The Independent Hostel Guide [...] 9

England
Wales
Scotland
Northern Ireland

Edited by

Sam Dalley and Penny MacGregor

ISBN 978-0-9565058-8-0

Independent Hostel Guide 2019: England, Wales, Scotland & Northern Ireland. 28th Edition.

Editors: Sam Dalley and Penny MacGregor.

British Library Cataloguing in Publication Data. A catalogue record for this book is available at the British Library **ISBN 978-0-9565058-8-0**

Published by: Independent Hostels UK, Speedwell House, Upperwood, Matlock Bath, Derbyshire, DE4 3PE.
Tel: +44 (0) 1629 580427.

Printed by: Cambrian Printers www.cambrian-printers.co.uk/

Front Cover Photo: Todor Tsvetkov © Istock

Back Cover Photos: Edens Yard Backpackers pg 76 and Alstonefield Camping Barn Pg 141.

Internal Photographs: Photos on page 301 credited to Tony Jones. Photo on page 357 credited to Brain Sutherland. Photo on page 362 credited to Ike Gibson. Photo on page 378 credited to Martin Thirkettle. Photo on page 232 credited to Mike Emmett. Photo on page 224 credited to Mick Garratt. Photos on page 205 credited to Rob Nobal. Photos on page 198 credited to Elliott Simpson. Photos on page 354 and 359 credited to VisitScotland/Paul Tomkins. Photos on page 331 credited to Allan Sutherland, Paul Higson, Colin McLean and Tom Daly. Photos on pages: 239, 104, 189, 284, 259, 154, 130,140, 35, 75, 86, 87, 73, 116, 229, 252, 267, 91, 107, 108, 105, 95, 175, 227, 88, 211, 206, 82, 134, 225, 166,177 © National Trust / Ross Hoddinott, Joe Cornish, Sarah Bailey, Robert Morris, Mike Henton, Roy Jones, Alex Green, John Millar, Peter Muhly, Roger Coulam, Paul Harris, Graham Bettis, James Dobson, Andrew Butler, Stuart Cox, Paul Delaney, David Noton, John Malley, Drew Buckley, Tracey Willis, Rob Joules, Sarah Harris, Justin Seedhouse, Arnhel de Serra, David Sellman, Hywel Lewis, Chris Lacey, David Noton,Robin Sutton. Other photos were donated by the accommodation and all copyright is retained.

Distributed in the UK by:
Cordee Books and Maps,
3a De Montfort Street, Leicester,
LE1 7HD.
Tel: 0116 2543579

CONTENTS

INDEPENDENT HOSTELS UK

Independent Hostels UK is a network of over 400 bunkhouses, hostels, camping barns and group accommodation centres. These provide a unique form of accommodation, ideal for groups, individuals and families who enjoy good company, travel and the outdoors.

Independenthostels.co.uk

INDEPENDENT HOSTELS

Independent hostels have shared areas, self-catering kitchens and bedrooms with bunks. They are great for group get-togethers and for those who enjoy the outdoors and independent travel. Bunkhouses, camping barns, boutique hostels, backpackers' hostels and outdoor centres are all types of independent hostel.

- **Self-catering facilities**
- **Stays of just one night or more**
- **Private bedrooms, en suite rooms and dorms**
- **Wild locations for outdoor activities**
- **City centre locations for independent travel**
- **Families, individuals and groups all welcome**
- **Can be booked 'sole use' for get-togethers & groups**
- **No membership requirements**
- **95% are extra to the hostels in the YHA / SYHA**

BEST PRICE GUARANTEE

The hostels and bunkhouses displaying the Best Price symbol on our website promise that you will get their accommodation at the lowest price if you contact them direct.

Why do we offer a Best Price Guarantee? Most websites take a large commission from your money before they pass it on to the accommodation. Independent hostel networks across the world have united to give their members the opportunity to offer a Best Price Guarantee. See **www.bestprice-hostels.com** for hostels overseas offering the Best Price Guarantee.

The website of Independent Hostels UK gives you direct access to the accommodations' own booking systems so you can book direct.

KEY TO SYMBOLS

Dormitories

Private rooms (often ideal for families)

Sleeping bags required

Hostel fully heated

Some areas heated

Drying room available

Cooking facilities available

Meals provided or available locally

WiFi available

Simple accommodation, basic, clean and friendly

Dogs by prior arrangement

Bike shed

Bronze, Silver, Gold, Green Tourism Award

Affiliated to Hostelling International

Operated by the National Trust

GROUPS ONLY Accommodation for groups only

pp per person

GR Ordnance Survey grid reference

Some accessible areas (See Index pages 380-384)

Independenthostels.co.uk

Follow our social media @indiehostelsUK for special offers.

IF YOU LIKE OUR GUIDE

You will love our website. It has :

- Lots of detailed information on each hostel / bunkhouse.
- Large photos of the accommodation and area.
- 'Book Now' facility and online availability.
- Links to the hostels' & bunkhouses' own websites.
- Direct contact with the accommodation owners
- Offers and late availability
- Holiday ideas and magazine features to inspire you.

YOU WILL LOVE OUR WEBSITE

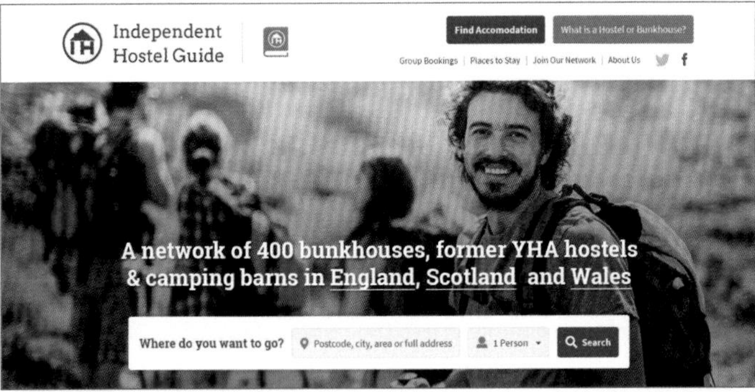

Every booking placed through the Independent Hostel Guide and the Independent Hostel's website is a direct booking.

Independenthostels.co.uk

WHY BOOK DIRECT ?

Independent Hostels UK is a network of over 400 hostels, bunkhouses and camping barns. We are very different to the giant online travel agents like Booking.com, Airbnb or Hostelworld.

When you book on one of those websites they take your money and withhold up to 20% as commission before passing the rest onto the accommodation provider.

As a network we don't do that. We provide a great selection of accommodation, easily searched and often with online booking. When you place a booking on our website the booking is placed directly with your hosts and they get 100% of your payment.

We provide the phone number of the accommodation so you can give them a call or you can contact them direct from our website.

With Independent Hostels UK everything you pay and everything you say goes direct to your hosts.

BOOK DIRECT BECAUSE

- **Everything you pay goes to your hosts**
- **You may get better rates**
- **You can chat with the staff and discuss your needs**
- **You may get preferential treatment**

Be good to your hosts

AND BOOK DIRECT

IHUK WORKING WITH

Independent Hostels UK is working with walking festivals to encourage walking, fresh air and friendship.

12-14 April	Kington Walks Spring Weekend	Herefordshire
24-28 April	Chepstow Walking Festival	Monmouthshire
27 Apr - 6 May	Ulverston WalkFest	Cumbria
30 Apr - 6 May	Settle-Carlisle Walking & Music Festival	N Yorks/Cumbria
10-12 May	Kendal Walking Festival	Cumbria
18 May - 2 June	Lincolnshire Wolds Walking Festival	Lincolnshire
1-9 June	Gower Walking Festival	W Glamorgan
7-15 June	Annual South Downs Way Walk	E Sussex/Hants
14-23 June	Moray Walking and Outdoor Festival	Moray
22-30 June	Otley Walking Festival	W Yorkshire
24 Aug - 1 Sept	Dartmoor Walking Festival	Devon
31 Aug -1 Sept	Corwen Walking Festival	Denbighshire
1-30 Sept	Guildford Walkfest	Surrey
7-22 Sept	South Pennines Walk and Ride Festival	Yorks/Lancashire
14-29 Sept	Autumn Footprints	Derbyshire
19-22 Sept	Kington Walking Festival	Herefordshire
27-29 Sept	Ross on Wye Walking Festival	Herefordshire
28 Sept - 6 Oct	Richmond Walking and Book Festival	N Yorkshire
28 Sep - 27 Oct	South Lincolnshire Walking Festival	Lincolnshire
5-12 Oct	Drovers' Tryst Walking Festival	Perthshire
10-13 Oct	Hay Walking Festival	Powys

Ride to Stride Walking & Music Festival on the Settle to Carlisle Line

WALKING FESTIVALS

kingtonwalks.org
walksinchepstow.co.uk
ulverstonwalkfest.co.uk
ride2stride.co.uk
kendalwalkingfestival.co.uk
woldswalkingfestival.co.uk
gowerwalkingfestival.uk
southdownsway.com
moraywalkoutdoorfest.co.uk
otleywalkingfestival.co.uk
dartmoorwalkingfestival.co.uk
corwenwalkingfestival.co.uk
guildfordwalkfest.co.uk
pennineprospects.co.uk
autumnfootprints.co.uk
kingtonwalks.org
walkinginross.co.uk
booksandboots.org
southlincswalking.com
droverstryst.com
haywalkingfestival.com

Independenthostels.co.uk/walking-festivals

Dartmoor Walking Festival

CITY, BACKPACKERS & BOUTIQUE HOSTELS

Independent city hostels, backpackers and boutique hostels cater for independent travellers exploring the UK. Close to public transport hubs, they are ideal for young travellers from overseas. They are also perfect venues for UK groups and individuals attending city events. These hostels are great places to meet people and make new friends, with many offering social events.

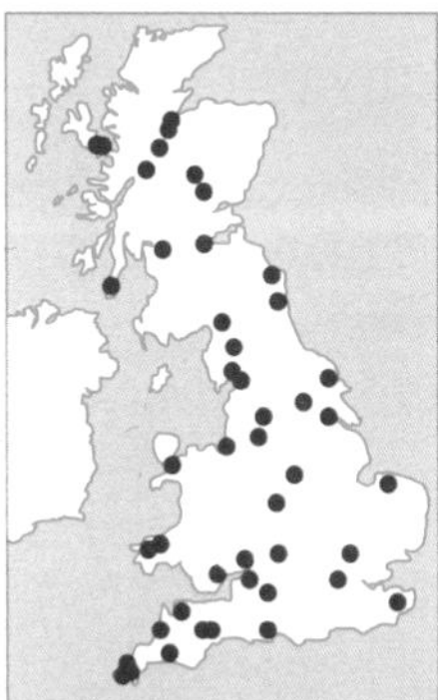

Independenthostels.co.uk/city

Clink261 pg 114

Reckoning House pg 146

KITCHENS

Kitchens like hostels vary.

Some are large and fully equipped.

Others are small and simple.

Look for the self-catering symbol

Some camping barns and bothies just have a stone slab for your own stove.

For economy and flexibility

Bretton Hostel pg 148

MEALS NEARBY

Many hostels are close to pubs that serve food or restaurants.

If there are meals available at the hostel or locally you will see this symbol

When you fancy eating out

Publove @ The White Ferry pg 111

MEALS PROVIDED

Some hostels and bunkhouses provide optional breakfasts, packed lunches and evening meals.

When you don't want to cook

Cote Ghyll Mill pg 167

High Street Hostel pg 315

Hull Trinity Backpackers pg 164

ban Backpackers pg 343

MORE THAN A BED

Hostels and bunkhouses have shared living areas, lounges, games rooms and gardens.

Space to relax and meet other guests.

A Home from Home

Hebden Bridge Hostel pg 170

Old Red Lion pg 136

Lowick School Bunkhouse pg187

Edens Yard pg 76

GARDENS

Many hostels have outdoor spaces. For evening sun, BBQs, glorious views and space for children to play.

Fresh air back at base

Mid Wales Bunkhouse pg 272

BUNKS

Most bunkhouses and hostels have bunks in the bedrooms.

You can either book a bunk in a room, ideal for lone travellers. Or a room full of bunks, great for large families.

Flexible and economical

Thorney How pg 194

ROOMS
are ideal for families
P
amily holidays

PRIVATE ROOMS

Many bunkhouses and hostels have private rooms. Sometimes with en suite facilities.

Look for this symbol P

For extra privacy

Hamilton Bpkrs pg 262

Falmouth Lodge Backpackers pg 74

Elterwater Hostel pg 192

NO MEMBERSHIP

There are no membership requirements at Independent Hostels.

Don't forget to book

Lodge Dinorwig pg 294

Llanfyllin Workhouse pg 280

WEDDINGS

Some hostels specialise as alternative wedding venues.

Great value and unique

Marthrown of Mabie pg 308

SOLE USE

You can book the whole hostel or bunkhouse for your group.

Perfect for celebrations

Old Brooder Bunkhouse pg 117

Hagg Farm Outdoor Centre pg 158

Dunfield House pg 123

GROUPS

Bunkhouses and hostels provide great accommodation for groups. School groups, outdoor clubs, universities and gatherings of friends all use independent hostels.

Ideal for schools and clubs

St Michaels Centre pg 151

Bath YMCA pg 97

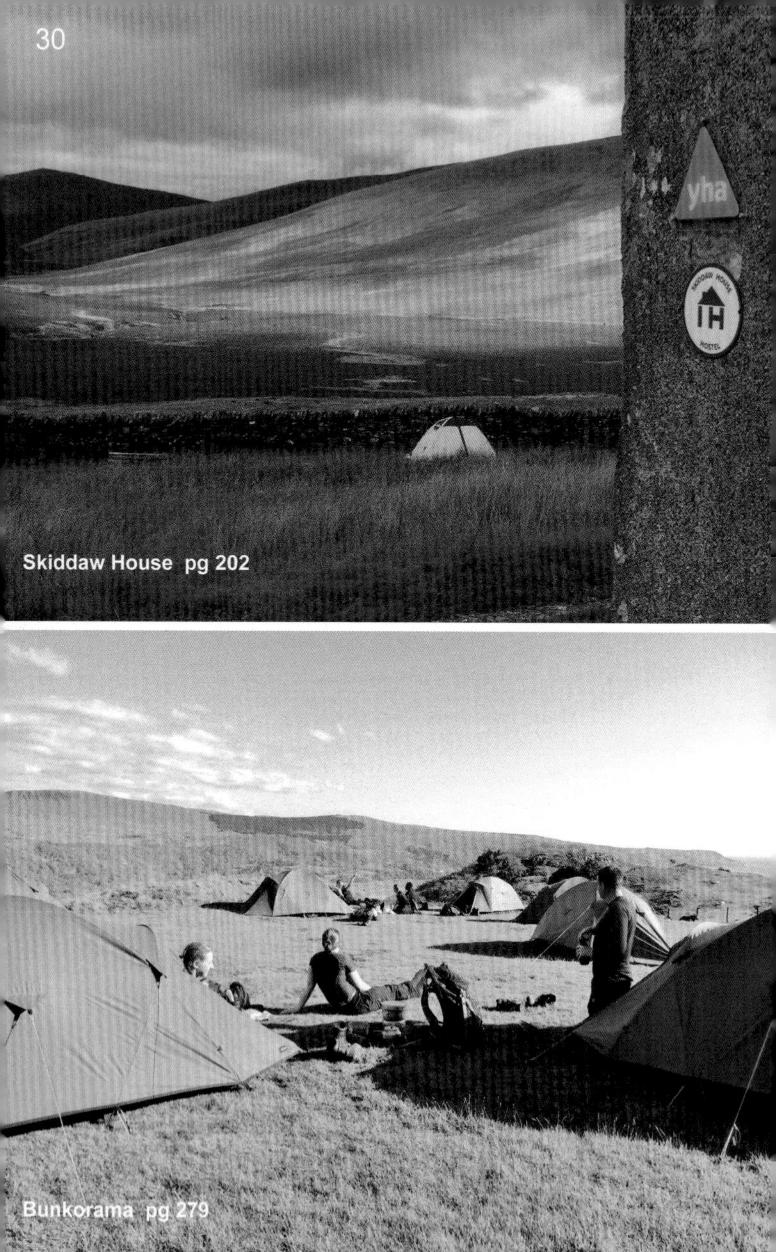

Skiddaw House pg 202

Bunkorama pg 279

CAMPING

Over 100 hostels and bunkhouses offer camping as a way to accommodate larger groups. Some also operate independent campsites.

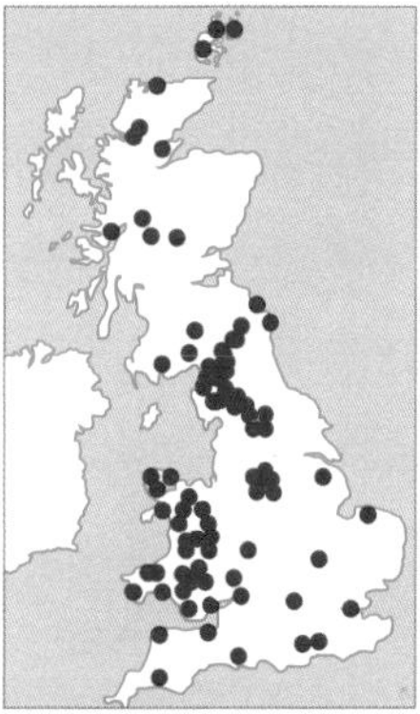

Independenthostels.co.uk/camp

Badrallach Bothy pg 361

Isle of Tiree pg 352

OUTDOOR ACTIVITIES

Many hostels and bunkhouses are in prime outdoor locations with activity providers on site or nearby.

Your hosts will know the best places to go and give advice on activities in their area.

Take on a challenge

Hardraw Old School Bunkhouse pg 180

Wayfarers Hostel pg 213

BIKE SHEDS

More and more hostels and bunkhouses have secure bike and equipment stores.

Look out for the symbol

Dry and secure

Hull Trinity Backpackers pg 164

DRYING ROOMS

Many hostels and bunkhouses have drying facilities, so you can go out in all weathers and be sure of a dry start the next day

Look out for the symbol 

Because it sometimes rains!

Hardraw Old School Bunkhouse pg 180

Viking Centre pg 137

Big Mose Bunkhouse pg130

Comrie Croft pg 323

CYCLISTS

Hostels are ideal stop-overs on long distance rides and great bases for off road challenges.

Many have wash down facilities and indoor repair areas.

Stay for one night or more

Dales Bike Centre pg 181

Deepdale Groups Hostel pg 133

ACCOMMODATION

There are over a hundred hostels and bunkhouses in the network which offer dog friendly accommodation. They provide ideal self-catering accommodation for holidays which is dog friendly by arrangement. Many provide accommodation for periods as short as one night so are ideal for a stop-over on a long journey. Always contact the accommodation in advance to find out about arrangements for your dog.

Look out for this symbol

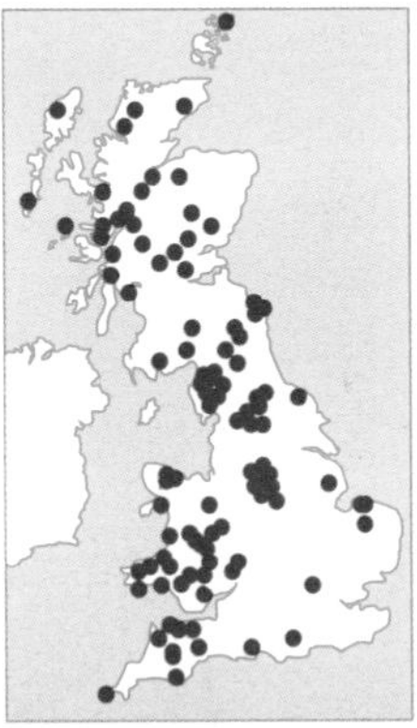

Independenthostels.co.uk/dog

Bunkorama pg 279

Mid Wales Bunkhouse pg 272

FRESH AIR

Many bunkhouses and hostels are in ideal locations for holidays in the fresh air.

Healthy family holidays

Big Mose Bunkhouse pg 130

Skiddaw House pg 202

Snowdonia

MOUNTAINS

You will find hostels and bunkhouses at the bottom and half way up mountains all over the UK.

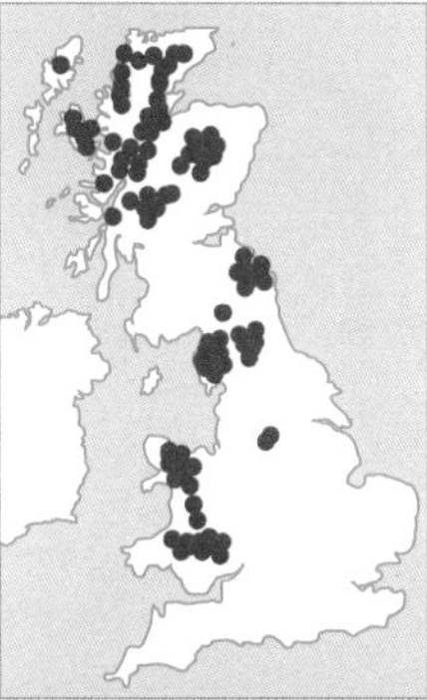

Independenthostels.co.uk/mountains

© Pentre Bach Bunkhouse pg 297

Bunkorama pg 279

Dalehead Bunkhouse pg 154

Pindale Farm pg 153
NATIONAL PARKS
All of the UK's National Parks are well provided for with independent hostels, bunkhouses & camping barns.
Independenthostels.co.uk/parks
Thorney How pg 194

Brancaster Activity Centre pg 135

Ocean Backpackers pg 83

BEACHES & COAST
There are lots of hostels and bunkhouses along the coasts and islands of the UK.
Independenthostels.co.uk/sea

Shielings Holidays pg 346

BUNKHOUSES AND BOTHIES

There are over 30 National Trust bunkhouses and bothies in the Independent Hostel Guide, all in spectacular locations. The bunkhouses are ideal for groups and provide self-catering accommodation in the grounds of National Trust Estates, within National Parks or along unspoiled coastlines. Most bunkhouses provide sleeping in bunk bed dormitories, a social area to gather and cook, showers, electricity and heating. National Trust bothies are often in isolated locations, and are the perfect getaway for those who really want to escape from modern life. Fitted with wooden sleeping platforms, there is usually no electricity and water often comes from a hand pump.

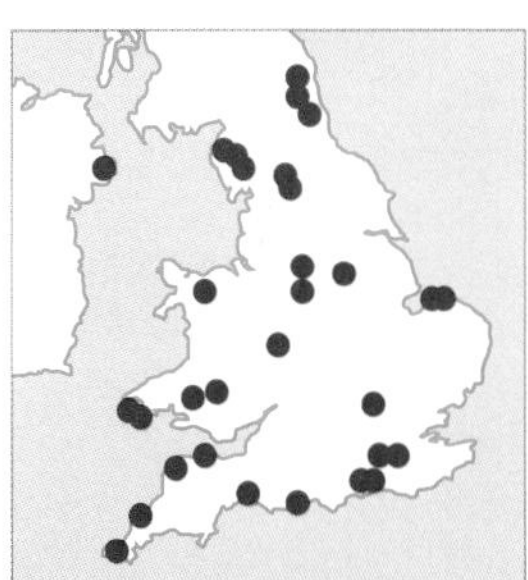

Independenthostels.co.uk/nt

Dalehead Bunkhouse pg 154

Campbeltown Backpackers pg 318

Derwentwater Independent Hostel pg 203

Dunfield House pg 123

HISTORIC BUILDING

Hostels and bunkhouses are found in many old and interesting buildings. From grand country mansions to old schools and barns.

Sleep surrounded by history

Viking Centre pg 137

Elterwater Hostel pg 192

Bretton Hostel pg 148

YOUTH HOSTELS
PAST AND PRESENT

The YHA has sold many hostels over the last twenty years and some of these have been rescued from closure by private individuals or local interest groups. There are now over 60 former YHA properties in the Independent Hostels network including bunkhouses and camping barns. These continue to provide great value self-catering accommodation to promote a greater knowledge, love and care of the countryside.

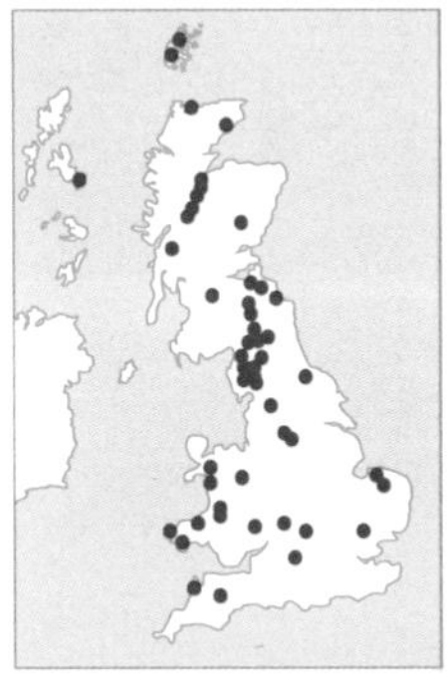

Independenthostels.co.uk/yha

Borth Youth Hostel pg 273

Clink78 pg 112

Green Man Backpackers pg 244

CITY HOSTELS

If central city locations are what you are after then city hostels are for you. Shared accommodation makes staying in the heart of the city economical and fun.

Stay at the heart of the city

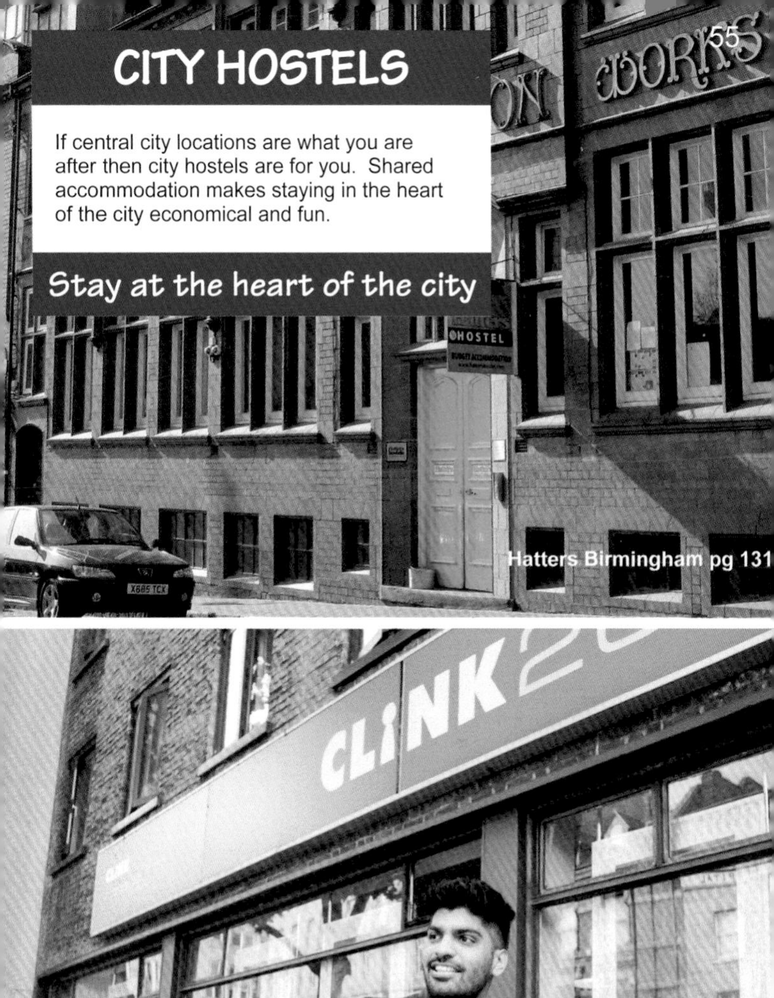

Hatters Birmingham pg 131

Clink261 pg 114

Alstonefield Camping Barn pg 141

Cragg Camping Barn pg 208

CAMPING BARNS AND BOTHIES

Camping barns and bothies offer simple accommodation in stunning rural locations. There is a platform to lay your sleeping roll, a table, benches and a safe area for your camping stove. It is common for camping barns to be off-grid with no heating or lighting and some have a wood-burning stove to gather around. Created to provided shelter for walkers but also ideal for family escapes, camping barns are owned and run by local farms and the community.

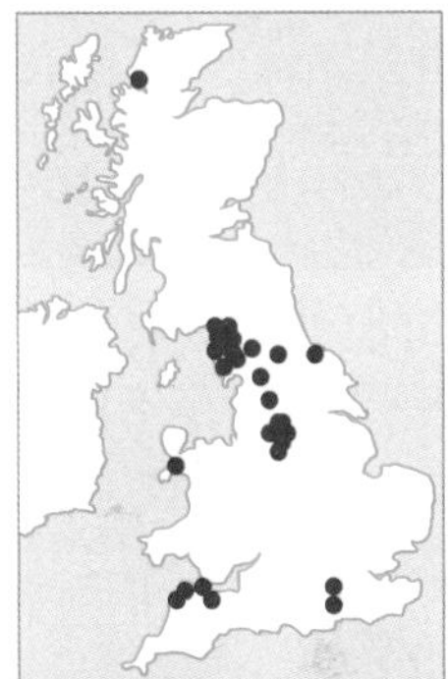

Independenthostels.co.uk/barns

Bowderstone Bunkhouse pg 205

Green Man Backpackers pg 244

Full Moon Backpackers pg 98

BOOK DIRECT

The large online booking sites keep up to 20% of your money.

Every booking placed through Independent Hostels is a direct booking, with 100% of your payment and all your communications going direct to your hosts.

You may get preferential treatment.

Be good to your hosts

Hamilton Backpackers pg 262

Glamping at The Dragons Back pg 249

Chellington Centre pg 118

Kyle Blue Hostel Boat pg 99

QUIRKY

There are some wonderful quirky hostels. Chose from a floating hostel, a canvas hostel, a hostel in a workhouse and an old railway carriage, to name but a few.

Seek out the unusual

Railway Carriage accommodation, Sleeperzzz pg 363

ECO HOSTELS

AND BUNKHOUSES

Hostels and bunkhouses have a naturally low CO2 footprint. Shared accommodation means shared resources, making the accommodation naturally sustainable Cyclists and walkers use the ultimate in carbon free travel and some hostels and bunkhouses provide a discount for those without a vehicle.

The hostels and bunkhouses on the map below make a special effort to run their accommodation in a sustainable way. Some of them have achieved Green Tourism Awards and these have the symbols shown opposite on their pages.

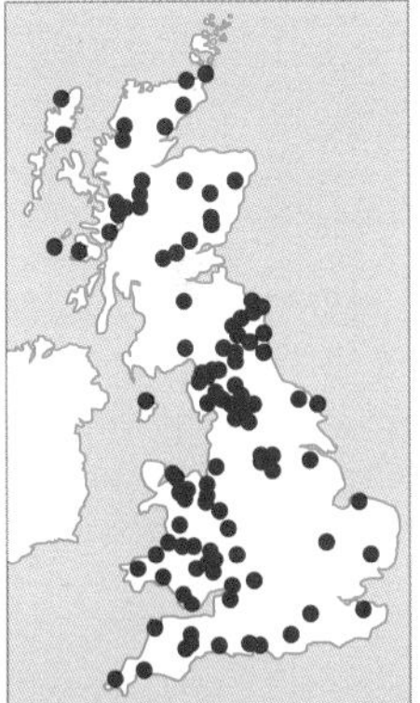

Independenthostels.co.uk/eco

Palace Farm Hostel pg 109

HOSTELS AND BUNKHOUSES ON

Keep checking - new routes are added every month

North England
North England
Scotland
Scotland
South Wales
Derbyshire
Wales
South West England
North Scotland
North England
North England
North Pennines
North England
Scotland
Welsh Borders
Wales
Wales
Outer Hebridies
UK
Cumbria
Staffordshire/Derbyshire
UK
Yorkshire
Scotland
West Country
Cornwall
North England

Independenthostels.co.uk/trails

Slack House Farm pg 220

THE LONG DISTANCE TRAILS

The Independent Hostels' website features each of the routes below showing the location of bunkhouses and hostels all along the way.

90 miles	The Pennine Way	Walk
192 miles	Wainwrights Coast to Coast Walk	Walk
75 miles	Great Glen Way	Walk
96 miles	West Highland Way	Walk
95 miles	Beacons Way	Walk
60 miles	White Peak Loop	Cycle/Walk
250 miles	Lon Las Cymru Cycle Route	Cycle
630 miles	South West Coast Path	Walk
516 miles	Scottish North Coast 500	Road Route
200 miles	Mountain Bike Coast to Coast Route	Mountain Bike
80 miles	The Dales Way	Walk
36 miles	Isaac's Tea Trail	Walk
84 miles	Hadrian's Wall	Walk
80 miles	The Rob Roy Way	Walk
177 miles	Offa's Dyke	Walk
291 miles	The Cambrian Way	Walk
861 miles	Wales Coast Path	Walk
156 miles	Hebridean Way	Walk/Cycle
850 miles	LEJOG Walk	Walk
70 miles	Cumbria Way	Walk
46 miles	The Limestone Way	Walk
874 miles	LEJOG Cycle Route	Cycle
73 miles	Settle to Carlisle Railway	Train
537 miles	The Scottish National Trail	Walk
350 miles	Mary Michael Pilgrim's Way	Walk
303 miles	Land's End Trail	Walk
140 miles	C2C (Sea to Sea) Cycle Route	Cycle

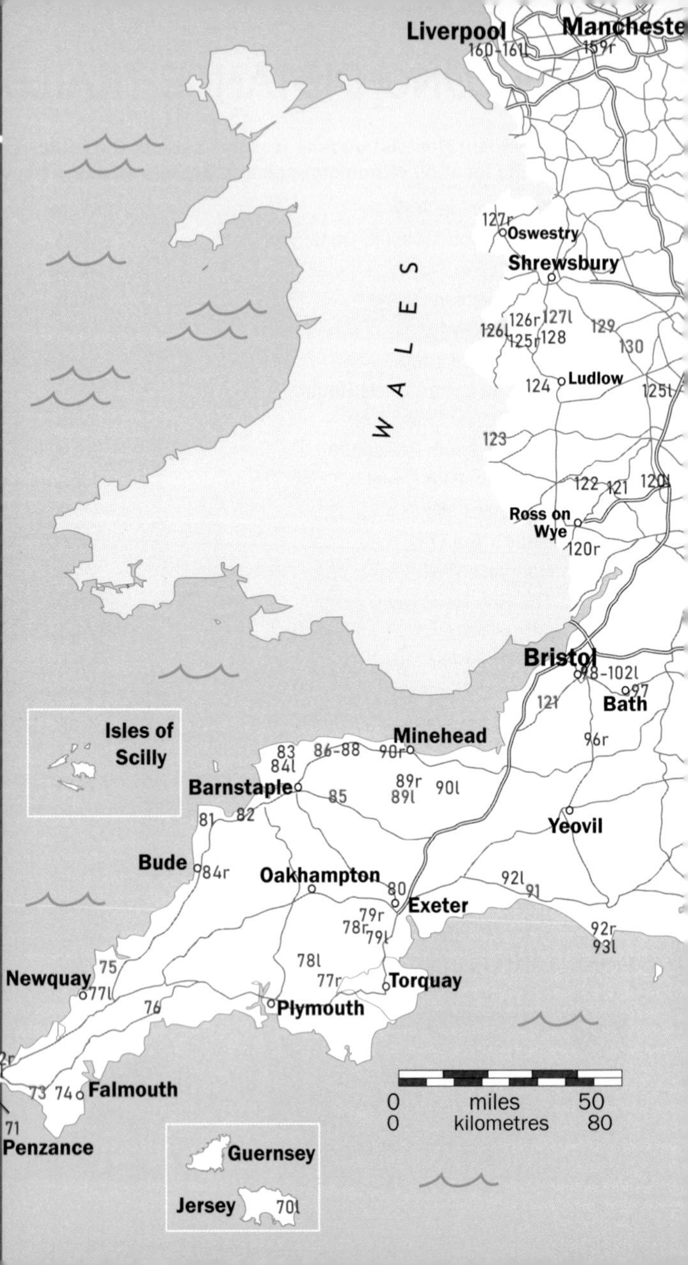

Liverpool 160–161l
Manchester 159r
127r Oswestry
Shrewsbury
126r 127l
126l 125r 128
129
130
124 Ludlow
125l
WALES
123
122 121 120l
Ross on Wye
120r
Bristol 98–102l
97 Bath
121
96r
Isles of Scilly
Minehead
83 86–88 90r
84l
Barnstaple
85
89r 90l
89l
81 82
Yeovil
Bude 84r
Oakhampton
80
Exeter
92l
91
79r
78r 79l
92r
93l
78l
75
Newquay 77l
77r Torquay
76
Plymouth
72r
72l
70r
71
73 74 Falmouth
Penzance
0 miles 50
0 kilometres 80
Guernsey
Jersey 70l

Sheffield
137
Lincoln
Skegness
Derby
Nottingham
132l
132r 133l-135
King's Lynn
136
Norwich
Leicester
Peterborough
Birmingham
131l,131r
Coventry
Northampton
Cambridge
118
117 Ipswich
Luton
Colchester
116
119l
Oxford
London
111l-115r
119r
Reading
109
110
Canterbury
Dover
108
106
107
Guildford
96l
Salisbury
103r
103l
104
105
Hastings
Portsmouth
102r
Brighton
95
Bournemouth
94
93r
KEY
45 - Page number
45l - Left side of page
45r - Right side of page
45 - Groups only

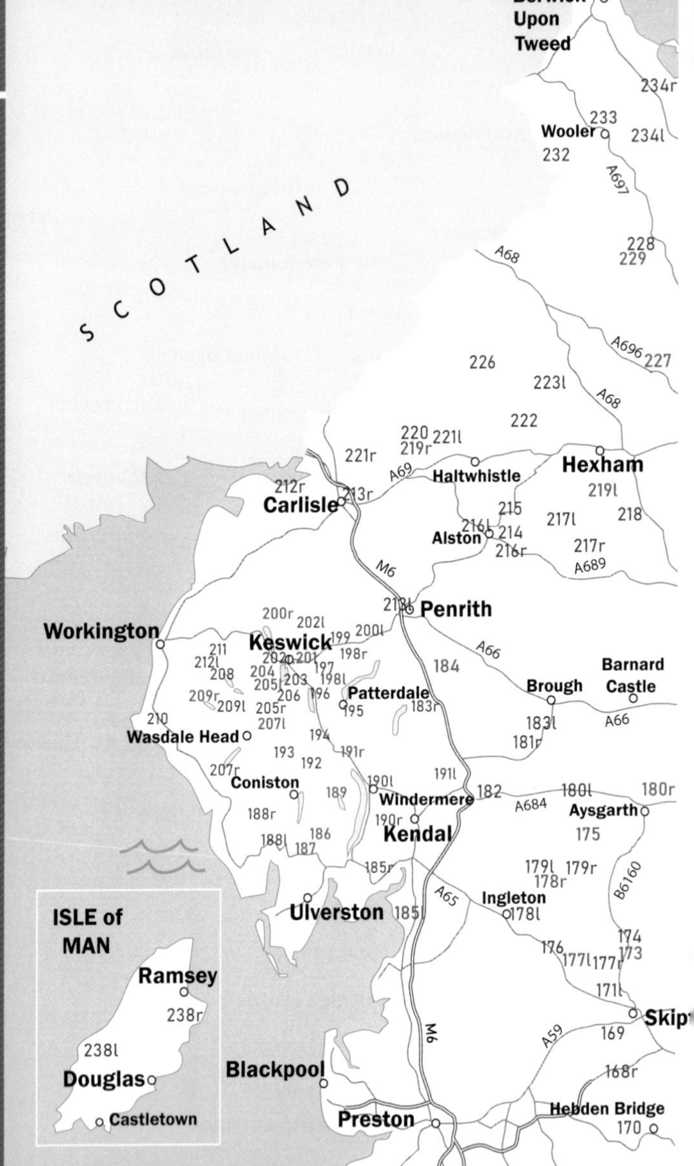
Berwick Upon Tweed
234r
233
Wooler
234l
232
A697
SCOTLAND
A68
228
229
A696
227
226
223l
A68
222
220
219r
221l
221r
Hexham
A69
Haltwhistle
212r
213r
Carlisle
219l
215
217l
218
216l
214
Alston
216r
217r
A689
M6
213l
Penrith
200r
202l
Workington
Keswick
199
200l
211
212l
202r
201
198r
197
208
204
203
198l
184
A66
Barnard Castle
205l
206
196
Patterdale
Brough
209r
209l
205r
195
183r
210
207l
183l
A66
Wasdale Head
194
181r
193
191r
192
207r
191l
Coniston
190l
189
182
180l
180r
Windermere
A684
Aysgarth
188r
190r
Kendal
175
188l
186
187
185r
179l
179r
178r
B6160
A65
Ingleton
Ulverston
185l
178l
ISLE of MAN
174
176
177l
177r
173
Ramsey
171l
238r
Skip
A59
169
M6
238l
Douglas
168r
Blackpool
Hebden Bridge
Preston
170
Castletown

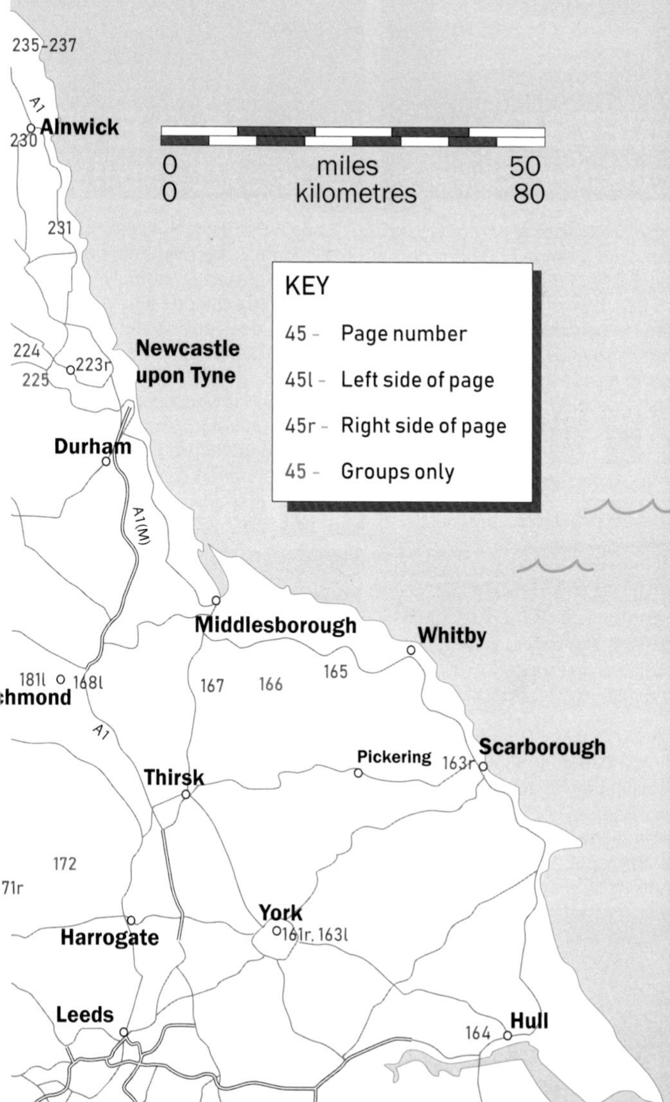

235-237
A1
Alnwick
230
0
miles
50
0
kilometres
80
231
KEY
45 - Page number
45l - Left side of page
45r - Right side of page
45 - Groups only
224
223r
225
Newcastle upon Tyne
Durham
A1(M)
Middlesborough
Whitby
181l
168l
167
166
165
chmond
A1
Pickering
163r
Scarborough
Thirsk
172
71r
York
161r, 163l
Harrogate
Leeds
164
Hull

JERSEY

ACCOMMODATION CENTRE

70l

Close to the pretty fishing port of Gorey in St Martin, with a range of B&B rooms, private en suites & dorms with shared showers plus camping. On & off-site activities including zip wire (U12s), archery, bush craft, low velocity paintball or escape from a castle by doing physical & problem solving tasks.

DETAILS

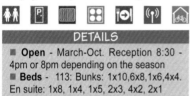

- **Open** - March-Oct. Reception 8:30 - 4pm or 8pm depending on the season
- **Beds** - 113: Bunks: 1x10,6x8,1x6,4x4. En suite: 1x8, 1x4, 1x5, 2x3, 4x2, 2x1
- **Price/night** - B&B:Bunks £30.75-£32.75pp. En suites: bunks, single, family 3, 4, 5 & 8 £32.75-£34.75pp. Twin £65.50-£69.50 per room. Youth groups £27.75pp.

CONTACT: Anna Stammers
Tel: 01534 498636
info@jerseyhostel.co.uk
www.jerseyhostel.co.uk
La Rue de la Pouclee et des Quatre Chemins, Faldouet, St Martins, Jersey, Channel Islands JE2 6DU.

LANDS END

HOSTEL AND B&B

70r

Land's End Hostel, in the hamlet of Trevescan, is 1/2 mile from Land's End. Double glazed & centrally heated it has a fully equipped kitchen & dining areas inside & out. Modern bathrooms and bedrooms with TV's & WiFi. New bunk beds with USB ports & LED lights. Bedding / towels supplied. Bicycle storage, parking & small on-site shop. Separate double/twin en suite B&B room with own entrance & outside dining area

DETAILS

- **Open** - All year.
- **Beds** - 14: 2×2, 1×4, 1×6 plus double B&B ensuite bedroom in the farmhouse.
- **Price/night** - From £25pp (cont. b/fast £5.50). B&B from £75 per room which includes continental breakfast

CONTACT: Lou
Tel: 07585 625774
lou@landsendholidays.co.uk
www.landsendholidays.co.uk
Mill Barn, Trevescan, Sennan, Nr Land's End, Penzance, TR19 7AQ

PENZANCE

BACKPACKERS

Whether you're looking for sandy beaches and sheltered coves, the storm lashed cliffs of Land's End, sub-tropical gardens, international artists, the remains of ancient cultures, or just somewhere to relax and take time out, Penzance Backpackers is for you. Situated close to the sea front and the town centre. Accommodation is mostly in small bunk-bedded rooms. Linen is provided. Lots of local information and a warm welcome all included.

 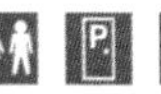     

DETAILS

- **Open** - All year. 10am-Noon, 5-10pm.
- **Beds** - 30: 2 double, 1x4 (double + 2 bunks), 3x6, 1x7.
- **Price/night** - From £18 per person. £40 for 2 people in private room.

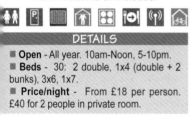

CONTACT: Mathew
Tel: 01736 363836
info@pzbackpack.com
www.pzbackpack.com
The Blue Dolphin, Alexandra Road,
Penzance, TR18 4LZ

LOWER PENDERLEATH

FARM HOSTEL

72l

Just three miles from St Ives' beaches & 5 miles from Penzance, Lower Penderleath Farm Hostel provides self-catering accommodation in four twin rooms and one alpine dormitory for 12. Plus a self contained family maisonette with small kitchen and private shower & toilet. BYO sleeping bags. Pub food in two local villages is within walking distance. Bedding not provided.

DETAILS

- **Open** - Easter-Oct. Arrive between 9am-6pm, depart by 10am.
- **Beds** - 24: 4x2 + dorm platform of 12, 1x4 self contained maisonette
- **Price/night** - £20pp, £45 twin room. £100 maisonette. Minimum of 2 nights. Sorry no cards. Cash payment only.

CONTACT: Russell Rogers
Tel: 07723 014567
rusrogers60@gmail.com
www.stivescampingandhostel.com
Lower Penderleath Farm, Towednack, St.Ives, Cornwall, TR26 3AF

COHORT

HOSTEL

72r

Located in the centre of St Ives, Cohort is a stylish, friendly hostel. Great facilities include a hot shower in the courtyard for surfers, through to a laundry and dry room. The on-site bar is cheap; there's free WiFi, a TV room and comfortable pod beds - all with USB ports, lights, curtains & under-bed storage and a big guest kitchen. Free tea and coffee before 10am. Walk outside to find cafés, bars, galleries, 5 spectacular beaches & the coastal path on your doorstep.

DETAILS

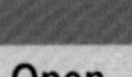

- **Open** - February - December. 8am - 10pm
- **Beds** - 61: 1x8, 7x6, 1x4, 2x twin, 1x twin/triple
- **Price/night** - From £15

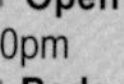 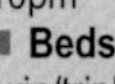 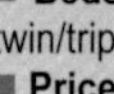 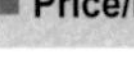 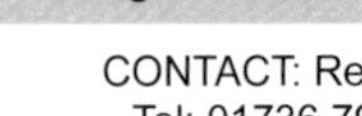

CONTACT: Reception
Tel: 01736 791664
hello@stayatcohort.co.uk
www.stayatcohort.co.uk
The Stennack, St Ives, Cornwall, TR26 1FF

 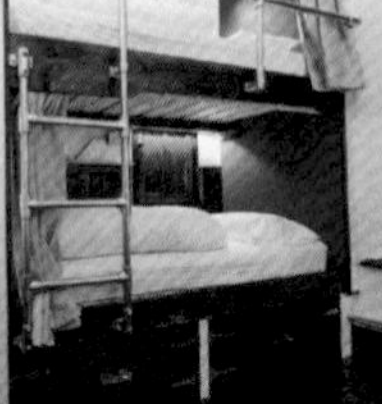

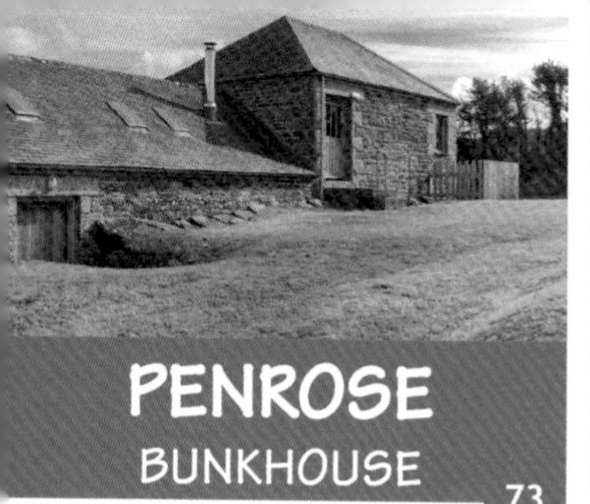

PENROSE

BUNKHOUSE

73

On the edge of the Penrose Estate, the gateway to The Lizard Peninsula.

Penrose bunkhouse is right next to the SW Coast Path and has great access to many local walks, trails and cycling routes. Penrose, is home to many rare species of wildlife as well as Cornwall's largest freshwater lake, the Loe. The perfect location to base your group for wildlife adventures, walking and activity holidays or a break away from it all. The bunkhouse sleeps 16 in three rooms and is well equipped for self catering.

DETAILS

- **Open** - All year. All day
- **Beds** - 16: 2x7, 1x2,
- **Price/night** - From £350 for two nights.

CONTACT: National Trust Holidays
Tel: 03443 351296
bunkhouses@nationaltrust.org.uk
www.nationaltrust.org.uk/holidays
Penrose Bunk House, Gunwalloe,
Helston, Cornwall TR12 7PY

FALMOUTH

LODGE BACKPACKERS

Judi will be your host at Falmouth Lodge. Relaxed, friendly and clean, Falmouth Lodge Backpackers is just two minutes' walk from the Blue Flag Gyllyngvase beach and the South West Coast Path. Only eight minutes' walk into town with its exotic gardens, art galleries, Maritime Museum, Pendennis Castle, and the harbour. Free parking and Wifi. Complimentary tea, coffee and breakfast. Well-equipped kitchen and cosy lounge.

DETAILS

- **Open** - Open Jan-Nov incl New Year. Reception open from 5pm
- **Beds** - 28: 2x2/3, 2 x4/5, 1x6/7, 1xdbl/family en suite (some sea views).
- **Price/night** - From £19 pp. Sole use £616 pn. Discounts for multiple nights

CONTACT: Judi
Tel: 01326 319996 or 07525 722808
judi@falmouthlodge.co.uk
www.falmouthbackpackers.co.uk
9 Gyllyngvase Terrace, Falmouth,
Cornwall, TR11 4DL

BEACH HEAD

BUNKHOUSE

With fantastic views out to sea and along the north Cornish coast to Trevose Head, the National Trust run Beach Head Bunkhouse provides great value basic self-catering holiday accommodation.

The self-catering facilities and great location just 1.5 miles from the beach at Porthcothan and close to the South West Coast path make it the perfect base for family holidays and walking groups alike.

Not suitable for very young children.

      GROUPS ONLY

DETAILS

- **Open** - All year. All day
- **Beds** - 14: 2x1 2x6
- **Price/night** - 2 nights from £340.

CONTACT: National Trust Holidays
Tel: 03443 351296
bunkhouses@nationaltrust.org.uk
www.nationaltrust.org.uk/holidays
Park Head, St Eval, Wadebridge,
Cornwall, PL27 7UU

EDENS YARD

BACKPACKERS

76

Welcome to this quirky, camino inspired eco hostel up-cycled from an old stable block to include mixed bunk rooms, a courtyard kitchen & a communal lounge. It's just a short leafy lane from the Eden Project situated on National Cycle routes 2 & 3, two miles from the Northwest Coast Path at Carlyon Bay and close to the historic Saints Way pilgrimage trail. Walkers and cyclists are welcomed and pick-ups from the station or parking can be arranged. Come and be welcome in Cornwall at Edens Yard.

DETAILS

- **Open** - Easter to mid October. Arrive between 4pm and 10pm please.
- **Beds** - 1x6, 1x8
- **Price/night** - £15

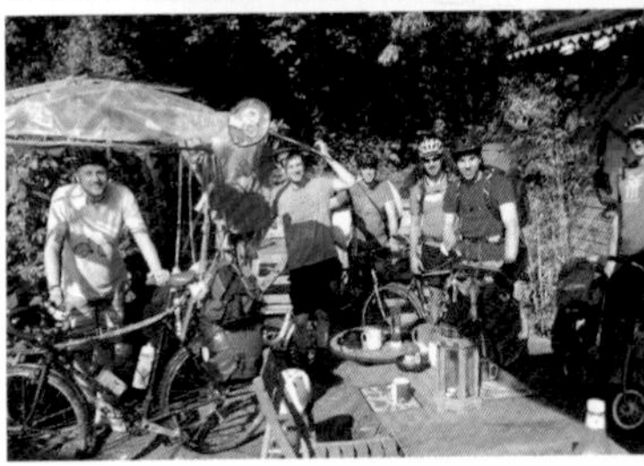

CONTACT: Neal or Julia
Tel: 01726 814907
info@edensyard.uk
www.edensyard.uk
17 Tregrehan Mills, St. Austell, Cornwall, PL25 3TL

REEF

LODGES

77l

Whether you are visiting Newquay for a holiday, stag or hen party, celebration, club event or just a great weekend, you can't go wrong with Reef Lodges. With singles, doubles, surfer accommodation or group accommodation in a fantastic centre of town location Reef Lodges offers amazing surf and stay packages, surfing breaks, learn to surf breaks and discount deals on accommodation. Perfect for a surfing break in Newquay.

DETAILS

- **Open** - All year. All day
- **Beds** - 109: 2x10, 3x8, 2x7, 3x6, 1x5, 4x4, 2x3 doubles and twins
- **Price/night** - From £15pp. Extra for private rooms, en suite, bank holidays and breakfast. Mid-week discounts.

CONTACT: Reception Team
Tel: 01637 838354
ReefLodgesTeam@gmail.com
www.surfinnewquay.com
10 - 12 Berry Road, Newquay, Cornwall, TR7 1AR

HARFORD

BUNKHOUSE

77r

Harford Bunkhouse & Camping offers comfortable budget accommodation on the edge of stunning South Dartmoor. An ideal choice if you are planning to start the Two Moors Way walk from south to north. Run alongside a working Dartmoor farm, the bunkhouse offers dormitory style accommodation with self catering facilities for up to 50 people. The campsite is on two of the farm's meadows. There are also two camping pods and a cabin which sleep up to 6 people each.

DETAILS

- **Open** - All year. All day.
- **Beds** - 40-50 beds
- **Price/night** - From £17pp. Camping pods/cabin £50 each. Camping £7.50pp

CONTACT: Julie Cole
Tel: 07968 566218
julie.cole6@btinternet.com
www.harfordbunkhouse.com
West Combeshead, Harford, Ivybridge, Devon, PL21 0JG

FOX TOR

CAFE & BUNKHOUSE

78l

An ideal base for anyone wishing to spend time on Dartmoor whether it is to walk, climb, cycle, kayak or just relax and enjoy the spectacular scenery. Fox Tor Bunkhouse is situated near the centre of the village of Princetown. Guests can book packed lunches and breakfasts.

The café has wood-burning stoves and provides lovely home made food cooked to order. Guided walks & mountain biking are available as is mountain bike hire.

DETAILS

- **Open** - All year. All day. Arrive from 4.30pm, leave by 10.30am.
- **Beds** - 12: 3 x 4
- **Price/night** - Please phone or see website for prices.

CONTACT: Abbi or Dave
Tel: 01822 890238
enquiries@foxtorcafe.com
www.foxtorcafe.co.uk
Two Bridges Road, Princetown,
Dartmoor, Devon, PL20 6QS

SPARROWHAWK

BACKPACKERS

78r

A small, friendly eco-hostel in the centre of Moretonhampstead, Dartmoor National Park. Popular with cyclists, hikers, bikers, wild swimmers, artists and photographers, A beautifully converted stone stable, with solar-heate showers, kitchen, courtyard, BBQ and secure bike shed. High open moorland, rocky tors, ancient burial sites, stone circles, woods and clear rivers close by. Moretonhampstead has shops, cafés, ar galleries and pubs. Cicerone LEJOG & Dartmoor Way cycle routes pass by.

DETAILS

- **Open** - All year
- **Beds** - 18: 1x14 + double/family room.
- **Price/night** - Adults dorm £19. U14 £10. Double room £42 (for 2 people).

CONTACT: Alison
Tel: 01647 440318 or 07870 513570
ali@sparrowhawkbackpackers.co.uk
www.sparrowhawkbackpackers.co.uk
45 Ford Street, Moretonhampstead,
Dartmoor, Devon, TQ13 8LN

COLEHAYES

PARK

79l

Colehayes Park is a Grade II listed Georgian Manor on Dartmoor with 20 acre grounds and views over the rolling hills of the Devon. Perfect for school and university groups, large gatherings of family/friends and DIY weddings. It has a commercial kitchen for self-catering or meals can be provided. Friendly with a warm laid back atmosphere.

  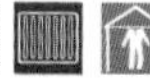     GROUPS ONLY

DETAILS

- **Open** - All year
- **Beds** - 81: Manor 70: in 21 bedrooms Cottage 11:
- **Price/night** - Schools and universities with meals £38pp+VAT, min of 30 (Manor) 11(Cottage). Self catering sole use: 3 night weekend or 4 nights midweek, Manor from £2995, Cottage from £630.

CONTACT: Kate
Tel: 01626 833033
mail@colehayes.co.uk
www.colehayes.co.uk
Haytor Road, Bovey Tracey, South Devon, TQ13 9LD

BLYTHESWOOD

HOSTEL

79r

In secluded, native woodland on the eastern edge of Dartmoor, the cabin has been a hostel since the 1930s. Friendly and peaceful, with a homely living room, wood burner, self-catering kitchen, picnic tables, BBQ and fire pit. Walk straight from the door to Heltor and Blackingstone Rock or along the river to Fingle Bridge and Castle Drogo. Cross stepping stones to Dunsford village. Moretonhampstead and Chagford are nearby. On the LEJOG cycling route.

DETAILS

- **Open** - All year.
- **Beds** - 16: 1x6, 1x4 (family), 1x2 (cabin) and 1x4 (family cabin)
- **Price/night** - £16 per adult. U16 £10. Sole Use: £240pn 2+nights. £280 1night.

CONTACT: Lewis or Sarah
Tel: 07758 654840
hello@blytheswood.co.uk
www.blytheswood.co.uk
Steps Bridge, Dunsford, Devon, EX6 7EQ

EXETER GLOBE

BACKPACKERS

Globe Backpackers offers clean, comfortable, self catering accommodation. It is just a few minutes' walk from Exeter's city centre with its cathedral, picturesque historic waterway, quay and wide range of shops, pubs, clubs, cafés and restaurants.

DETAILS

- **Open** - All year (phone for Xmas). Check in/check out: Mon-Fri: 8.30-12 noon and 3.30-11pm. Sat,Sun: 8.30am-11pm. Earlier check out by arrangement only.,
- **Beds** - 46-52: 1x10, 3x8, 1x6, 3x2/4 (dbl/twin plus bunk bed)
- **Price/night** - Dorms from £17.50pp or £80pp per week. Private rooms from £50 for two people, £80 for four people. £5 key deposit.

CONTACT: Duty Manager
Tel: 01392 215521
info@exeterbackpackers.co.uk
www.exeterbackpackers.co.uk
71 Holloway Street, Exeter, EX2 4JD

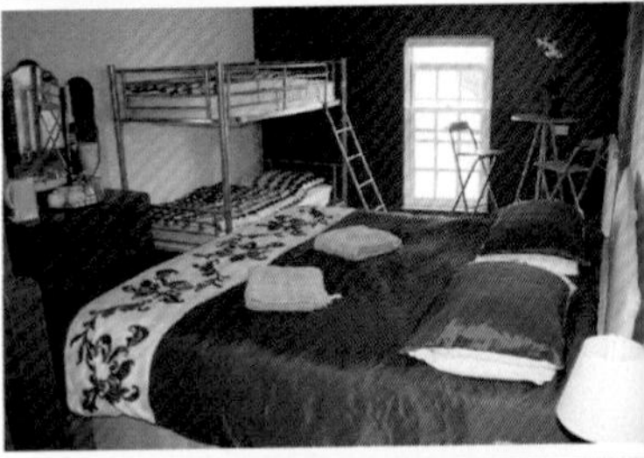

ELMSCOTT
HOSTEL

Elmscott Hostel is surrounded by unspoiled coastline with sea views of Lundy Island. Great for walking, cycling, surfing and bird watching. The South West Coast Path is just a few mins' walk away. The hostel is well equipped for all your self-catering needs and has a games room and shop. In winter it is only available for sole use bookings.

DETAILS

- **Open** - All year.
- **Beds** - 32 (35 in winter): 1 unit of 20: 2x6, 2x4; 1 unit of 12: 1x6, 1x4, 1x2. Extra 3 bed room for sole use in winter.
- **Price/night** - Adult £20-£22, under 16s £15.50-£17. Discounts for groups or longer stays.

CONTACT: John, Thirza and Kate
Tel: Hostel 01237 441367/ Owners 01237 441276/ Kate 01237 441637
john.goa@virgin.net
www.elmscott.org.uk
Elmscott, Hartland, Bideford, Devon, EX39 6ES

PEPPERCOMBE

BOTHY

Located in a quiet, tranquil, wooded valley with views across Bideford Bay towards Lundy, Peppercombe Bothy is effectively a stone tent. A perfect stopover on the South West Coast Path which passes through the valley close by or for those who really do want to get away from it all. With access to it's own secluded beach you will not be disappointed.

There is no light or heating so bring your own sleeping, cooking and eating equipment and a torch!

DETAILS

- **Open** - All year. All day
- **Beds** - 4: BYO mats & sleeping bags
- **Price/night** - From £22 for whole bothy.

CONTACT: National Trust Holidays
Tel: 03443 351296
bunkhouses@nationaltrust.org.uk
www.nationaltrust.org.uk/holidays
Peppercombe, Bideford, Devon, EX39 5QD

OCEAN
BACKPACKERS

Close to picturesque Ilfracombe Harbour, this clean and friendly hostel offers fantastic facilities for walkers, cyclists, surfers, families, schools and activity groups. Providing self-catering accommodation with great facilities including, communal lounge (free WiFi), bike/surfboard storage, drying area and free parking. Ilfracombe is full of cafés, galleries, shops and restaurants and is home to Damien Hirst's statue, Verity.

DETAILS

- **Open** - March-Nov. Reception 9-12 noon and 4pm-10pm. No curfew.
- **Beds** - 54:- 1x8, 5x6, 1 x single, 2 x double, 3 x double & bunk
- **Price/night** - Dorm beds £13-£20pp. Double/twin rooms £45-£50 per room.

CONTACT: Chris and Abby
Tel: 01271 867835 Mob: 07866 667716
info@oceanbackpackers.co.uk
www.oceanbackpackers.co.uk
29 St James Place, Ilfracombe, Devon, EX34 9BJ

MULLACOTT

CAMPING BARN

84l

Set in 30 acres on the North Devon coast, the farm boasts sea views overlooking Woolacombe, Lundy Island, Lee Bay, Ilfracombe, and the Welsh coast. A former stable block with all accommodation on ground level with raised sleeping areas with mattresses. BYO sleeping bag/bedding and warm clothing. There is a dining area and well equipped kitchen. Toilets/coin operated showers are in a nearby block. No stag/ hen parties. Dogs welcome with sole use bookings. B&B, camping and a static caravan are also available on site.

DETAILS

- **Open** - March - November
- **Beds** - 20
- **Price/night** - £10 per person. Sole use: by arrangement.

CONTACT: Alison and Adrian Homa
Tel: 01271 866877
relax@mullacottfarm.co.uk
www.mullacottfarm.co.uk
Ilfracombe, Devon, EX34 8NA

NORTHSHORE

BUDE

84r

An ideal base to see the South West's attractions: The Eden Project, Tintagel Castle, The Tamar Lakes, Dartmoor and Bodmin Moor or as a stop off on the South West Coast Path. There are competition standard surfing beaches nearby. Families with children aged over 5 welcome. Meet old friends or make new ones, on the deck, in the lounge or around the dining room table after cooking up a storm in the fully fitted kitchen. No stag groups please.

DETAILS

- **Open** - All year, except Christmas week. 8.30am-1pm & 4.30-10.30pm.
- **Beds** - 41: 2x6, 4x4, 1x3, 1x2, 4xdbl
- **Price/night** - From £22pp dorm rooms (single night supplement)

CONTACT: Sean or Janine
Tel: 01288 354256
northshorebude@uk2.net
www.northshorebude.com
57 Killerton Road, Bude, Cornwall, EX23 8EW

ROCK AND RAPID

BUNKHOUSE

Perfect for an adventurous or relaxing break. The Rock and Rapid Adventure Centre offers activities such as climbing (climbing wall on site for lessons or use by experienced climbers) coasteering, raft building and canoeing. The bunkhouse can be rented out for sole use. Or an activity package can be put together for your group. This can vary rom a few activities to a full programme, including food.

Just 20 mins from the North Devon coastline. Hen and stags welcome as are family and school groups.

DETAILS

- **Open** - All year. 24 hours.
- **Beds** - 40: 2 x 18, 2 x 2
- **Price/night** - £250 per night sole use.

CONTACT: Gareth Chalker
Tel: 01769 309003
info@rockandrapidadventures.co.uk
www.rockandrapidadventures.co.uk
Hacche Mill, South Molton, EX36 3NA

BUTTER HILL

BARN

86

This cosy National Trust bunkhouse can be found at Countisbury close to Lynton and Lynmouth on the North Devon Coast. Surrounded by the dramatic Watersmeet Valleys and Exmoor, it is perfect for accessing the South West Coastal Path and the Atlantic surf beaches.

It is also great for those wanting to experience Exmoor's dark skies. Perfect for families, groups and walkers, the barn is just along the road from Exmoor Bunkhouse (see page 87), so it can be used as an overspill for larger groups.

GROUPS ONLY

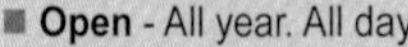

DETAILS

- **Open** - All year. All day
- **Beds** - 6: 1x6
- **Price/night** - 2 nights from £120.

CONTACT: National Trust Holidays
Tel: 03443 351296
bunkhouses@nationaltrust.org.uk
www.nationaltrust.org.uk/holidays
Countisbury, Lynton, Devon, EX35 6NE

EXMOOR
BUNKHOUSE

)wned & managed by the National Trust, providing comfortable, high standard accommodation, Exmoor Bunkhouse is the perfect base for families or groups visiting Exmoor National Park.

Located at Countisbury, the bunkhouse is close to the Watersmeet Valleys and the North Devon villages of Lynton and Lynmouth. Take part in the many activities Exmoor has to offer such as walking & horse riding or go surfing on ıearby beaches. Larger groups overspill at Butter Hill Barn (see page 86).

        GROUPS ONLY

DETAILS

- **Open** - All year. 24 hours.
- **Beds** - 18: 2x8, 1x2
- **Price/night** - 2 nights' minimum stay from £270 mid week and £390 weekend.

CONTACT: National Trust Holidays
Tel: 03443 351296
bunkhouses@nationaltrust.org.uk
www.nationaltrust.org.uk/holidays
Countisbury, Lynton, Devon, EX35 6NE

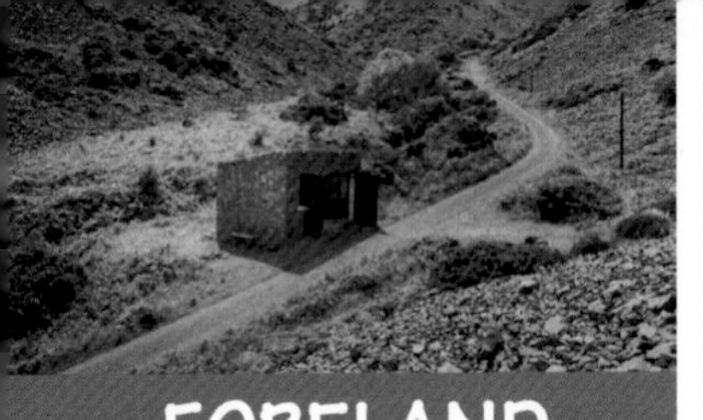

FORELAND

BOTHY

88

Foreland Bothy on the National Trust Foreland Point Estate on the Exmoor coast offers very basic accommodation, but rewards you with a fantastic location right on the South West Coast Path. Treat it like camping but without the tent, so you need to bring camping mats, sleeping bags and cooking equipment. There is a composting loo but no hot water. The perfect location for a night or two for those who want to explore the area on foot or want to escape technology in this wilderness under some stunning dark skies.

GROUPS ONLY

DETAILS

- **Open** - All year. All day
- **Beds** - 4: 1x4 platforms
- **Price/night** - From £22 sole use.

CONTACT: National Trust Holidays
Tel: 03443 351296
bunkhouses@nationaltrust.org.uk
www.nationaltrust.org.uk/
holidaysLighthouse Road, Countisbury,
Lynton, Devon, EX35 6NE

NORTHCOMBE

CAMPING BARNS

89l

A mile outside the town of Dulverton on Exmoor, Northcombe Camping Barns nestle in the Barle river valley with good canoeing, walking and bridleways. A perfect base for groups on Exmoor. The barns sleep 16 and 28 in partitioned dormitories. Smaller groups can be catered for. Heated by wood-burning stoves with a well equipped kitchen, you just need to bring your own pillows, sleeping bags or duvets.

GROUPS ONLY

DETAILS

- **Open** - All year. Arrive after 4pm, depart before 10.30am
- **Beds** - 44: Barn16: 1x6, 1x10. Barn28: 1x6, 1x10, 1x12
- **Price/night** - Sole use: Barn16 from £160, Barn28 from £260. Showers 20p. Electric meter £1 coins.

CONTACT: Sally Harvey
Tel: 01398 323602
sallyeharvey17@gmail.com
www.northcombecampingbarns.co.uk/
Hollam, Dulverton, Somerset, TA22 9JH

EXMOOR

BUNKBARN

89r

Formerly a granary on a working farm, this eco-friendly bunkbarn is just 1km from Winsford Hill. Perfect for exploring Exmoor on foot, bike or canoe. Hot water, central heating & good WiFi included in price. Well equipped, open-plan kitchen/dinning with room for all. Large drying room & BBQ area. BYO bedding & towels plus shoes/slippers to protect feet from rough barn floor. Sole use at weekends (2 nights min). Rooms can be booked individually in the week.

DETAILS

- **Open** - All year. All day.
- **Beds** - 25: 1x14, 1x8, 1x3
- **Price/night** - Weekend sole use: £350. Mon-Thur sole use: £300. Rooms: 14/bed £240, 8/bed £150, 3/bed £75.

CONTACT: Julia or Guy Everard
Tel: 01643 851410
bookings@exmoorbunkbarn.co.uk
www.exmoorbunkbarn.co.uk
Week Farm, Bridgetown, Dulverton TA22 9JP

CHITCOMBE FARM

CAMPING BARNS

90l

A small family farm in West Somerset on the edge of Exmoor, Chitcombe Farm provides inexpensive, basic, warm & dry accommodation. Perfect after a day hiking on Exmoor, or training for an event. The Hay Barn, is a dormitory style open plan barn whilst The Cart Shed is an open plan chalet. Both have well equipped kitchens, bathroom with showers, seating areas and central heating. Beds are in bunks. BYO pillows and sleeping bag.

DETAILS

- **Open** - All year.
- **Beds** - 16: The Hay Barn 14, The Cart Shed 4. More by arrangement
- **Price/night** - £20pp. Sole use: The Hay barn £200. The Cart Shed £75.

CONTACT: Ali Kennen
Tel: 01398 371274
stkennen@hotmail.co.uk
chitcombebarns.co.uk
Chitcombe Farm, Huish Champflower, Taunton, Somerset, TA4 2EL

BASE LODGE

90r

Base Lodge is your perfect base for exploring Exmoor, the Quantocks and North Devon. The South West Coast Path starts in Minehead and there is excellent mountain biking. Guided bikin[g], navigational training, climbing, surfing pony trekking and natural history walks can all be arranged. Base Lodge is clean, comfortable with self-catering an[d] a cosy log burner.

DETAILS

- **Open** - All year. All day access once booked (reception open from 3pm).
- **Beds** - 22: 2x2, 1x7, 1x6, 1x5
- **Price/night** - Dorms £17.50 (£20 one night), private single £7.50 supplement, twin/double £40. Sole use of Base Lodge from £200. Family room discount.

CONTACT: Wendy or Graham
Tel: 01643 703520 or 07731 651536
togooutdoors@hotmail.com
www.togooutdoors.co.uk
16 The Parks, Minehead, Somerset, TA24 8BS

STONE BARROW

FORMERLY GOLDEN CAP

On the National Trust Golden Cap Estate, this bunkhouse has been converted from an old MoD radar station and provides fantastic group accommodation for families, walkers or special interest groups.

With great views over Golden Cap, Lyme Bay and Chesil Beach it is the perfect base for a walking or beach holiday with Charmouth beaches only half an hour walk away. Stone Barrow Bunkhouse sleeps 8 in two 4 bed dorms and is well equipped for group self-catering.

    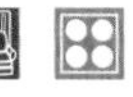  

DETAILS

- **Open** - All year. All day
- **Beds** - 8: 2x4
- **Price/night** - From £160 for two nights.

CONTACT: National Trust Holidays
Tel: 03443 351296
bunkhouses@nationaltrust.org.uk
www.nationaltrust.org.uk/
holidaysStonebarrow Lane, Charmouth,
Dorset, DT6 6RA

MONKTON WYLD

COURT

92l

This Victorian neo-Gothic mansion in Dorset's AONB has easy access to the Jurassic Coast at Lyme Regis as well as the Wessex and Monarch's Way long distance footpaths. Guests can use the vegetarian self-catering kitchen to prepare their own meals or vegetarian meals can be pre-booked. There is also camping in the grounds. Run by a charity that promotes sustainable living. Fruit and vegetables are grown in the organic garden and Jersey cows provide the dairy products.

DETAILS

- **Open** - All year. Office opening hours: 9am-5pm.
- **Beds** - 41 beds in a variety room sizes.
- **Price/night** - £20 - £35pp.

CONTACT: Office Team
Tel: 01297 560342
info@monktonwyldcourt.org
www.monktonwyldcourt.co.uk
Elsdon's Lane, Charmouth, Bridport, Dorset, DT6 6DQ

BHP BUDGET

ACCOMMODATION

92r

In the heart of Weymouth, the gateway to the Jurassic coast. With a mixture of bunk rooms with the Plus of double en suite rooms. Close to the town centre, the safe swimming waters of the beach & the old harbour which hosts fantastic festivals of the sea. Go wind and kite surfing, fishing, sailing, diving or rock climbing. Sole use possible for groups of up to 23. Facilities include large self catering kitchen, lounge with Freeview TV & DVD. No stag/hen or party groups

DETAILS

- **Open** - All year. Arrivals 2 pm onwards.
- **Beds** - 23: 3×4, 1×3, 2×2, 2x double en suites
- **Price/night** - Dorms from £18.50. Private rooms from £32. Sole use of building from £216 (sleeps 23).

CONTACT: BhP Budget Accommodation
Tel: 01305 789257
bunkhouseplus@gmail.com
www.bunkhouseplus.co.uk
47 Walpole Street, Weymouth, DT4 7HQ

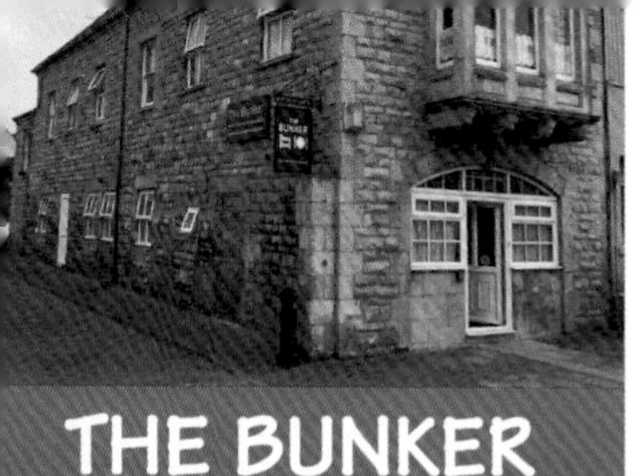

THE BUNKER

PORTLAND

93l

ıe Bunker is on the South West Coastal ²ath, with Chesil Beach on its doorstep and world class sport climbing, diving sites and water-sports a short distance way. Sleeping up to 18 in 6 private bunk rooms, each with a shower and sink, he Bunker offers bunk & breakfast and elf-catering accommodation for groups nd individuals. It has a large communal rea, kitchen with tea and coffee making acilities and free WiFi. Packed lunches nd evening meals available on request.

DETAILS

- **Open** - All year. Check in from 3pm, check out by 10am.
- **Beds** - 18: 3x4,3x2, private bunkrooms
- **Price/night** - Ranging from £15 to £27 per person. Exclusive hire available.

CONTACT: Tony or Sally
Tel: 07846 401010
stay@thebunkerportland.com
www.thebunkerportland.com
The Bunker, Victoria Square, Portland,
Dorset, DT5 1AL

MYTIME

OUTDOOR CENTRE

93r

Located on the Isle of Purbeck, just outside the picturesque village of Worth Matravers, the rustic MyTIME Outdoor Centre provides ideal accommodation for groups wishing to explore the magnificent Jurassic coastline and experience the enviable range of outdoor activities nearby; from walking and cycling to coasteering and kayaking. Groups have sole use of the centre.

GROUPS ONLY

DETAILS

- **Open** - All year.
- **Beds** - 40: 24 inside: 1x2, 1x4 en suite, 1x8, 1x10. 16 camping.
- **Price/night** - Whole centre from £330 (24 people). 16 more can camp (BYO tents) at £7pp. Bedding £5pp. Dog £15. Winter fuel supplement £10 (Oct-Mar).

CONTACT: MyTIME Outdoor Centre
Tel: 01202 710701
enquiries@mytimecharity.co.uk
www.mytimecharity.co.uk/Outdoor_Centre.html
Off Renscombe Rd, Worth Matravers,
Isle of Purbeck, Dorset. BH19 3LL

SWANAGE

AUBERGE

Family run, Swanage Auberge is a refuge for climbers, cyclists, walkers & divers at the eastern end of the Jurassic Coast. In the centre of Swanage, a stone's throw from the South West Coast Path, there is excellent walking, mountain biking, diving and rock climbing close by. There is a fully equipped self-catering kitchen and a packed lunch service if required. Parking for 2 vehicles is available on a first come first served basis & free on-street parking is close by.

DETAILS

- **Open** - All year (phone mobile if no reply). All day.
- **Beds** - 15: 1x6, 1x4,1x5
- **Price/night** - £20pp, £18 for 2+ nights. Inc bedding/towel, cereal breakfast, tea & coffee. Group rates. No credit cards.

CONTACT: Pete or Pam
Tel: 01929 424368 or 07711 117668
bookings@swanageauberge.co.uk
www.swanageauberge.co.uk
45 High St, Swanage, Dorset, BH19 2LX

SOUTH SHORE
LODGE

ɔuth Shore Lodge is on the south coast of Brownsea Island in Poole Harbour. t is a Victorian lodge, available to hire ɜar-round by youth, community, special nterest, corporate and school groups. ɿere is also some availability for hire by groups of families and friends.

With its own garden, beach access, hower block and views of the Purbeck ills, the lodge sleeps 24 in 5 rooms and well equipped for self-catering. Access ɔ Brownsea Island is by foot on a ferry from Sandbanks/Poole.

GROUPS ONLY

DETAILS

- **Open** - All year. All day
- **Beds** - 24: 3x6, 1x4, 1x2
- **Price/night** - 1 night £330.

CONTACT: National Trust Holidays
Tel: 01202 707744
rownseagroupbooking@nationaltrust.org.uk
www.nationaltrust.org.uk
ɔlidaysBrownsea Island, Poole, Dorset, BH13 7EE

CHOLDERTON
YOUTH HOSTEL

96l

Situated on a delightful family owned farm, this 4* youth hostel provides family/child friendly accommodation for groups or individuals. The hostel is located 8 miles from historic Salisbury with its cathedral, and only 5 miles from Stonehenge. Cooked breakfasts are available from the Ewe Tree Café and packed lunches & evening meals can be pre-booked. Guests get free admission to Charlie's rare breeds farm and large indoor play barn, just next door. Or why not explore the tree top trail, zip wire and woodland walk in the grounds?

  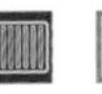    

DETAILS

- **Open** - All year
- **Beds** - 70
- **Price/night** - Enquire for prices.

CONTACT: Reception
Tel: 01980 629438
info@choldertonyouthhostel.co.uk
www.choldertonyouthhostel.co.uk
Beacon House, Amesbury Road,
Cholderton, Salisbury, Wilts, SP4 0EW

MENDIP
BUNKHOUSE

96r

Larkshall (Mendip Bunkhouse) is the Cerberus Spelaeological Society's headquarters and offers well appointec modern and comfortable accommodatic on The Mendips. It is an ideal base fo caving, walking, cycling, climbing, divin at Vobster Quay and for exploring the Somerset countryside. Popular tourist attractions, including Wells, Wookey Hole, Cheddar Gorge and the city of Bath, are all within reach. Camping available. Ample parking.

DETAILS

- **Open** - All year. All day.
- **Beds** - 30 in 3 rooms (plus camping).
- **Price/night** - £8pp. (Sole use only by arrangement). Min charge £15 pp pe stay.

CONTACT:
Tel: 08454 750954
hostelbookings@cerberusspeleo.org.u
www.cerberusspeleo.org.uk
Cerberus Spelaeological, Larkshall,
Fosse Rd. Oakhill, Somerset, BA3 5H

BATH YMCA

97

Bath YMCA offers great value accommodation. Centrally located, all the sights of this World Heritage city are easily reached on foot. With 210 beds, Bath YMCA specialises in making guests feel comfortable. Fully air conditioned lounge with TV, laundry, lockers, football table and WiFi. Couples, families, groups and backpackers all welcome.

DETAILS

- **Open** - All year. All day.
- **Beds** - 210: Dorms: 1x10, 3x12, 1x15, 1x18. Rooms: 7 x quad, 6 x triple, 29 x twin, 5 x double, 9 x single
- **Price/night** - From: dorm £16pp, single £32pp, twin £28pp, double £30pp, double ensuite £40pp, triple £23pp, quad £22pp. Inc breakfast.

CONTACT: Reception
Tel: 01225 325900
stay@ymcabathgroup.org.uk
www.ymcabathgroup.org.uk
International House, Broad Street Place,
Bath, BA1 5LH

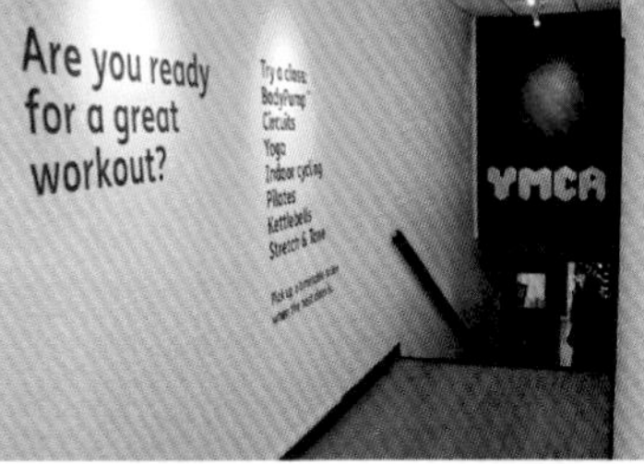

FULL MOON

BACKPACKERS

A live music venue and travellers' hostel at the heart of Bristol's arts and cultural area, Stokes Croft. Just 10 minutes' walk from the city centre and bus station. This historic coaching inn is not a place for an early night, as guests get free entry to live music and DJ's at the Full Moon's Attic Bar. Beds are available in dorms and private rooms. There is kitchen, common room and a large courtyard with plenty of opportunities to get to know people from around the world.

DETAILS

- **Open** - All year
- **Beds** - 78: 2xdbl, 2xtwin, 1x3, 1x4, 1x5, 2x6, 2x8, 3x10
- **Price/night** - From £19pp in a dorm. £40 / £50 for private twin / double.

CONTACT: Reception
Tel: 0117 924 5007
info@fullmoonbristol.co.uk
www.fmbristol.co.uk
1 North St, Stokes Croft, Bristol, BS1 3PR

KYLE BLUE

HOSTEL BOAT

99

Moored in the heart of Bristol's historic harbour, only a five minute stroll to the city centre. The Kyle Blue Hostel Boat is a converted Dutch Barge with private and shared cabins and a spacious upper deck providing fabulous views of the harbour from its tranquil lounge and well equipped self-catering kitchen. Great for independent travellers or small groups wanting to visit this vibrant city. Sleeping is in various sized cabins with private shower rooms. The Kyle Blue is moored in a residential area so no noise after 11pm.

DETAILS

- **Open** - All year. All day
- **Beds** - 30: 4x1/small dbl, 3x5 1x4 1x7
- **Price/night** - From £29 per person

CONTACT:
Tel: 0117 929 0609
kylebluebristol@gmail.com
kylebluebristol.co.uk
Wapping Wharf, Museum Street, Bristol
BS1 6GW

ROCK AND BOWL

100

The Rock n Bowl Hostel is in the heart of Bristol. It occupies 2 floors of an historic 1930s building with The Lanes, a bowling alley, bar and club venue on the ground floor (hostel guests get great discounts). With its huge range of rooms there will be a bed to suit your budget. And everyone gets a free breakfast! Facilities include a well equipped large kitchen, lounge with Sky TV including Sky Sports/ BT Sports, laundry and free WiFi.

DETAILS

- **Open** - All year. All day.
- **Beds** - 144: 1×20, 3×12, 1×10, 3×10 weekly bed dorm, 2×8, 2×6, 3×4, 1×4 female, 1xdouble/twin/3bed, 1xdouble
- **Price/night** - Dorms from £10pp. Private rooms from £39. Weekly rooms from £90.

CONTACT: The Reception Team
Tel: 0117 325 1980
bookings@rocknbowlmotel.com
www.thelanesbristol.co.uk/hostel/
22 Nelson Street, Bristol, BS1 2LE

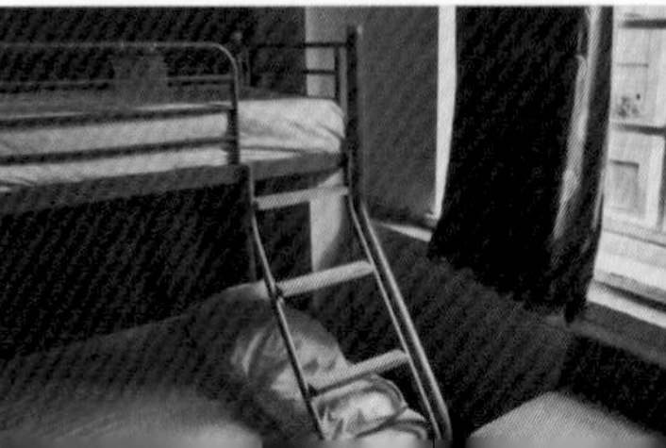

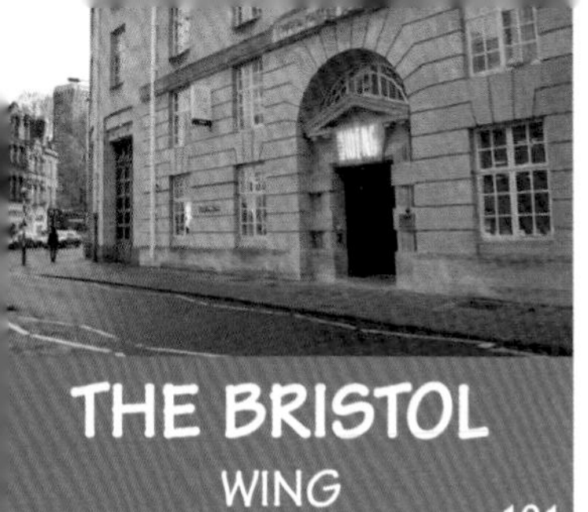

THE BRISTOL
WING

This brand new hostel, in the historic old police headquarters, is in the heart of the city centre. A mix of private, en suite and dorm rooms makes it ideal for single travellers, couples and families. The communal spaces on the ground floor include an award winning café offering tasty breakfasts, great coffee and a super fresh lunch menu. Close to the bus station, just 20 mins from Bristol Temple Meads and perfectly located for Bristol's best shopping from the independent shops of Park Street & Clifton, to big name brands in Cabot Circus or quirky market stalls in St Nicholas's Market.

DETAILS

- **Open** - All year. All day.
- **Beds** - 88
- **Price/night** - From £18 per person

CONTACT: Reception
Tel: 0117 428 6199
enquiries@thebristolwing.co.uk
www.thebristolwing.co.uk/
9 Bridewell Street, Bristol, BS1 2QD

BRISTOL

BACKPACKERS HOSTEL

102l

Bristol's most central backpacker hostel. Clean & comfortable beds - mixed/single sex dorms - private rooms - individual bathrooms & free hot showers - free linen - large self-catering kitchen - free tea, coffee & hot chocolate. Late night basement bar - piano & guitar room - DVD lounge - free WiFi - luggage storage room - laundrette.
Run by backpackers for backpackers - No curfew after check in.

DETAILS

- **Open** - All year. Reception hours 9am -11.30pm (no curfew).
- **Beds** - 90: Bunk bed accommodation in private twin, private triple or 6, 8 and 10 bed dorms.
- **Price/night** - From £18pp. £90 per week. From £35 for private rooms.

CONTACT:
Tel: 0117 925 7900
bristol.backpackers.hostel@gmail.com
www.bristolbackpackers.co.uk
17 St Stephen's Street, Bristol, BS1 1EQ

SOUTHSEA ROCKS

HOTEL

102r

Southsea Rocks Hotel has a variety of rooms from great value hotel rooms with en suite options to cool hostel dorms.

There are social areas, an outdoor courtyard to sit in the sun and space for guests to enjoy take outs from local restaurants. It is within walking distance of the castle, common and aquarium and is a great base for exploring other attractions including Portsmouth's historic dockyard, Charles Dickens' birthplace and The Mary Rose Museum.

DETAILS

- **Open** - All year. All day
- **Beds** - 28: 2x2, 3x3, 1x4, 1x5, 1x9
- **Price/night** - Private rooms from £40, beds in dorm also available.

CONTACT: Reception
Tel: 02392 820110 or 07510 800761
info@southsearockshotel.co.uk
www.southsearockshotel.co.uk
4 Florence Rd, Portsmouth, Southsea
PO5 2NE

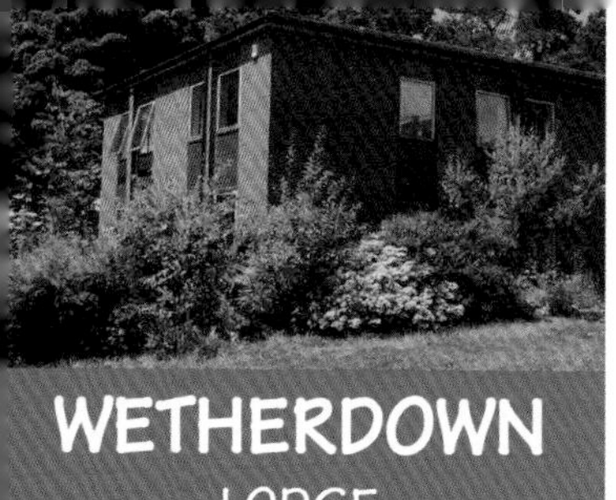

WETHERDOWN LODGE

103l

An award winning eco-renovation in the heart of the South Downs National Park right on the South Downs Way National Trail. The perfect base for walkers, cyclists, business away-days and family get-togethers. The Lodge offers well appointed self-catering accommodation while the campsite has yurts and secluded woodland pitches. The centre has large grounds with woodland trails and a café. Pubs, shops within 2 miles.

DETAILS

- **Open** - Hostel and campsite open all year. Yurts closed from Nov to April
- **Beds** - 38: 10 x 3, 4 x 2
- **Price/night** - See sustainability-centre website.

CONTACT: Dan
Tel: 01730 823549
accommodation@sustainability-centre.org
www.sustainability-centre.org
The Sustainability Centre, Droxford Road, East Meon, Hampshire, GU32 1HR

THE PRIVETT CENTRE

103r

In glorious East Hampshire countryside (AONB), The Privett Centre offers low cost, comfortable, short-stay accommodation in a unique rural setting. It has been designed to accommodate small to medium-sized groups who like to have the place to themselves. Outside a large paddock and asphalt playground provide secure and spacious recreational and parking space. It is available for weekday, weekend and day use all year. The Privett Centre is an ideal residential setting for family & friends' get-togethers.

DETAILS

- **Open** - All year.
- **Beds** - 29: 1x1, 1x2, 2x4, 1x6, 1x12
- **Price/night** - From £15 pp. Minimum charges apply. (Contact for exact prices).

CONTACT: Mehalah Piedot
Tel: 01256 351555
info@privettcentre.org.uk
www.privettcentre.org.uk
Church Lane, Privett, Hampshire, GU34 3PE

GUMBER
CAMPING BARN

A converted Sussex flint barn on a working sheep farm within the National Trust's Slindon Estate, Gumber Camping Barn provides simple overnight accommodation & camping for walkers, horse riders and cyclists, just off the South Downs Way. A tranquil and remote location for you to get away from it all. Just five minutes' walk from Stane Street, the Roman Road that crosses the South Downs Way at Bignor Hill. NO CARS. Not suitable for under fives.

DETAILS

- **Open** - Mar-Oct. Flexible opening hours
- **Beds** - 25: 1x16, 1x5, 1x4 plus overflow area
- **Price/night** - £12, £6 (under 16s).

CONTACT: Gumber Bookings Team
Tel: 01243 814484
gumberbothy@nationaltrust.org.uk
www.nationaltrust.org.uk/holidays
Gumber Campsite and Camping Barn,
Gumber Farm, Slindon, West Sussex,
BN18 0RN

SLINDON

BUNKHOUSE

105

This bunkhouse on the National Trust Slindon Estate has so much to offer all year round.

In the winter months enjoy the benefit of the wood burner in the lounge, and in the summer enjoy a barbeque in the walled garden.

Perfect for all types of groups and families wanting to get together and enjoy the fabulous South Downs National Park, its surroundings and the miles of footpaths that criss-cross the estate.

GROUPS ONLY

DETAILS

- **Open** - All year. All day
- **Beds** - 17, 1x6, 1x10, 1x1
- **Price/night** - 2 nights from £430

CONTACT: National Trust Holidays
Tel: 0344 335 1296
bunkhouses@nationaltrust.org.uk
www.nationaltrust.org.uk/holidays
Slindon Estate Yard, Top Road, Slindon, Arundel, West Sussex, BN18 0RG

PUTTENHAM

ECO CAMPING BARN

This eco project on North Downs Way offers simple overnight accommodation in a beautifully converted historic barn. Self-catering (or local pubs for food within walking distance); three shared sleeping areas; garden with picnic bench and cycle shed. NO CARS ON SITE, even for off-loading. Nearest rail stations: Wanborough 3.5 km, Guildford 7 km.

DETAILS

- **Open** - April 13th to Oct. arrive after 5pm leave before 10am. No access 10am-5pm.
- **Beds** - Sleeping platforms for 11.
- **Price/night** - £15 adults; £12 aged 5-17 (accompanied by adult). Sole use by arrangement. £3 `green` voucher if arriving on foot, cycle or public transport.

CONTACT: Bookings
Tel: 01483 811001
bookings@puttenhamcampingbarn.co.uk
www.puttenhamcampingbarn.co.uk
The Street, Puttenham, Nr Guildford, Surrey, GU3 1AR

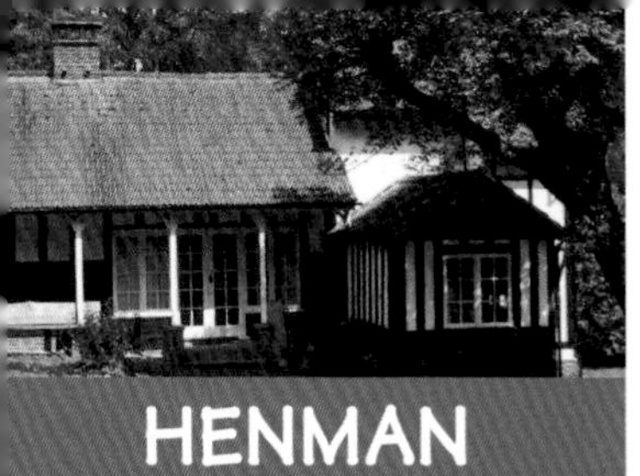

HENMAN

BUNKHOUSE

107

Perfect for groups wanting to walk or cycle around Leith Hill or beyond. This National Trust owned bunkhouse in the Surrey Hills AONB sleeps up to 16 in 6 and 4 bunk dorms. Well equipped with a self-catering kitchen, large dining table and comfy seating around an open fire. Walkers can directly access the Greensand Way and other local routes and there are many bridleways and tracks suitable for cycling. This is a great place for a holiday only 30 miles from London but in stunning countryside.

GROUPS ONLY

DETAILS

- **Open** - All year. All day except for Christmas and New Year
- **Beds** - 16: 2x6, 1x4
- **Price/night** - £225 Friday to Sunday, £180 Monday to Thursday

CONTACT: National Trust Holidays
Tel: 01306 712711
leithhill@nationaltrust.org.uk
www.nationaltrust.org.uk/holidays
Broadmoor, Dorking, Surrey, RH5 6JZ

OCTAVIA HILL

BUNKHOUSE

Converted from former farm buildings, Octavia Hill Bunkhouse is located on Outridge Farm on the National Trust Toys Hill Estate. Sleeping 10 in two rooms it is the perfect base for families or groups of walkers wanting to explore this lovely part of the Kent Downs Area of Outstanding Natural Beauty.

This bunkhouse has plenty of communal space and a well equipped kitchen for those who want to self-cater. Easily accessible by car, train and bus (the bus stop is just 15 minutes' walk away).

DETAILS

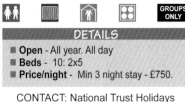

- **Open** - All year. All day
- **Beds** - 10: 2x5
- **Price/night** - Min 3 night stay - £750.

CONTACT: National Trust Holidays
Tel: 03443 35 1296
bunkhouses@nationaltrust.org.uk
www.nationaltrust.org.uk/holidaysPipers Green Road, Brasted Chart, Westerham, Kent, TN16 1ND

PALACE FARM
HOSTEL

Palace Farm Hostel is a relaxing and flexible 4* hostel on a family run farm. Situated in the village of Doddington, (which has a pub!), in the North Kent Downs AONB, the area is great for walking, cycling (cycle hire available £10 a day) and wildlife. The accommodation consists of ten fully heated en suite rooms sleeping up to 39. Duvets, linen and continental breakfast included.

DETAILS

- **Open** - All year. 8am to 10pm flexible, please ask.
- **Beds** - 39: 1x8, 1x6, 2x5 (family room), 1x4, 1x3 and 4x2
- **Price/night** - From £18-£37.50 pp (all private en suite rooms). Group reductions.

CONTACT: Graham and Liz Cuthbert
Tel: 01795 886200
info@palacefarm.com
www.palacefarm.com
Down Court Road, Doddington, Sittingbourne / Faversham, Kent, ME9 0AU

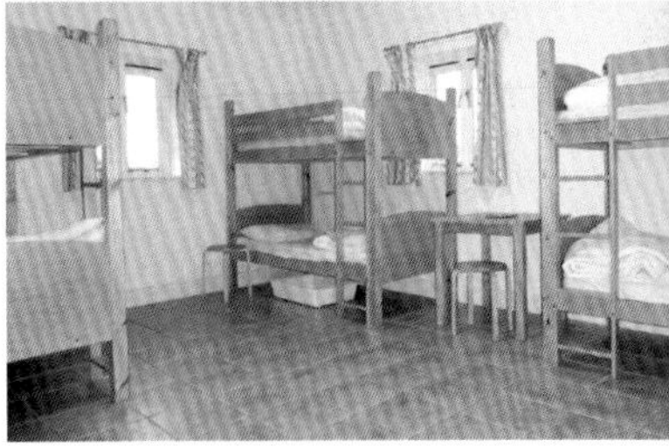

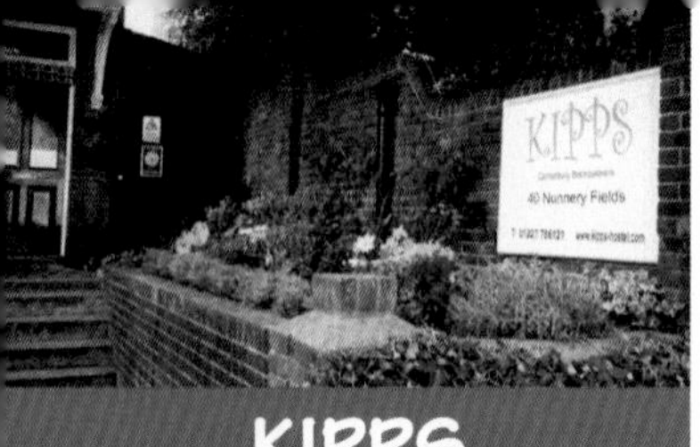

KIPPS

CANTERBURY

110

Perfect for backpackers, visitors to Canterbury or groups. Close to the the city centre & Canterbury Cathedral.

Ideal for visiting Dover, Leeds Castle, Whitstable & Herne Bay. Fully equipped kitchen, dining room, TV lounge, large garden with outdoor pool table. Free WiFi. Private rooms have TV/tea/coffee & mini safe. Dorms have free lockers

DETAILS

- **Open** - All year. No curfew. Reception 7.30am to 11pm.
- **Beds** - 41: 2x1, 3x2, 1x4, 2x6, 1x8, 1x9. Most rooms en suite.
- **Price/night** - From: Mixed dorm £15pp. Sgle room £25pp. Dble/twin £45, Family £60. Weekly/winter rates. Parking permits for street parking from reception.

CONTACT: Reception
Tel: 01227 786121
kippshostel@gmail.com
www.kipps-hostel.com
40 Nunnery Fields, Canterbury, CT1 3JT

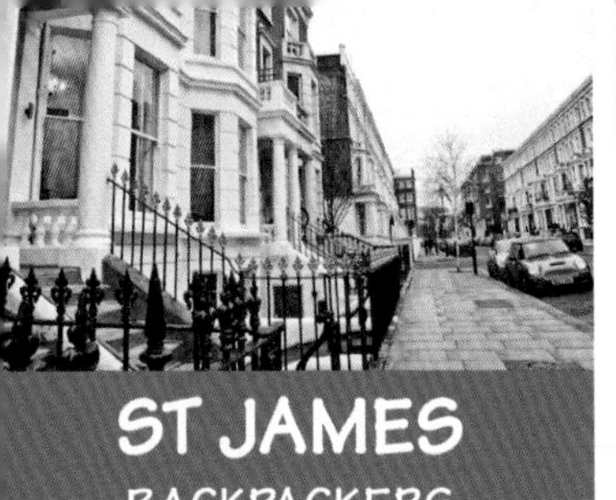

ST JAMES

BACKPACKERS

111l

St James Backpackers is a family-run hostel welcoming global travellers in central London's Earls Court. A great place for people who like to mingle, with a communal dinner each night and a warm community vibe helped along by the lovely staff. Just around the corner from Earl Court Tube station (Zone 1, central London). Free fast WiFi. Free dinner, breakfast and 24hr hot drinks. Lots of space for socialising including a lovely garden and lounge with HD TV.

DETAILS

- **Open** - All year. 24 hour reception,
- **Beds** - 108: Double, twin & triple private rooms (some en suite). Dorms sleeping 4, 6 or 8.
- **Price/night** - From £20, depending on season and room.

CONTACT: Reception
Tel: 07450 645573
info@saint-james-hostel.co.uk
www.saint-james-hostel.co.uk
21 Longridge Road, London, SW5 9SB

PUBLOVE

THE WHITE FERRY

111r

The White Ferry House is a stunning Victorian flat-iron building steeped in history. It provides accommodation in central London, close to Victoria, The Houses of Parliament and Buckingham Palace. In the traditional pub atmosphere you can enjoy chilling out and playing board games, locally sourced drinks and award-winning burgers. There's a 24 hour reception, free WiFi, individual power sockets and guest food & drink discounts. Publove@The White Ferry offers a classic night out and a great location for exploring London by day.

DETAILS

- **Open** - All year.
- **Beds** - 75: 1x3, 1x9, 2x12, 1x15, 1x24
- **Price/night** - From £14 per person.

CONTACT: The Bar
Tel: 020 7233 6133
whiteferry@publove.co.uk
www.publove.co.uk/white-ferry-victoria
The White Ferry House, 1 Sutherland Street, London, SW1V 4LD

CLINK78

In the centre of London in a 200 year old courthouse, Clink78 combines original features with modern interior design to create a friendly & unique hostel. In the heart of King's Cross, with easy tube access to the whole city. The friendly team will happily help with your itinerary and provide discounted attraction tickets. Kitchen, games area, TV/film lounge. Meet new people in The ClashBAR.

DETAILS

- **Open** - All year. 24 hours - no curfew or lockouts.
- **Beds** - 500: 4-16 bed dorms, triple, twin, single, en suite, cell rooms (for 2)
- **Price/night** - From £15pp. Bedlinen, WiFi & London walking tour inc. Group discounts.

CONTACT: Maud
Tel: 020 7183 9400
reservations78@clinkhostels.com
www.clinkhostels.com
78 Kings Cross Road, King's Cross, London, WC1X 9QG

PUBLOVE

THE CROWN

113l

A hip hangout for locals and travellers, The Crown at Battersea has easy-going vibes. Check in and find your bed, then lounge on the cosy sofas with a tipple or get involved with some board games. Newly refurbished in 2018 The Crown is in south-west London on the lively Lavender Street. Hostel beds are in mixed dormitories, with WiFi, fresh linen, duvet and pillow, 24hr bar, reception and security all included. With food and drink discounts for hostel guests, experience the fun and lively atmosphere of PubLove culture in London.

DETAILS

- **Open** - All year.
- **Beds** - 27: 1x3, 1x9, 1x15
- **Price/night** - From £15 per person.

CONTACT: The Bar
Tel: 020 7738 1122
crown@publove.co.uk
www.publove.co.uk/crown-battersea
PubLove@The Crown,102 Lavender Hill,London, SW11 5RD

PUBLOVE

THE EXMOUTH ARMS

113r

Five minutes' stroll from Euston Station and just 15 minutes' walk from the Eurostar at St Pancras, with The British Museum, Madame Tussauds, Regents Park and many of London's attractions an easy stroll away. PubLove@The Exmouth Arms not only gives you a bed for the night, but also the great atmosphere of a British pub. Complete with pub quizzes every Tuesday, hand crafted burgers and a wide range of drinks including local gins and ales. Explore London by foot in the day with a night of cracking PubLove ahead.

DETAILS

- **Open** - All year
- **Beds** - 31: 1x2, 2x6, 1x8, 1x9
- **Price/night** - From £14 per person.

CONTACT: The Bar
Tel: 020 7387 5440
exmoutharms@publove.co.uk
www.publove.co.uk/exmouth-arms-euston
PubLove @The Exmouth Arms, 1 Starcross Street, London, NW1 2HR

CLINK261

One of London's top backpacker hostels, Clink261 offers simple, comfortable, self-catering accommodation in the city centre. King's Cross is a creative area close to the British Museum, Covent Garden & Camden Market or a short tube ride to Piccadilly Circus & Leicester Square. Guests can go round the corner to Clink78 (see page 112) for entertainment and good value drinks at the ClashBAR.

DETAILS

- **Open** - All year. All day (except for Xmas) - no curfew or lockouts.
- **Beds** - 170: 4-6 8-10 & 18 bed dorms, 4 private rooms (up to 2 beds)
- **Price/night** - From £15pp. Breakfast bookable. Group discounts.

CONTACT: Maud
Tel: 020 7833 9400
reservations261@clinkhostels.com
www.clinkhostels.com
261-265 Gray's Inn Road, King's Cross, London, WC1X 8QT

PUBLOVE

THE GREEN MAN

115l

Spend your night above a pub, 5 mins from Paddington Station & experience the real & exciting local London. PubLove@The Green Man, has great transport connections to all the famous sites, 24 hour reception & bar, free WiFi, personal power sockets, bed screens & guest food & drink discounts. You can book by the bed or book a private room. There are friendly bar-staff who like to chat, so ask about places to go and the events happening because there's nothing better then advice from a local.

DETAILS

- **Open** - All year
- **Beds** - 18: 1x3, 1x6, 1x9
- **Price/night** - From £15

CONTACT: The Bar
Tel: 020 7723 7980
greenman@publove.co.uk
www.publove.co.uk/green-man-paddington
PubLove@The Green Man, 308 Edgware Road, Paddington, London W2 1DY

PUBLOVE

THE STEAM ENGINE

115r

Book a bed upstairs, then relax on one of the snug Chesterfield sofas in this classy British pub in the heart of Waterloo. Everything you need is on hand, 24 hour reception, a beer garden for summer evenings, free WiFi, hand crafted burgers & the best of London's beers & gins. Publove@The Steam Engine is a short walk from London's main attractions. Head to the river to see London in all its glory, Big Ben and the London Eye. Enjoy a classic night out in central London in the heart of British pub culture.

DETAILS

- **Open** - All year
- **Beds** - 33: 2 x 12, 1x9
- **Price/night** - From £16 per person.

CONTACT: The Bar
Tel: 020 7928 0720
steamengine@publove.co.uk
www.publove.co.uk/steam-engine-waterloo
PubLove@The Steam Engine, 41-42 Cosser Street, London, SE1 7BU

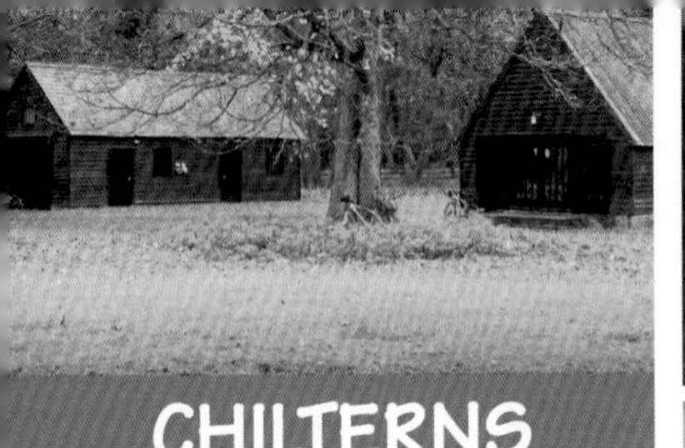

CHILTERNS
BUNKHOUSE

116

Located on the National Trust's Ashridge Estate in the heart of the Chilterns Area of Outstanding Natural Beauty, this bunkhouse provides rustic, basic accommodation which comprises two restored barns located amongst the woodlands and grassland of the estate.

A well equipped, self-catering kitchen, lounge and outdoor eating area make it perfect for self-catering groups whilst the nearby picture postcard village of Aldbury has two pubs. There is no mobile reception at the bunkhouse.

   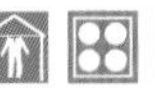    GROUPS ONLY

DETAILS

- **Open** - All year. All Day
- **Beds** - 16: 2x8
- **Price/night** - From £220

CONTACT: National Trust Holidays
Tel: 03443 351296
bunkhouses@nationaltrust.org.uk
www.nationaltrust.org.uk/holidays
Outwood Kiln, Aldbury, Tring,
Hertfordshire, HP23 5SE

OLD BROODER

BUNKHOUSE

117

;omfy, farm self-catering in rural Suffolk close to historic Lavenham. Sleeps 20 singles in four bedrooms. Mix of oak ›unks/conventional beds. Relax in cosy sitting room; BBQ, ping-pong, croquet & badminton in the garden; explore the farm, picnic in a meadow. 20 bikes ncluded to explore quiet country lanes, ›r kayak down the River Stour, Go Ape, visit castles, print workshop courses.

       GROUPS ONLY

DETAILS

- **Open** - Check booking arrangements
- **Beds** - 20: 2x2, 2x8
- **Price/night** - W/ends: 2nt min from £1400. 3nts Bk Hols £1800. Xmas-New Yr (3nts+) £1900+. 2nt midweek stay £900. Ask for a quote for small groups or one-night stays.

CONTACT: Juliet Hawkins
Tel: 01787 247235
hawkins@thehall-milden.co.uk
www.thehall-milden.co.uk
The Hall, Milden, Lavenham, Sudbury, Suffolk CO10 9NY

CHELLINGTON CENTRE

A unique and memorable venue for group stays. Situated in the beautiful Bedfordshire countryside with amazing views across the Great River Ouse, it's easily accessible from the M1 but a world apart. The converted 12th century church can sleep 30 in bunkrooms, with modern facilities, an industrial style kitchen for self-catering and two breakout rooms. Youth group discounts available.

DETAILS

- **Open** - All year
- **Beds** - 30: 2 x 5, 5 x 4
- **Price/night** - Youth Groups: week night £385, weekend (Fri&Sat exit by 2pm Sunday) £840. Other groups: week night £440, weekend £1050.

CONTACT: Claire or Scott
Tel: 01234 720726
admin@chellington.org
www.chellington.org
The Chellington Centre, St Nicholas Church, Felmersham Road, Carlton, Bedford MK43 7NA

HARLOW

INTERNATIONAL

119l

Harlow International Hostel is in the centre of a landscaped park and is one of the oldest buildings in Harlow. The town of Harlow is your ideal base for exploring London, Cambridge and the est of South East England. The journey me to central London is only 35 minutes rom the hostel door and it is the closest ostel to Stansted Airport. National Cycle Route 1 passes the front door. Meals can be provided for groups. There's a children's zoo, orienteering course and outdoor pursuits centre in the park.

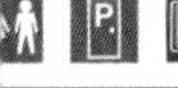      

DETAILS

- **Open** - All year. 8am - 10.30pm (check in 3-10.30pm).
- **Beds** - 30: 2x1, 5x2, 1x4, 1x6, 1x8
- **Price/night** - Please see the website.

CONTACT: Richard Adams
Tel: 01279 421702
mail@h-i-h.co.uk
www.h-i-h.co.uk
13 School Lane, Harlow, Essex, CM20 2QD

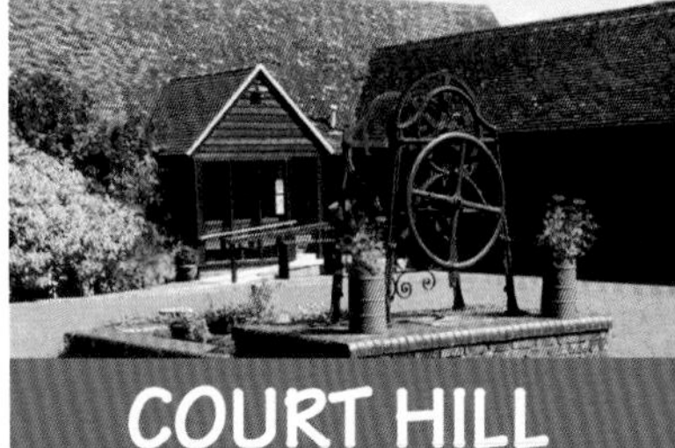

COURT HILL

CENTRE

119r

Just 2 miles south of Wantage, and only a few steps from the historic Ridgeway National Trail, Court Hill Centre enjoys breathtaking views over the Vale of the White Horse. Reclaimed barns surround a pretty courtyard garden. Providing accommodation to families, groups and individuals, the centre offers evening meals, breakfasts and picnic lunches.

There is a beautiful high-roofed dining room which retains the atmosphere of the old barn. A meeting/class-room camping and self-catering available.

DETAILS

- **Open** - All year. To check availability please call 01235 760253.
- **Beds** - 59: 1x15,1x9,1x6,1x5,6x4,1x2
- **Price/night** - From £22.50. U18 £15.50

CONTACT: Reception
Tel: 01235 760253
info@courthill.org.uk
www.courthill.org.uk
Letcombe Regis, Wantage, OX12 9NE

CROFT FARM

WATERPARK

120l

Just outside Tewkesbury in the scenic River Avon Valley, with it's own lake. Accommodation is in cabins, a pod village, chalets and camping. Great for touring the Cotswolds, Malverns, Bredon Hill and the Forest of Dean. There are also a wide range of watersports activities and tuition on offer providing added interest for those wanting a more active holiday. A footpath meanders through the meadow to the River Avon, and free river fishing is available to all guests.

DETAILS

- **Open** - All year. 9am-9pm.
- **Beds** - 250: 58x4 9x2
- **Price/night** - Bed £12, B&B £18, half board £24, full board £30

CONTACT: Martin Newell
Tel: 07736 036967 or 01684 772321
alan@croftfarmleisure.co.uk
www.croftfarmwaterpark.com
Bredons Hardwick, Near Tewkesbury, Gloucestershire GL20 7EE

YE OLD FERRIE INN

BUNKHOUSE

120r

This beautiful riverside pub has been standing on the banks of the River Wye since the 15th century. With charming traditional features, warming open fires and stunning views across the valley, Ye Old Ferrie Inn is the ideal base for your exploration of the Wye Valley. Ye Old Ferrie Inn Bunkhouse, adjoining the inn, is the perfect place for you to hang up your rucksack, kick off your walking boots and relax. Popular with canoeists, walkers and climbers. If you don't fancy self-catering there is B&B in the Inn.

DETAILS

- **Open** - All year. All day.
- **Beds** - 20:1x14, 1x6 + dbl B&B rooms.
- **Price/night** - From £15 per person For sole use please ring to enquire.

CONTACT: Jamie
Tel: 01600 890 232
hello@yeoldferrieinn.com
www.yeoldferrieinn.com
Ferrie Lane, Symonds Yat West, Herefordshire HR9 6BL

BERROW HOUSE

BUNKHOUSE

Visit Berrow House Bunkhouse in the Malvern Hills with direct access to Ragged Hill and Eastnor Castle. Berrow House is near to the old spa town of Malvern and within half an hour of the Welsh Border and the Forest of Dean. It's an ideal base for walkers on the Worcestershire Way. In the garden around Berrow House there is a selection of simple accommodation and camping with a picnic area and nature area. Good for star gazing and enjoying the views of the Cotswold Hills.

DETAILS

- **Open** - All year. All day.
- **Beds** - 7 (Bunkhouse), 4 (Fold), 3 (Nook), 3 (Bandsaw Barn) & 8 tents.
- **Price/night** - £14 per person

CONTACT: Bill or Mary Cole
Tel: 01531 635845
berrowhouse@tiscali.co.uk
www.berrowhouse.co.uk
Hollybush, Ledbury, Herefordshire, HR8 1ET

WOODSIDE LODGES
BUNKHOUSE

Woodside Lodges Bunkhouse sits in a landscaped park with pools & wild flower meadows, along with Scandinavian self-catering lodges, a campsite and camping pods. The bunkhouse offers 5 self-catering units. Guests enjoy private rooms but share the campsite shower block. Close to the Herefordshire Trail, Malvern Hills & the Forest of Dean it's ideal for walkers, cyclists & nature lovers.

DETAILS

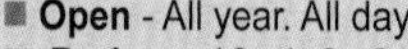

- **Open** - All year. All day.
- **Beds** - 16: 1x2, 2x3, 2x4 (max 20 using camp beds)
- **Price/night** - From £12.50 based on 4 sharing. Sole use of rooms. Phone/check website for full prices. £5 per pet.

CONTACT: Woodside Lodges Country Park
Tel: 01531 670269
info@woodsidelodges.co.uk
www.woodsidelodges.co.uk
Woodside Lodges, Falcon Lane, Ledbury, Herefordshire, HR8 2JN

DUNFIELD HOUSE

In rural Herefordshire, close to the Welsh border, Dunfield House provides accommodation for groups of up to 95 with sole use of the house, stables, parkland & swimming pool. From November to March the house & stables can also be hired individually by smaller groups. The house provides fully catered accommodation & the stables have a self-catering kitchen. A great choice for school, youth, music or church groups, training courses & family get-togethers.

GROUPS ONLY

DETAILS

- **Open** - All year. All day.
- **Beds** - 95: main house 73, stables: 22
- **Price/night** - Sole hire of site from £25pp fully catered. Stables (sleeping 22) self-catering from £350 per night.

CONTACT: The Reception Team
Tel: 01544 230563
info@dunfieldhouse.org.uk
www.dunfieldhouse.org.uk
Dunfield House, Kington. Herefordshire.
HR5 3NN

LUDLOW MASCALL
CENTRE

124

A beautiful Victorian building in the heart of Ludlow, extended to provide en-suite accommodation with twin rooms, a family room, and a room designed for those with limited mobility. Within walking distance of restaurants, shops and pubs and near to the Shropshire Hills and Mortimer Forest with miles of stunning landscapes to explore. Fresh towels, bedlinen, complimentary toiletries, tea- and coffee-making facilities, parking and WiFi included. Breakfasts available.

DETAILS

- **Open** - All year, not Xmas & New Year
- **Beds** - 19: 7 x 2, 1 x 1, 1 x 4
- **Price/night** - Family Room (4 bed) £60-£75, Twin Room £45-£60, Single Room: £30-£45.

CONTACT:
Tel: 01584 873882
info@ludlowmascallcentre.co.uk
www.ludlowmascallcentre.co.uk
Lower Galdeford, Ludlow, Shropshire
SY8 1RZ

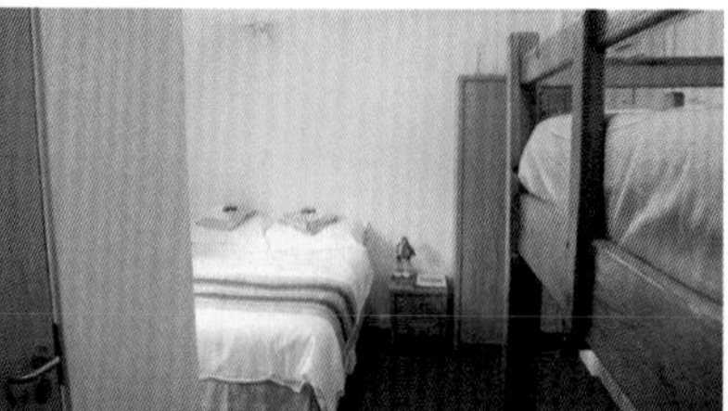

HAYE FARM

SLEEPING BARN

125l

his bunkhouse on a working farm has a fully equipped self-catering kitchen, ning room and lounge. Enjoy the quiet ural location on the covered decking, atio (with BBQ) and lawn. The nearby Wye Forrest is one of the largest remaining ancient forests in England. n the Worcestershire Way and close to e Severn Way and Mercian Way (NCN oute 45) at Bewdley (1 mile). The West Aidland Safari Park and Severn Valley Railway are also very close.

  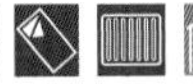    

DETAILS

- **Open** - All year. 24 hour access.
- **Beds** - 15: 1x2, 1x3, 1x4, 1x6
- **Price/night** - From £20pp. Book bed n dorm, private room or exclusive use of whole barn. Visit website for full prices.

CONTACT: Stuart Norgrove
Tel: 07732 489195
enquiries@haye-farm.co.uk
www.haye-farm.co.uk
Haye Farm, Ribbesford, Bewdley,
Worcestershire, DY12 2TP

FOXHOLES

CASTLE BUNKHOUSE

125r

Foxholes Castle Bunkhouse, is situated within a relaxed, family-run campsite, with glorious views of South West Shropshire's beautiful hills. Just a few minutes' walk from the Shropshire Way, Offa's Dyke Path and the Sustrans cycle network, it is the perfect base for walkers, cyclists, photographers, families or couples. The lively town of Bishops Castle with its pubs, cafés, restaurants and take-aways is just a 10 minute walk away. In addition to the bunkhouse there are 2 cabins nearby. The Datcha sleeps 6 and the Eco cabin sleeps 8.

DETAILS

- **Open** - All year.
- **Beds** - 7
- **Price/night** - £15 pp. Sole use: £90.

CONTACT: Adam Smith/Wendy Jones
Tel: 01588 638924
foxholes.castle@googlemail.com
www.foxholes-castle.co.uk/bunkhouse.html
Foxholes Camping, Montgomery Rd,
Bishops Castle, Shropshire, SY9 5HA

BROUGHTON

BUNKHOUSE

126l

Clean and cosy accommodation in a 17th century barn with a wealth of exposed beams and full of character. There is a fully equipped kitchen, central heating, hot water and showers. Clothes washing and drying facilities are also provided. Located just outside Bishops Castle in South Shropshire, perfect for walking on the nearby Stiperstones and Long Mynd. Ideal for cycling around Clun or just enjoying the real ale brewed in two of Bishop Castle's own pubs.

DETAILS

- **Open** - All year. 24 hours.
- **Beds** - 12: 2 x 6
- **Price/night** - From £10pp. Sole use hire by groups, weekend or mid week is welcomed. Please phone for prices.

CONTACT: Kate
Tel: 01588 638393
lbrfarm@fastmail.co.uk
www.broughtonfarm-shropshire.co.uk
Lower Broughton Farm, Nr Bishops Castle, Montgomery, Powys SY15 6SZ

BRIDGES

YOUTH HOSTEL

126r

Tucked away in the tranquil Shropshire hills, close to Long Mynd & Stiperstones Bridges Hostel is an ideal spot for walkers with the Shropshire Way passing close by. It is also handy for the End to End cycle route and good mountain biking routes. The hostel has a good kitchen, lounge with wood fire, drying room, shop and a large garden. Home cooked, home grown three course evening meals are available. Camping available and there is a pub nearby.

DETAILS

- **Open** - All year. Reception open 8-10 am & 5-10 pm. Hostel closes at 11pm.
- **Beds** - 38: 2x4 en suite, 1x6 or 8 1x10, 1x12 plus camping
- **Price/night** - Adults £22. Under 18's £14.50, discounts for YHA. Camping £8.

CONTACT: Bridges Youth Hostel
Tel: 01588 650656
bridges@yha.org.uk
Ratlinghope, Shrewsbury, Shropshire, SY5 0SP

WOMERTON FARM

BUNKHOUSE

127l

Womerton Farm Bunkhouse sits right next to the Long Mynd in the heart of the Shropshire Hills. It offers small select accommodation for 8 with a well appointed kitchen and living area. It is just 3 miles from Church Stretton, 12 miles from Shrewsbury and 15 miles from Ludlow. Local attractions include Acton Scott Working Farm Museum, Stokesay Castle and Museum of Lost Content. Well behaved dogs allowed.

GROUPS ONLY

DETAILS

- **Open** - All year. All day. Closed from 11 am to 4pm on change over days.
- **Beds** - 8: 1x6 bunks + dble sofa bed.
- **Price/night** - £80 Christmas/New Year & Easter to Sept, £60 off peak. Discounts for 4+ nights and mid-week.

CONTACT: Ruth or Tony
Tel: 01694 751260
ruth@womerton-farm.co.uk
www.womerton-farm.co.uk
Womerton Farm, All Stretton, Church Stretton, Shropshire, SY6 6LJ

SPRINGHILL

FARM BUNKHOUSE

127r

Part of a Welsh hill farm on the Wales/ Shropshire border at 1475ft above sea level, with beautiful views over the Ceiriog Valley and Berwyn Mountains. Great for walking, riding, cycling, team building, meetings, or just to relax. There is a heated games and lecture room. The bunkhouse has under-floor heating, entrance hall, drying room, large self catering kitchen, dining area & lounge. The patio and lawn have a BBQ and hot tub. Horse riding and archery on site. Horses and pets welcome on request.

DETAILS

- **Open** - All year by arrangement.
- **Beds** - Bunkhouse: 25, Cottages: 2x6
- **Price/night** - £20pp (including bedding but not towels)

CONTACT: Sue Benbow
Tel: 01691 718406
sue@springhillfarm.co.uk
www.springhillfarm.co.uk
Springhill Farm, Selattyn, Oswestry, Shropshire, SY10 7NZ

ALL STRETTON

BUNKHOUSE

128

All Stretton Bunkhouse offers comfortable, cosy, self-catering accommodation for individuals and groups of up to 10. It has easy access to the Long Mynd with walks and bike rides for all levels. It is within easy reach of the busy town of Church Stretton and just 10 minutes' walk from the local pub. There's a well equipped kitchen, a shower, two toilets and a tumble dryer. Sole use bookings may bring dogs.

DETAILS

- **Open** - All year. Winter 4pm-10.30am. Summer 5pm-10.30am.
- **Beds** - 10: 2x4, 1x2
- **Price/night** - £20; children half price; £1 pppn discount for those arriving without a vehicle.

CONTACT: Frankie Goode
Tel: 01694 722593 or 07815 517482
info@allstrettonbunkhouse.co.uk
www.allstrettonbunkhouse.co.uk
Meadow Green, Batch Valley, All Stretton, Shrops, SY6 6JW

STOKES BARN

BUNKHOUSES

On top of Wenlock Edge AONB, in the heart of Shropshire, Stokes Barn has two bunkhouses with comfortable, centrally heated, dormitory accommodation. Perfect for corporate groups, walkers, field study, schools, stag and hen parties or a reunion with friends/family. Ironbridge World Heritage Site is 6 miles away. Much Wenlock is walking distance with shops, pubs and sports facilities.

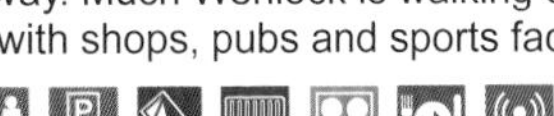

GROUPS ONLY

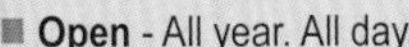

DETAILS

- **Open** - All year. All day.
- **Beds** - Threshing Barn 28: 1x12,1x10,1x6 Granary 16: 1x10,1x4,1x2
- **Price/night** - Prices per min 2 nights: Barn: £560 midweek, £910 weekend. Granary: £398 midweek, £615 weekend. Both units weekend 2 nights: £1365.

CONTACT: Helen
Tel: 01952 727491
info@stokesbarn.co.uk
www.stokesbarn.co.uk
Stokes Barn, Newtown Farm, Much Wenlock, Shropshire, TF13 6DB

BIG MOSE
BUNKHOUSE

Situated on the National Trust Dudmaston Estate, 4 miles south east of Bridgnorth, Big Mose Bunkhouse accommodates groups of up to 18 in 4 bunkrooms of varying sizes. It has spacious communal areas.

The bunkhouse is perfect for groups of family/friends, walkers and clubs. Dudmaston has lots to offer with managed woodlands, beautiful walks, tranquil pools with plenty of wildlife.

DETAILS

- **Open** - All year.
- **Beds** - 18: 1x2, 1x4, 1x6, 1x6
- **Price/night** - 2 nights: £336 (Jan-April), £376 (May-Dec). Discounts for longer stays.

CONTACT: National Trust Holidays
Tel: 03443 351296
bunkhouses@nationaltrust.org.uk
www.nationaltrust.org.uk/holidays
Big Mose Bunkhouse, Quatford,
Bridgnorth, Shropshire, WV15 6QR

HATTERS HOSTELS

BIRMINGHAM

131l

Your perfect base for exploring central
irmingham, Hatters has combined hotel
uality en suite accommodation with the
social buzz of an international hostel.
Groups of all sizes and independent
avellers will enjoy free WiFi & breakfast,
arge communal areas and helpful staff.
ull/half board possible for larger groups.
Ask about discounts for Cadbury World,
Warwick Castle, The Sealife Centre and
other attractions.

DETAILS

- **Open** - All year. All day. Check in 2pm, check out 11am.
- **Beds** - 100: single, double, twin, triple, 4, 6, 8 and 12 bed rooms.
- **Price/night** - From £12 dorms, from £32 private rooms, inc b/fast & linen. Enquire for group bookings.

CONTACT: Reception
Tel: 0121 236 4031
birmingham@hattersgroup.com
www.hattersgroup.com/#bham
2-95 Livery Street, Birmingham, B3 1RJ

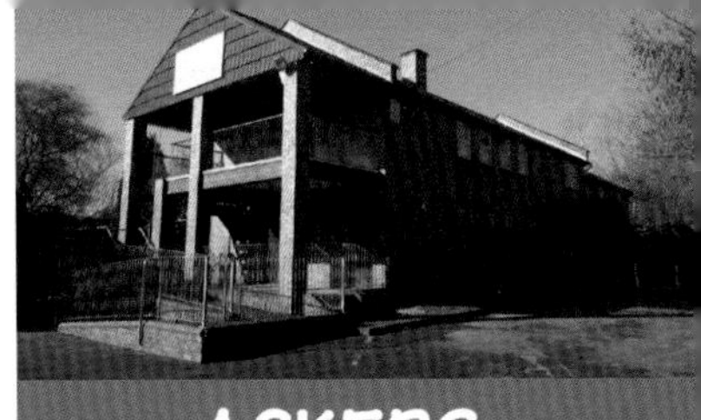

ACKERS

ADVENTURE

131r

Ackers Residential Centre (ARC) is a purpose built accommodation set in 70 acres of semi rural land just 2 miles from the centre of Birmingham. Perfect for The Sea Life Centre, Cadbury World, Thinktank, The Bull Ring shopping centre, National Motorcycle Museum, the NEC. With 9 sleeping rooms, a fully equipped self-catering kitchen, dining area and a rec room with TV, DVD, games and comfy seating. Akers Adventure provide instructor led outdoor activities on site which can be incorporated into your stay.

GROUPS ONLY

DETAILS

- **Open** - All year.
- **Beds** - 26: 4x4, 5x2
- **Price/night** - Enquire for price.

CONTACT: Emma Simon
Tel: 0121 772 5111
emma.simon@ackers-adventure.co.uk
www.ackers-adventure.co.uk
Ackers (ARC), Waverley Canal Basin,
Small Heath, Birmingham, B10 0DQ

IGLOO

HYBRID

132l

On Market Square, right in the centre of Nottingham, Igloo offers great value and comfort. Rooms are decorated using locally sourced, up-cycled furniture and feature street art murals. With a fully equipped self-catering kitchen, free WiFi, power showers, lockers, lounge, outdoor courtyard and laundry facilities. Igloo Annexe & Pods, offers further accommodation with the same standard.

DETAILS

- **Open** - All year. All day. Reception open 7am-1am Sun-Fri, 24hrs Sat.
- **Beds** - 49: singles, twins, doubles, triples, quads and family rooms.
- **Price/night** - Dorms: from £19pp. Singles from £29. Triples from £48. Quads from £64.

CONTACT: Igloo Hybrid
Tel: 01159 483822
hybrid@igloohostel.co.uk
www.igloohostel.co.uk
Igloo Hybrid, 4-6 Eldon Chambers, Wheeler Gate, Nottingham, NG1 2NS

HUNSTANTON

BACKPACKERS & YHA

132r

This family-run, family friendly licensed hostel is ideal for schools (classroom available) & groups as sole use or for families & individuals in private rooms. Close to the beach, town centre, Sealife sanctuary, cliff walks and buses serving the Norfolk Coast. Perfect for walking, cycling, birding and fun on the beach. Food served or self-cater in the kitchen. Enjoy sea views from the garden patio.

DETAILS

- **Open** - All year. 8-10am, 5-9:30pm.
- **Beds** - 48: 1x dbl, 2x3, 4x4, 1x5/6, 2x6/8, 1 grd floor 2 bed. Some en suite.
- **Price/night** - Prices from: Dorms £24, 2 bed £55, 4 bed £80. Ask re multi night discounts, family rooms, sole use & schools/groups full board packages.

CONTACT: Neal or Alison Sanderson
Tel: 01485 532061 or 07771 804831
enquiries@hunstantonhostel.co.uk
www.norfolkbeachholidays.co.uk
15-17 Avenue Road, Hunstanton, Norfolk, PE36 5BW

DEEPDALE

BACKPACKERS

133l

Deepdale Backpackers offers a range of comfortable self-catering rooms with private en suite shower/toilet facilities, plus single sex dorms. All bedding is provided, just BYO towels. With underfloor heating throughout, laundry & drying facilities, all rooms have shared access to a large well equipped kitchen, communal dining area and living room.

DETAILS

- **Open** - All year. All day. Collect key from Deepdale Visitor Information Centre
- **Beds** - 50: 5 x dbl, 1 twin, 1 quad, 1 family quad, 2 female dorms, 2 male dorms
- **Price/night** - From £12 in a shared dorm room. From £30 twin/double room.

CONTACT: Deepdale Backpackers & Camping
Tel: 01485 210256
stay@deepdalebackpackers.co.uk
www.deepdalebackpackers.co.uk
Deepdale Farm, Burnham Deepdale, Norfolk, PE31 8DD

DEEPDALE

GROUPS HOSTEL

133r

Deepdale Groups Hostel is at the heart of Burnham Deepdale on the beautiful North Norfolk Coast. The Groups Hostel offers comfortable, self-catering accommodation for groups. Sleeping up to 18 people in 4 bedrooms, it is perfect for friends, larger family gathering, clubs or reunions. A great base for a walking break, cycling tour or for bird/wildlife watching groups. The knowledgeable staff will give advice and share their passion for the area.

DETAILS

- **Open** - All year. All day. Collect key from Deepdale Visitor Information Centre
- **Beds** - 18: 2x6, 1x4, 1x2
- **Price/night** - From £216 (18 people)

CONTACT: Deepdale Groups Hostel
Tel: 01485 210256
stay@deepdalebackpackers.co.uk
www.deepdalebackpackers.co.uk/groups-hostel
Deepdale Farm, Burnham Deepdale, Norfolk, PE31 8DD

TOWER
WINDMILL

134

Built in 1816 and last used as a working corn mill in 1914, this National Trust bunkhouse has panoramic views of the surrounding countryside and the Norfolk coastline.

A perfect venue and location for groups of family and friends to get together and explore the local beaches and miles of public footpaths. Featuring a well equipped ground floor kitchen, sitting/dining area, a third floor library and large enclosed garden. BYO bedding and linen.

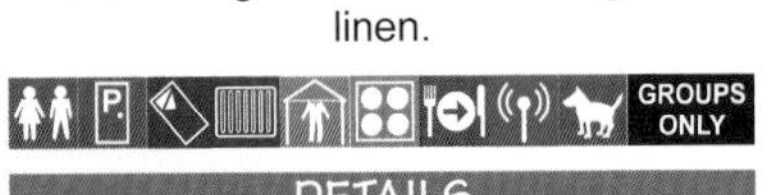

DETAILS

- **Open** - All year.
- **Beds** - 19: 2x8, 1x twin, 1x single
- **Price/night** - 3 night weekend break from £487 - £919

CONTACT: National Trust Holidays
Tel: 03443 351296
bunkhouses@nationaltrust.org.uk
www.nationaltrust.org.uk/holidays
Tower Windmill, Tower Road, Burnham Overy Staithe, Norfolk, PE31 8JB

BRANCASTER

ACTIVITY CENTRE (BAC)

This National Trust Grade II listed flint cottage lies in the picturesque harbour of Brancaster Staithe on the North Norfolk Coast. With stunning sea views across the beautiful marshes. Groups of up to 22 or 48 can be accommodated (sole occupancy). Self-cater in the well equipped kitchen, or eat out in nearby pubs and cafés. The upstairs 'snug' has a TV and woodburner and there is a garden with seating and gas BBQ. Perfect for sailing, walking, kite surfing, bird watching & the Norfolk Coast Path.

GROUPS ONLY

DETAILS

- **Open** - All year. Booking essential
- **Beds** - 48:1x8, 1x7, 2x6, 3x5, 1x4, 1x2
- **Price/night** - From £719 (2 nights/22 beds/low) to £1526 (2 nts/48 beds/high)

CONTACT: National Trust Holidays
Tel: 03443 351296
bunkhouses@nationaltrust.org.uk
www.nationaltrust.org.uk/holidays
Dial House, Harbour Way, Brancaster Staithe, Kings Lynn, Norfolk PE31 8BW

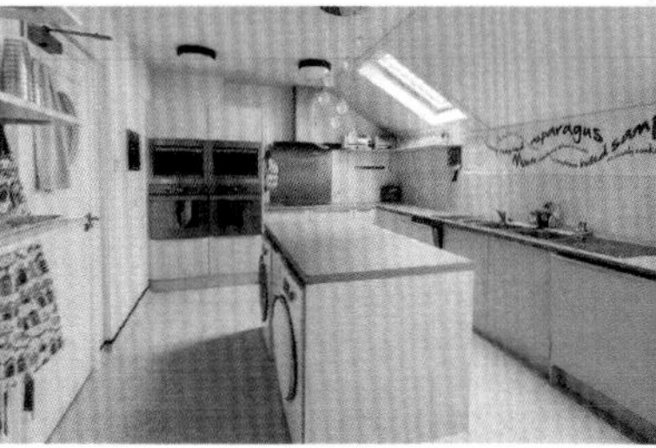

OLD RED LION

136

The medieval walled town of Castle Acre is on the Peddars Way ancient track/ long distance path. This former pub, continues to serve travellers who seek refreshment and repose. Stay in private rooms or dorms (bedding/linen supplied). There are quiet communal areas and 2 large areas suitable for group activities.

DETAILS

- **Open** - All year. All day. Arrival times by arrangement.
- **Beds** - 22: 1x8, 1x6, 1x double, 2x double en suite, 2x twin
- **Price/night** - Double ensuite £70. Wet room (ground floor) £70/Sgle occ.£55. Double £65/Sgle occ £45. Twin £55/Sgle occ £40. Discounts for 2+ nights. Dorms £22.50. B/fast, bedding, towel included.

CONTACT: Alison Loughlin
Tel: 01760 755557
oldredlion@yahoo.co.uk
www.oldredlion.org.uk
Old Red Lion, Bailey Street, Castle Acre, Norfolk, PE32 2AG

VIKING

CENTRE

Situated in the village of Claxby in the Lincolnshire Wolds AONB this low cost hostel has a well equipped kitchen and good sized communal area. Within easy reach of Lincoln, Gainsborough, Scunthorpe and Grimsby. The perfect location for: walking, cycling, field studies, outdoor pursuits, educational activities and conservation projects. Popular with schools, scouts, guides, walkers, cycling groups and other youth organisations. Ideal for groups wanting an educational and/or adventurous break deep in rural surroundings.

        GROUPS ONLY

DETAILS

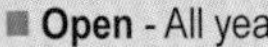

- **Open** - All year
- **Beds** - 20: 2x4, 2x6
- **Price/night** - £90 per night per group

CONTACT: Susannah Boulton
Tel: 01673 828025
info@thevikingcentre.org
thevikingcentre.org/
Pelham Road Claxby Market Rasen,
Lincolnshire, LN8 3YR

GLENORCHY

CENTRE

The Glenorchy Centre is found on the edge of the Peak District National Park in the historic market town of Wirksworth. The High Peak Trail for walking, pony trekking and cycling and Black Rocks for bouldering and climbing are within a couple of miles. Nearby Cromford has Arkwright's mills, a World Heritage Site, and Cromford Canal. Suitable for self-catering groups, the accommodation is well appointed and boasts a spacious multi-purpose room with a large stage.

DETAILS

- **Open** - Mid Feb to early Dec. 24 hours.
- **Beds** - 26: 1x12, 1x8, 1x4, 1x2
- **Price/night** - Mon-Thurs £995 (4nts); Fri-Sun £620 (2nts); Sat-Sat £1425 (7nts) Small grps £20pp. 1 nt: min charge £410.

CONTACT: The Secretary
Tel: 01629 824323
secretary@glenorchycentre.org.uk
www.glenorchycentre.org.uk
Chapel Lane, Wirksworth, Derbyshire, DE4 4FF

MOUNT COOK

ADVENTURE CENTRE

This not-for-profit organisation is based on the outskirts of the Peak District. Their mission is to provide access to the outdoors for all, especially young people and those who would not otherwise have the opportunity. Mount Cook offers a range of exciting outdoor activities including Archery, Bush Craft, High Ropes and Zip Wire. The purpose-built Centre can accommodate up to 140 guests in modern ensuite bedrooms, and a further 40 guests in Glamping Pods.

GROUPS ONLY

DETAILS

- **Open** - All year. Office hours; weekdays 9-5.
- **Beds** - 140 Beds: 34x4 + 2x2 (disabled access), 10 Pods: 10x4 + 40 Camping
- **Price/night** - Contact Mount Cook.

CONTACT: The Office
Tel: 01629 823702
Explore@mountcook.uk
www.mountcook.org
Porter Lane, Middleton-by-Wirksworth, Matlock, DE4 4LS

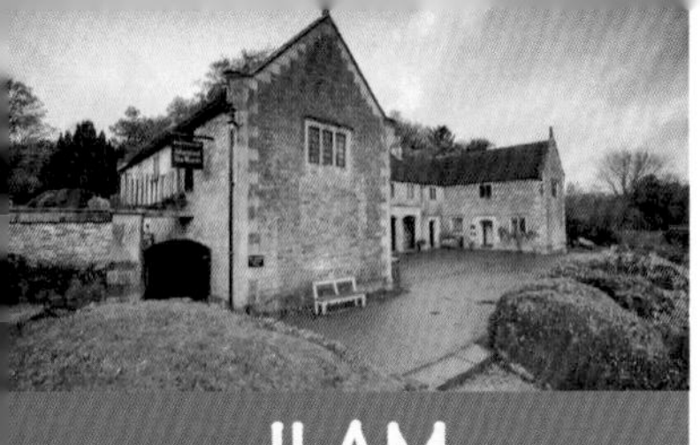

ILAM
BUNKHOUSE

140

The former 18th century stable block of Ilam Hall in the Peak District National Park close to Dove Dale. Now managed by the National Trust and providing high quality group accommodation. Each bunk has a locker, night light and plug socket. The sociable main living area has a large dining table with benches, an open plan kitchen and large comfortable sofas. Explore the limestone hills, dales, rivers and woodland of the picturesque White Peak.

   GROUPS ONLY

DETAILS

- **Open** - All year. All day.
- **Beds** - 16: 2x6, 1x4
- **Price/night** - Week: £170. Weekend £250. Minimum bookings apply weekends and bank holidays. Dogs: £15/dog/stay.

CONTACT: National Trust Holidays
Tel: 03443 351296
bunkhouses@nationaltrust.org.uk
www.nationaltrust.org.uk/holidays
Ilam Bunkhouse, Ilam Park, Ilam, nr Ashbourne, DE6 2AZ

ALSTONEFIELD

CAMPING BARN

Close to Dovedale, the Manifold Valley Cycle Trail, Carsington Water, AltonTowers and the Roaches Rocks (great for climbers). Ideal for quiet group get-togethers/parties, families, cyclists, walkers, DofE, Scouts, school groups and team building.

Camping in the comfort of a remote cosy barn with log burning stove. No electric and no distractions, it is the perfect place to switch off from the hassles of a hectic life. BYO all camping equipment.

DETAILS

- **Open** - All year. All day apart from Christmas and New Year.
- **Beds** - 12: BYO sleeping mats & bags
- **Price/night** - £9pp, £108 for sole use.

CONTACT: Robert or Teresa Flower
Tel: 01335 310349
gateham.grange@btinternet.com
www.gatehamgrange.co.uk
Gateham Grange, Alstonefield,
Ashbourne, Derbys. DE6 2FT

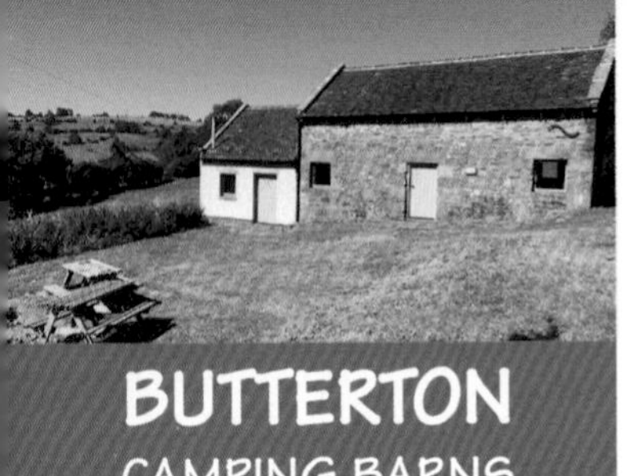

BUTTERTON

CAMPING BARNS

Waterslacks Camping Barn is perched on the edge of the Manifold Valley with breathtaking views of the surrounding hills. BYO all camping gear including stove and sleep mats. Wills Barn is a fully equipped bunkhouse with stunning views of this unspoiled area of the Peak District National Park. A rustic log-burning stove provides heating and cooking facilities. Fenns Barn 4* self-catering holiday let and camping are also available

GROUPS ONLY

DETAILS

- **Open** - All year. All day
- **Beds** - Waterslacks: 15. Wills: 6. Fenns: 7 + Camping.
- **Price/night** - Waterslacks from £127, Wills from £90, Fenns Barn from £100.

CONTACT: Jason and Michelle
Tel: 07708 200282
fennsfarmaccommodation@gmail.com
www.peakdistrictbarns.co.uk
Fenns Farm, Wetton Road, Butterton, Leek, Staffordshire, ST13 7ST

SHEEN
BUNKHOUSE

143

Sheen Bunkhouse is in a quiet corner of the Peak District, close to the beautiful Dove and Manifold valleys. It has a TV lounge, well equipped self-catering kitchen, two bunkrooms with wash basins and separate toilets & showers. The Manifold Track, Tissington Trail and High Peak Trail give easy access to beautiful countryside, ideal for families and cyclists. Dovedale, the Upper Dove Valley and the remote moors around Flash and Longnor offer stunning walking. Buxton, Leek and Bakewell are within 12 miles and Alton Towers is 20 minutes away by car.

DETAILS

- **Open** - All year. 24 hours access, reception 8am - 9pm.
- **Beds** - 14: 1x8, 1x6
- **Price/night** - Adults from £17,u16s £12

CONTACT: Jean or Graham Belfield
Tel: 01298 84501
grahambelfield11@gmail.com
Peakstones, Sheen, Derbys, SK17 0ES

MOORSIDE FARM

BUNKHOUSE

144l

A 300-year-old farmhouse set 1300 feet up in the beautiful Derbyshire/ Staffordshire Peak District National Park. Five miles from historic Buxton and a perfect base for all the Peak District has to offer. The 2 sleeping areas sleep 14 and 6 - perfect for a small group or family. A 3 course breakfast and optional packed lunch / substantial evening meal are provided. Vegetarians catered for. Hot drinks can be made in the small kitchen. Ample parking space.

GROUPS ONLY

DETAILS

- **Open** - All year. 24 hours.
- **Beds** - 20: 1 x 14, 1 x 6
- **Price/night** - Full board (b/fast, packed lunch, eve meal) £40pp, B&B £30pp. Groups only (Min booking of 4 people).

CONTACT: Charlie
Tel: 01298 83406
charliefutcher@aol.com
www.moorsidefarm.com
Hollinsclough, Longnor, Buxton, Derbyshire, SK17 0RF

ROACHES

BUNKHOUSE

144r

The Roaches Bunkhouse is at the foot of The Roaches gritstone edge in the Peak District. The area has some of the best climbing in the country plus walks and cycling in stunning scenery. An ideal base for climbers, walkers and cyclists. It has a drying room and bedrooms sleeping 2 or 4 in bunks. The communal area has tables and chairs, log fire, TV and board games. Self-catering facilities are available in a small kitchen. Parking available on site. Close to Ye Old Rock Inn and 3 miles the bustling market town of Leek.

DETAILS

- **Open** - All year.
- **Beds** - 42: 9x4, 3x2
- **Price/night** - £12 per person per night.

CONTACT: Emma Baines
Tel: 01538 300308 or 07836 628868
info@roachesbunkhouse.com
www.roachesbunkhouse.com
Upper Hulme Mill, Roach Road, Upper Hulme, Nr Leek, Staffordshire, ST13 8TY

ROYAL OAK

BUNKBARN

145

A refurbished stone barn next to an award winning Peak District country pub, The Royal Oak Bunkbarn, is perfectly situated with direct access onto the High Peak and Tissington Trails (disused railways for easy off-road cycling). The area is also very popular with climbers and walkers with limestone gorges and stone circles to explore. The bunkbarn offers comfortable, clean bunk bed style rooms. The five separate bunk rooms are all heated and lockable. Campsite and holiday cottages also available.

DETAILS

- **Open** - All year. All day.
- **Beds** - 34: 3x8, 1x6, 1x4
- **Price/night** - April to Sept £17pppn, Oct to March £15pppn.

CONTACT: The Royal Oak
Tel: 01298 83288
hello@peakpub.co.uk
www.peakpub.co.uk
The Royal Oak, Hurdlow, Nr Buxton, SK17 9QJ

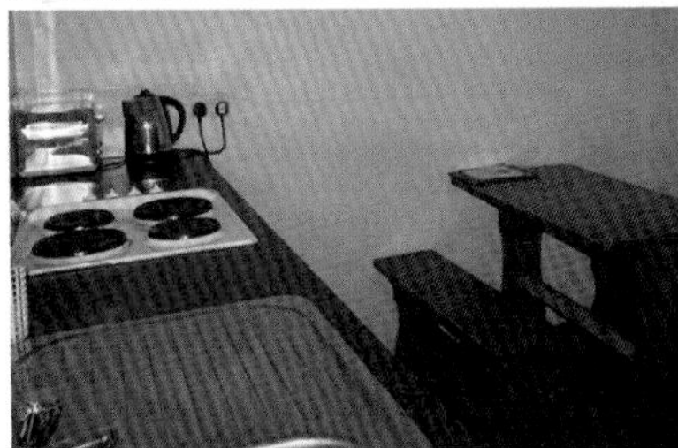

THE RECKONING
HOUSE

146

Renovated to a high standard including double glazing and insulation, the Reckoning House is situated 3 miles from Bakewell. It is on the edge of the Lathkill Dale National Nature Reserve, full of interesting flora and fauna as well as outstanding geological features. Horse riding, fishing, golf and cycle hire are available locally. Local walks include the Limestone Way. Facilities include: cooking area, 4 calor gas rings (gas supplied), hot water for washing up & showers, storage heaters in all rooms.

DETAILS

- **Open** - All year. By arrangement.
- **Beds** - 12: 2x6 bunk rooms.
- **Price/night** - £15 per person. Sole use £95 per night.

CONTACT: Rachel Rhodes
Tel: 01629 812416 or 07540 839233
mandalecampsite@yahoo.co.uk
www.mandalecampsite.co.uk
Mandale Farm, Haddon Grove,
Bakewell, Derbyshire, DE45 1JF

THORNBRIDGE

OUTDOORS

Thornbridge Outdoors offers excellent flexible group accommodation. With its superb location in the heart of the Peak District you have access to wonderful countryside, interesting places and the traffic free Monsal Trail, popular with walkers and cyclists.

GROUPS ONLY

DETAILS

- **Open** - All year. All day.
- **Beds** - 90 + camping: Lodge 38: 4×5, 4×3, 1×6. Farm House 38: 2×8, 2×6, 1×5, 1×3, 1×2. Woodlands 10: 1×5, 1×4 1×1. 2 The Woodlands 4: 2x2. Teepees 45: 9 x 4/5 & camping.
- **Price/night** - Weekend breaks from £240 (2 The Woodlands Cottage), £360 (Woodlands), £1,110 (Farm House), £1,398 (Lodge). Ask for activity costs.

CONTACT: Reception
Tel: 01629 640491
info@thornbridgeoutdoors.co.uk
www.thornbridgeoutdoors.co.uk
Great Longstone, Bakewell, Derbyshire, DE45 1NY

BRETTON

HOSTEL

148

Bretton Hostel is surrounded by meadows on Bretton Edge, near historic Eyam in the heart of the Peak District. With glorious far-reaching views, the sense of space & tranquility is immense. Duvets, pillows and bed linen provided; well equipped kitchen; secure bike store. Lovely timber studio for additional space and workshops. A perfect place for relaxing or enjoying outdoor activities.

DETAILS

- **Open** - Groups (sole use): All year. Individuals: Apr-Oct (Mon-Thu). Open all day. Check in from 4pm, check out 11am.
- **Beds** - 17: 1x8, 1x6, 1x3
- **Price/night** - Sole use from £280 (min 2 nights stay). Individuals from £20. Apply for Xmas, NY and bank holiday prices.

CONTACT: Clare Palmer
Tel: 07792 385134
bookings@brettonhostel.co.uk
brettonhostel.co.uk
Bretton, near Eyam, Hope Valley,
Derbyshire S32 5QD

FOUNDRY

ADVENTURE CENTRE

149

With all of the Peak District National Park within easy access, the centre is an ideal location for activities and tourism and it welcomes a wide range of groups. 31 or 52 bed configurations can be booked.

The spacious centre includes; a large lounge with library, TV and wood burning stove, well equipped kitchens & dining areas. An extensive network of paths give access to the countryside. Adventure activities available, great for team building & courses.

        GROUPS ONLY

DETAILS

- **Open** - All year. All day.
- **Beds** - 52 or 31 in 9 bedrooms
- **Price/night** - 31 beds from £790 per night, 52 beds from £1120 per night.

CONTACT: Tim Gould
Tel: 07786 332702
tim@foundrymountain.co.uk
foundryadventurecentre.co.uk
The Old Playhouse, Great Hucklow,
Derbyshire, SK17 8RF

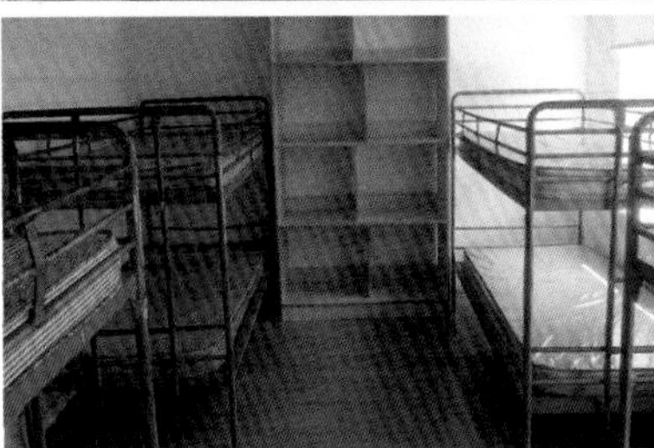

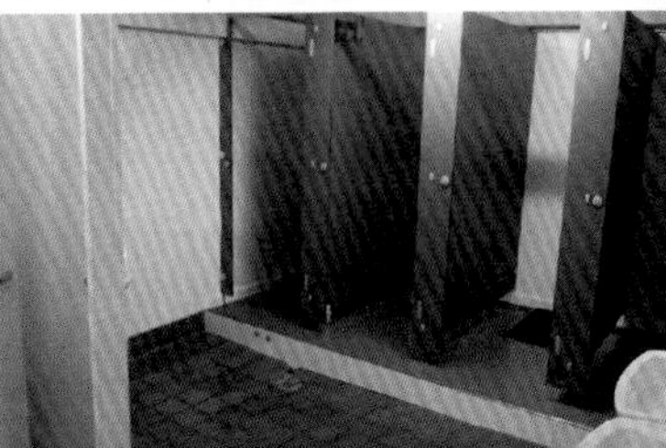

HOMESTEAD

AND CHEESEHOUSE

150

In the heart of Bamford these two bunkhouses are on a small farm just 3 miles from Stanage Edge. The Derwent Dams are close by. Perfectly located for visiting Castleton, Chatsworth House and Hathersage. Both bunkhouses are centrally heated have hot showers and have their own well equipped kitchens. Sheets and pillows are provided (BYO sleeping bags) Book separately or together. Sorry, no dogs.

DETAILS

- **Open** - All year, arrive after 2pm on day of arrival and leave by 11am on departure.
- **Beds** - Homestead 22: 1x10, 2x6. Cheesehouse 4: 1x4
- **Price/night** - From £15 pp. Sole use: Homestead £210, Cheesehouse £45. Min 2 nights for Homestead at weekends. Phone for a quote for single night.

CONTACT: Helena Platts
Tel: 01433 651298
The Farm, Bamford, Hope Valley, S33 0BL

ST MICHAELS

CENTRE

At the heart of Hathersage in the Hope Valley, close to Stanage and the other gritstone edges, the Derwent Valley Reservoirs, Chatsworth, Castleton and Hathersage outdoor pool. With limitless walking from the door. High quality accommodation for groups, with a well equipped self-catering kitchen, dining room, lounge & classroom. Outdoor activities available on request.

      GROUPS ONLY

DETAILS

■ **Open** - All year. Office open Monday to Friday 8.30 am - 4pm

■ **Beds** - 38: 2x2, 1x4, 2x6, 1x8, 1x10. Plus 4 in adjacent cottage.

■ **Price/night** - £23.50pp min, £470 a night, min stay: 2 nights. Activities: £300 per day (max 12 people) + transport cost.

CONTACT: Ian Weeks
Tel: 01433 650309
stmichaels@nottscc.gov.uk
www.nottinghamshire.gov.uk
Main Road, Hathersage, Derbyshire, S32 1BB

THORPE FARM

BUNKHOUSES

152

Close to Hathersage and 2 miles west of Stanage Edge, the bunkhouses are on a family-run dairy farm. Popular areas for climbing, walking from meadows to moorland with fantastic views & mountain biking. Each bunkhouse is heated and has a living room, kitchen, bathrooms with two toilets, showers and washbasins. Sleep in dorms with bunks or the Hayloft has mattresses on the gallery floor. Camping is available. Secure bike storage and free parking.

DETAILS

- **Open** - All year. No restrictions.
- **Beds** - Old Shippon 32: 2x12, 2x4. Old Stables 14 1x8, 1x6. Pondside 14: 1x8, 1x6. Byre 14: 1x6, 1x4. Living Room 4.
- **Price/night** - See own website.

CONTACT: Jane Marsden
Tel: 01433 650659
jane@hope-valley.co.uk
www.thorpe-bunk.co.uk
Thorpe Farm, Hathersage, Peak District, Via Sheffield, S32 1BQ

PINDALE
OUTDOOR CENTRE

A mile from Castleton in the heart of ıe Peak District, Pindale Farm offers a ange of accommodation. There's B&B ı the farmhouse. The Barn has 6 self-catering units. The Engine House is a elf-catering unit and The Powder House s a small camping barn. There is also a campsite. The ideal base for many ıtdoor activities. Instruction is available.

DETAILS

- **Open** - All year (camping March-October). 24 hours.
- **Beds** - 64: Farmhouse: 4. Engine House: 8. Powder House: 4. The Barn: 6x8 -10. Plus camping.
- **Price/night** - Camping £8pp (hook up £4). Barns £17pp + £1 electric tokens. Enquire for B&B.

CONTACT: Alan Medhurst
Tel: 01433 620111
info@pindalefarm.co.uk
www.pindalefarm.co.uk
Pindale Road, Hope, Hope Valley,
Derbyshire, S33 6RN

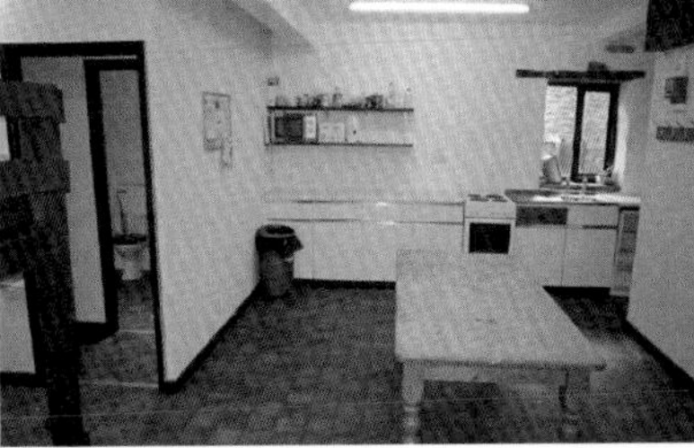

DALEHEAD

BUNKHOUSE

154

Dalehead Bunkhouse is on a working hill farm at the remote head of Edale Valley. Providing basic but comfortable accommodation heated by log burner & infrared radiant heat. There is a kitchen with fridge/freezer, a lounge, dining room and plenty of parking. Please bring sleeping bags, pillows and towels. Edale is a very popular destination for walkers, climbers, mountain bikers, hang-gliders or for enjoying the magnificent scenery.

GROUPS ONLY

DETAILS

- **Open** - All year. All day.
- **Beds** - 20: 1x6, 1x8, 1x6
- **Price/night** - Mon-Thurs £190 per night. Fri-Sun £275. Min 2 nights bookings Fri-Sun, 3 nights bank holidays. Dogs £15 per dog per stay.

CONTACT: National Trust Holidays
Tel: 03443 351296
bunkhouses@nationaltrust.org.uk
www.nationaltrust.org.uk/holidays
Dalehead Bunkhouse, Upper Booth,
Edale, Hope Valley, S33 7ZJ

EDALE BARN

COTEFIELD FARM

155l

verlooking Mam Tor, at the start of the ennine Way, Edale Barn is a traditional amping barn or stone tent with a basic eeping platform and a small communal ing area. Within easy reach of the high moorland of Kinder and the wooded Derwent Valley. Adjoining the barn, but vith external access, is a cooking area d separate toilet. There is no hot water or electricity. BYO sleeping & cooking equipment and torches. Pubs serving meals are within walking distance.

DETAILS

- **Open** - All year. Arrive after 4pm and depart before 10am.
- **Beds** - 8 on a raised wooden platform
- **Price/night** - £8.50 per person. £68 sole use per night.

CONTACT: Sally Gee or Rachael Gee
Tel: 01433 670273 or 07739 828383
reg1102@hotmail.com
www.fb.com/cotefieldfarmcottages
Cotefield Farm Olllerbrook Edale Hope Valley Derbyshire S33 7ZG

UPPER BOOTH

CAMPING BARN

155r

Next to a small campsite alongside Crowden Clough in the Peak District. Hire the simple barn and additional pitches on the campsite. There is space for cooking (BYO equipment and beds) and tables for eating. Toilets, sinks & showers are shared with the campsite. On a working hill-farm, the Pennine Way passes through the farmyard and there is great mountain biking locally.

DETAILS

- **Open** - March-November. Arrival between 3pm and 9pm. Departure before 10am. Not suitable for late night parties.
- **Beds** - 12 sleeping spaces & camping.
- **Price/night** - Sole use (up to 12 persons) from £90 per night plus vehicles. Individuals from £10 per person per night.

CONTACT: Robert, Sarah or Alice
Tel: 01433 670250
mail@helliwell.info
www.upperboothcamping.co.uk
Upper Booth Farm, Edale, Hope Valley, Derbyshire, S33 7ZJ

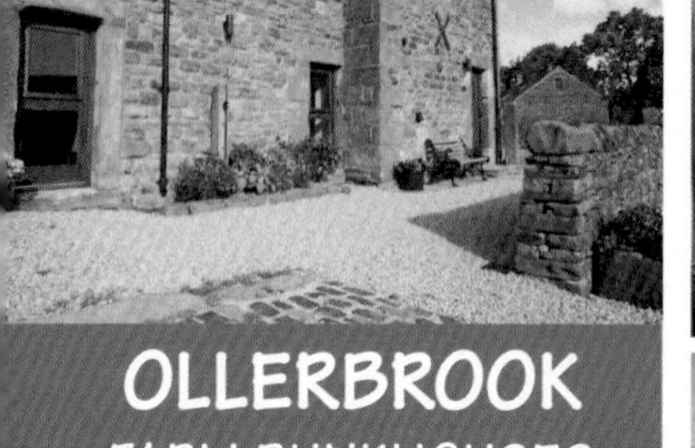

OLLERBROOK

FARM BUNKHOUSES

Close to the start of the Pennine Way with easy access to Kinder Scout and the village of Edale via a network of footpaths from the doorstep. Castleton, Buxton, Bakewell and Chatsworth House are all within 40 minutes' drive. There are 2 bunkhouses each with a fully equipped kitchen and available for sole use by groups. Bring your own sleeping bags.

GROUPS ONLY

DETAILS

- **Open** - All year. All day. Arrive after 4pm depart before 10.30am.
- **Beds** - Nab View 18: 3x6, Stables Bunkhouse 16: 4x4
- **Price/night** - Nab View: £330. The Stables: midweek £200, weekends £230. Enquire for longer stays and prices for room or bed. Minimum of two night stay.

CONTACT: Sheila
Tel: 01433 670235
ollerbrookfarm@gmail.com
www.ollerbrookfarm.co.uk
Ollerbrook Booth, Edale, Hope Valley, Derbyshire, S33 7ZG

JOHN HUNT

BASE

The John Hunt Base is situated in the gh Peak on the site of Hagg Farm (see page 158).

The base offers comfortable, family friendly accommodation ideal for ghtseeing, hill walking, trail running and biking as well as quieter pursuits such as photography. There is a picnic area, vildlife garden with fire pit and a playing eld with climbing boulder. Activities can be arranged including climbing, stream crambling, caving & on-site high ropes.

       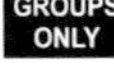 GROUPS ONLY

DETAILS

- **Open** - All year. Office, Mon-Thur 8.30am- 4.30pm, Fri 8.30-3.30pm
- **Beds** - 18: 1x8, 1x6, 2x2
- **Price/night** - £300 min 2 nights. Instruction (12 people) from £300 per day.

CONTACT:
Tel: 01433 651594
haggfarm@nottscc.gov.uk
www.nottinghamshire.gov.uk/haggfarm
Hagg Farm OEC, Snake Rd, Bamford, Hope Valley, S33 0BJ

HAGG FARM

OEC

Situated in the Peak District's Woodlands Valley, Hagg Farm offers comfortable accommodation for up to 44 people with an additional 18 beds in the John Hunt Base next door (see page 157). Part of Nottinghamshire C.C's Environmental & Outdoor Education Service, Hagg Farm is available for private hire by groups, families, clubs & charitable organisations. It can be booked on a self-catering or catered basis.

       GROUPS ONLY

DETAILS

- **Open** - All year. Office: Mon-Thurs 8:30am-4.30pm Fri 8:30am-4pm
- **Beds** - 44: 4 x 8, 2 x 4, 2 x 2
- **Price/night** - £24pp: min charge for 25 people, min 2 night stay. Outdoor activity instruction for 12 from £300 per day.

CONTACT: Kirsty Weatherall
Tel: 01433 651594
haggfarm@nottscc.gov.uk
www.nottinghamshire.gov.uk/haggfarm
Hagg Farm OEC, Snake Rd, Bamford, Hope Valley, S33 0BJ

BUSHEY HEATH

FARM

159l

Bushey Heath Farm in the heart of the Peak District offers 2 self contained bunk barns for groups of up to 20 and a summer campsite. The larger barn can accommodate occupants of both barns for meals. The farm has been developed with ground source heating, wind turbine and rainwater harvesting, so visitors can experience practical sustainable ideas. Sleeping bags/duvets/ sheet required.

GROUPS ONLY

DETAILS

- **Open** - All year. Campsite March-Oct.
- **Beds** - 20: Little Barn 6:1x6, Marmaduke's Rest 14: 1x6, 1x8.
- **Price/night** - Sole use: Little Barn: £144. Marmaduke Rest Barn: £350. Minimum stay of 2 nights.

CONTACT: Ruth Allen
Tel: 01298 605022 9am-8pm only.
busheyheathfarm@gmail.com
www.busheyheathfarm.com
Forest Lane, Tideswell Moor, Tideswell, Buxton, Derbyshire, SK17 8JE

HATTERS HOSTELS

MANCHESTER

159r

Hatters on Hilton Street combines hotel quality en suite accommodation with the social buzz of an international hostel. Located in the heart of the bohemian Northern Quarter of Manchester, it's your perfect base for all city centre attractions & transport links. Full/half board options for larger groups. Ask about discounts to Alton Towers, about Man Utd & City football stadium tours and about all that is FREE to do in Manchester!

DETAILS

- **Open** - All year. All day. Check in 2pm, check out 11am.
- **Beds** - 155: single, twin, double, triple, 4, 6, 8, and 12 bed rooms. All en suite.
- **Price/night** - From £12 dorms, from £32 private rooms inc linen & b/fast. Enquire for group bookings.

CONTACT: Reception
Tel: 0161 236 4414
hilton@hattersgroup.com
www.hattersgroup.com/#mcr
15 Hilton Street, Manchester, M1 1JJ

EMBASSIE
BACKPACKERS

160l

The Embassie is a majestic terraced house in an unspoilt Georgian square. Until 1986 it was the Consulate of Venezuela! Only 15 minutes' walk from the centre of Liverpool, known for its nightlife, it's in the perfect position. Recently refurbished, there are new kitchen facilities, a brand new shower suite and an all new games room & relax area with Sky Sports and HD television. The hostel is clean, safe and staffed 24 hours. Bedding is provided (including sheets) and free coffee, tea, toast and jam are available 24 hours.

  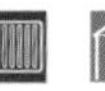    

DETAILS

- **Open** - All year. All day.
- **Beds** - 50
- **Price/night** - £19 (Sunday to Thursday), £25 Friday, £32 Saturday

CONTACT: Kevin
Tel: 0151 707 1089
embassie@gmail.com
www.embassie.com
1 Falkner Square, Liverpool, L8 7NU

EURO HOSTEL
LIVERPOOL

160r

Right in the heart of the city and a perfect base from which to experience Liverpool's legendary night life, shoppin and waterfront walks. Backpackers, couples, families and groups are all welcomed. Rooms vary from 8 bed dorms (mixed or female only), en suite private rooms for up to 8 people or VIF suites accommodating groups of 6 or 8 in bunks with private TV lounge and en suite facilities. The Hatch bar serve meals including breakfast and is a grea live music venue as well as providing good quality food and drink. Car park discounts provided on check out.

DETAILS

- **Open** - All year. All day.
- **Beds** - 220 approximately
- **Price/night** - From £14 pp

CONTACT: Reception
Tel: 08454 900971
liverpool@eurohostels.co.uk
www.eurohostels.co.uk/liverpool/
54 Stanley Street, Liverpool L1 6AU

HATTERS HOSTELS

LIVERPOOL

161l

atters Liverpool combines hotel quality en suite rooms with the social buzz of an international hostel. Conveniently cated for all city centre attractions and transport links it's your perfect base for experiencing the heart and soul of Liverpool. Full/half board options for rger groups. Ask at the reception about scounts to Alton Towers, Beatles tours, otball stadium tours, Albert Docks and many other FREE adventures.

DETAILS

- **Open** - All year. All day. Check in after 2pm, check out 11am.
- **Beds** - 300: sgle, dble, twin, triple, 4, 6, 8 and 12 bed rooms. All en suite
- **Price/night** - From £12 for dorms and rom £32 for privates inc linen and b/fast. Enquire for group bookings.

CONTACT: Reception
Tel: 0151 709 5570
liverpool@hattersgroup.com
www.hattersgroup.com/#lpool
56-60 Mt Pleasant, Liverpool, L3 5SH

STABLESIDE

YORK

161r

Stableside, a quiet & welcoming 4* hostel situated right on the historic Knavesmire, is the perfect location for enjoying a break in the beautiful, historic city of York. Guests can take advantage of the varied room options catering for the single traveller and larger groups. Free parking, free WiFi and a fabulous Yorkshire welcome. Meals can be provided for groups. On the NCN Route 65 for easy access to the city centre.

DETAILS

- **Open** - All year (except during race meetings). All day.
- **Beds** - 133: 2x6, 21x4, 8x triple, 1x twin, 11 x single.
- **Price/night** - B&B twin room £80 inc towels. Enquire for group rates.

CONTACT: Fay
Tel: 01904 709174
fay.waudby@yorkracecourse.co.uk
www.stablesideyork.co.uk
Stableside, York Racing Stables, York, YO24 1QG

HALIFAX COLLEGE

HOSTEL

Within walking distance of Heslington village and the University of York campus. Halifax College is the perfect base for exploring York. The city is famous for the iconic York Minster, exquisite architecture, The Shambles, boutique shopping, a vibrant café and restaurant culture and world class museums such as the National Railway Museum and the unique Jorvik Centre. All rooms are self-catering and single occupancy with a wash basin and the use of shared bathroom and kitchen within each house.

DETAILS

- **Open** - July - September
- **Beds** - 51
- **Price/night** - £26

CONTACT: Reception
Tel: 01904 328431
conferences@york.ac.uk
yorkconferences.com/hostel
Halifax College Reception, Garrowby Way, York, YO10 5GH

THE FORT

BOUTIQUE HOSTEL

163l

Step outside The Fort Boutique Hostel into an area of York steeped in history and surrounded by lively cafés, bars and restaurants. The hostel has comfortable, stylish accommodation with flat screen TV's and WiFi. Complimentary hot drinks are available. And if you are feeling hungry, meals are available locally as The Fort is situated above Kennedy's Bar and Restaurant, a popular, independently owned venue.

So, relax, order a drink and enjoy this vibrant, unique spot, smack bang in the heart of York.

DETAILS

- **Open** - All year. 24hrs.
- **Beds** - 60: 5x2 4x8 3x6
- **Price/night** - From £18 per person

CONTACT: Fiona Helme
Tel: 01904 639573
info@thefortyork.co.uk
www.thefortyork.co.uk
1 Little Stonegate, York, YO1 8AX

SCARBOROUGH

YOUTH HOSTEL

163r

For a fun filled, seaside break Scarborough is unbeatable: two safe, sandy beaches, penny arcades, pirate ship, three surf schools and the new Alpamare Waterpark. Once a 17th century water mill on a quiet riverside just outside the town, Scarborough Youth Hostel is also a perfect base for exploring the coast and country of the North York Moors and Wolds with miles of paths, tracks and quiet lanes for walkers and cyclists.

DETAILS

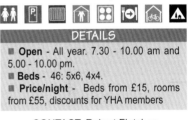

- **Open** - All year. 7.30 - 10.00 am and 5.00 - 10.00 pm.
- **Beds** - 46: 5x6, 4x4.
- **Price/night** - Beds from £15, rooms from £55, discounts for YHA members

CONTACT: Robert Fletcher
Tel: 01723 361176
scarboroughhostel@gmail.com
www.scarboroughhostel.com
The White House, Burniston Road,
Scarborough, YO13 0DA

HULL TRINITY
BACKPACKERS

164

In the heart of Hull, a few hundred yards from the marina and the Humber, this hostel is aimed at the individual traveller, small groups, cyclists and families alike. With flexible rooms including an en suite family room, it is perfect for visiting Hull's art exhibitions and family friendly attractions such as The Deep and newly opened Hull Bonus Arena. Self-catering kitchenette. Coffee lounge in reception welcoming you and passers by.

DETAILS

- **Open** - All year. All day. Except 25 & 26th Dec and New Year.
- **Beds** - 24: 1x6, 2x4, 1x4 en suite, 3 x single/twin. Can accommodate additional.
- **Price/night** - From £19pp (dorm) to £30pp single. £39 private share.

CONTACT: Glenn Gavin
Tel: 01482 223229 or 07853 000474
hulltrinitybackpackers@gmail.com
hulltrinitybackpackers.com
51/52 Market Place Kingston Upon Hull
HU1 1RU

BANK HOUSE

FARM HOSTEL

165

ıxury bunkbarn, camping barn and B&B ı an organic farm in beautiful Glaisdale Dale. Stunning views of the North York Moors and just 1 mile from the Coast to Coast route. The newly converted ›unkbarn is warm & well appointed with one dorm of mostly single beds. The camping barn provides simple, single-night shelter for walkers and cyclists.

DETAILS

- **Open** - All year. Phone calls 9am-9pm
- **Beds** - Bunkbarn: 1x11 (9 singles 1 bunk) Camping barn: 8: 2x4
- **Price/night** - Bunkbarn: W/ends £500 (2 nights), Bank Hols £600 (3 nights). Saturday £400. Midweek from £25pppn. Deals for longer stays. Camping Barn: £12pp. Farmhouse B&B: £40.

CONTACT: Chris or Emma Padmore
Tel: 01947 897297
info@bankhousefarmhostel.co.uk
www.bankhousefarmhostel.co.uk
Bank House Farm, Glaisdale, Whitby
YO21 2QA

BRANSDALE MILL

BUNKHOUSE

166

Bransdale Mill is an eighteenth century Grade II listed water mill, converted by the National Trust to provide comfortable bunkhouse accommodation for 12 people. It is full of historic character with flag-stone floors, wooden beams and a log burner. Situated at the head of an unspoiled and hidden valley in the North York Moors, 3 miles from the Coast to Coast walk. With no WiFi or phone signal, Bransdale Mill is an ideal base to get away from it all, surrounded by the working life of the Dale.

DETAILS

- **Open** - All year. All day
- **Beds** - 12: 2x6
- **Price/night** - From £300 for two nights sole use. (Min booking 2 nights).

CONTACT: National Trust Holidays
Tel: 03443 351296
bunkhouses@nationaltrust.org.uk
www.nationaltrust.org.uk/
holidaysBransdale Mill, Bransdale,
Fadmoor, York YO62 7JL

COTE GHYLL

MILL

167

n a beautiful and secluded valley in the North Yorkshire Moors National Park, is converted linen mill is a perfect base for exploring the moors, dales & coast. Osmotherley has pubs, tea room & shops. Explore the stream & woodlands or take part in organised activities for children and groups. Next to Cod Beck eservoir, Cleveland Way, Coast to Coast and the start of the Lyke Wake Walk. All refurbished, en-suite bedrooms.

DETAILS

- **Open** - All year. 7am -10am, 5pm-9pm.
- **Beds** - 71: Mill 61: 4x2, 6x4, 4x6 + 5 rollout beds. Annex: 10
- **Price/night** - Adults from £26. U18's from £20.80. Family rooms from £50. Enquire for groups & sole use.

CONTACT: Reception
Tel: 01609 883425
mill@coteghyll.com
www.coteghyll.com
Osmotherley, Northallerton, North Yorkshire, DL6 3AH

BROMPTON ON SWALE

BUNKBARN

168l

Located on a small working farm, just 3 miles east of Richmond, Yorkshire. Brompton on Swale Bunkbarn offers a welcome break from walking or cycling the Coast to Coast. A pot of tea for weary walkers upon arrival and safe storage for bikes makes this bunkhouse especially welcoming. Close to the Yorkshire Dales, Swaledale, Wensleydale, Easby Abbey, Richmond Castle & Ellerton Lakes. Dogs are welcome to stay but must be kept on a lead around the yard as there are ducks, hens and geese.

DETAILS

- **Open** - All year. All day
- **Beds** - 12: 3x4
- **Price/night** - £12pp. £144 sole use. Sleeping bag hire £1

CONTACT: Chris Wilkin
Tel: 01748 818326
chris01748@gmail.com
www.facebook.com/bromptononswalebunkbarn
24 Richmond Road, Richmond, North Yorkshire, DL10 7HE

TRAWDEN

CAMPING BARN

168r

Trawden Camping Barn is a listed stone barn on Middle Beardshaw Farm. Surrounded by stunning landscape, the nearby village of Wycoller has been much used by film crews. The barn is large and open with an ancient timbered roof. There is accommodation for 20: 7 beds/bunks and 13 mattresses (BYO sleeping bags) with plenty of communal space, a table tennis and pool table and a well equipped kitchen (in a separate building just 15m away). Pub & café just a short walk away.

DETAILS

- **Open** - All year. Warm clothes and sleeping bags required in winter
- **Beds** - 20 (7 beds + 13 mattresses)
- **Price/night** - £15 pp plus £10 per night per group for electricity.

CONTACT: Ursula
Tel: 01282 865257
ursula78beardshaw@gmail.com
Middle Beardshaw Head Farm, Burnley Road, Trawden Lancashire, BB8 8PP

EARBY HOSTEL

FRIENDS OF NATURE

Reopening in Spring 2019, Earby's newly refurbished Independent Hostel (Friends of Nature House), welcomes individuals, families and small groups to this historic, cosy cottage with picturesque garden. A perfect stop for Pennine Way walkers and great base for local day hikes, cycling or discovering the countryside and local heritage. Featuring comfortable lounges, wood burning stove, a well equipped kitchen and dining areas that seat 18. Real ale pub and meals nearby. Adults must accompany U16s.

DETAILS

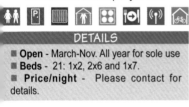

- **Open** - March-Nov. All year for sole use
- **Beds** - 21: 1x2, 2x6 and 1x7.
- **Price/night** - Please contact for details.

CONTACT: Warden
Tel: 01282 842349
earby@naturefriends.org.uk
www.thefriendsofnature.org.uk/houses/earby
9-11 Birch Hall Lane, Earby, Lancashire, BB18 6JX

HEBDEN BRIDGE

HOSTEL

170

Expect a warm welcome at Hebden Bridge Hostel. Comfy and welcoming, with private rooms and dorm beds from £15. Nestled into woodland only a short walk from the town centre, and less than 500m from the Hebden Bridge Loop on the Pennine Way, the hostel makes the perfect base for hiking, sight-seeing, relaxing or experiencing Hebden Bridge's vibrant café, music, arts & culture.

DETAILS

- **Open** - Easter to Nov. Sole use all year. Arrive 5-8pm, leave by 10am.
- **Beds** - 33 : 6x4 (or 2), 1x3 (or 2), 1x6
- **Price/night** - Bunkroom £15pp. Dorm £20pp. Twin £55. Double £60. Double+1 £75. Private 4-bed room £75. Midweek single £35. Sole use available.

CONTACT: Em or Dave
Tel: 01422 843183
mama@hebdenbridgehostel.co.uk
www.hebdenbridgehostel.co.uk
The Birchcliffe Centre, Hebden Bridge, W Yorks, HX7 8DG

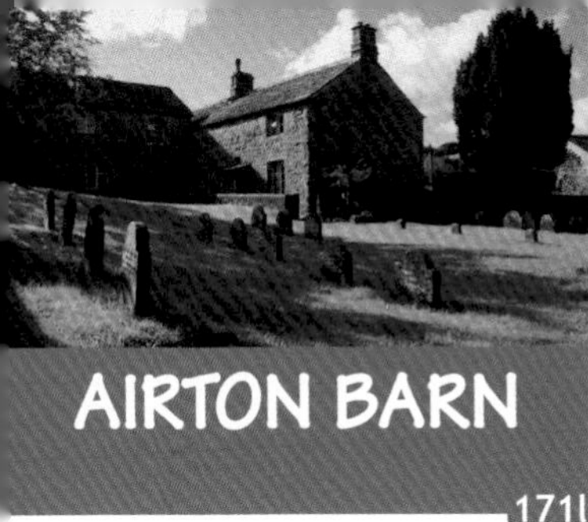

AIRTON BARN

171l

A friendly welcome awaits you in a unique setting at Airton Barn. Adjacent to the 17th century Friends Meeting House, Airton Barn is a simple bunkhouse sleeping up to 18 people over two floors, with storage space for up to 5 bicycles. Located on popular walking and cycling routes, and surrounded by some of Yorkshire's finest tourist destinations, the Barn is ideally placed for walkers and cyclists as well as small group getaways.

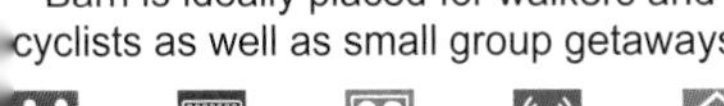

DETAILS

- **Open** - All year. Volunteer warden resident on site
- **Beds** - 6 bunk beds + 6 mattresses + 6 air beds. Overflow camping for 2 tents.
- **Price/night** - £18pp, reducing for larger groups. Call to discuss.

CONTACT:
Tel: 01729 830263
airtonbarn@gmail.com
www.airtonbarn.org.uk
The Nook, Airton, Skipton, North Yorkshire, BD23 4AE

GRASSINGTON

BUNKBARN

171r

With spectacular views of Wharfedale, Grassington Bunkbarn offers comfortable accommodation for individuals and groups. Featuring a well equipped kitchen and a lounge/games area with Freeview TV, WiFi, good mobile signal & a BBQ area. Walking, cycling, climbing, fishing, horse riding, archaeology, bird watching, geology, botany & golf nearby. There's something for everyone.

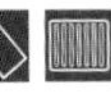

DETAILS

- **Open** - All year. Reception 9am - 5pm Mon - Fri, Sat 10am - 2pm.
- **Beds** - 34: 2x12, 1x6, 1x4
- **Price/night** - Sole use: W/E: £1100 (2 ngts). BH: £1350 (3 ngts). Midweek: £410pn. 4 ngts: £1250. 7 ngts: from £2150. Bed £26 (call for availability).

CONTACT: Paul, Mark or Janet Kent
Tel: 01756 753882
enquiries@grassingtonbunkbarn.co.uk
www.grassingtonbunkbarn.co.uk
Spring Croft, Moor Lane, Grassington, BD23 5BD

NIDDERDALE

BUNKHOUSE

172

Exclusive hire in the stunning Nidderdale Valley overlooking Gouthwaite reservoir. The bunkhouse has a well equipped, open plan kitchen, beautiful dining & seating areas with great views. The Nidderdale Way goes right past the house. The Yorke Arms, Michelin star restaurant, is nearby. The award winning village of Pateley Bridge has pubs, cafés and festivities throughout the year. The Nidderdale Museum is a short drive away. Perfect for walkers, wildlife lovers or to explore Yorkshire. No dogs.

GROUPS ONLY

DETAILS

- **Open** - All year. All day.
- **Beds** - 20: 1x8, 3x4
- **Price/night** - From just £18 per person. Exclusive group hire

CONTACT: Matt or Bev
Tel: 07597 645254
nidderdalebunkhouse@gmail.com
www.nidderdalebunkhouse.com
Ramsgill, Harrogate, North Yorkshire
HG3 5RH

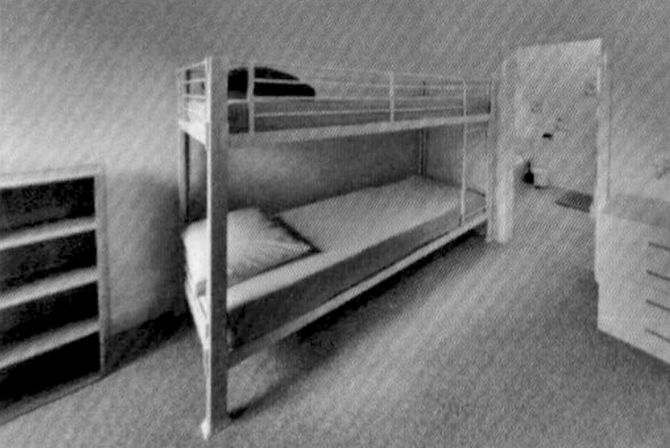

SKIRFARE
BARN

Skirfare Barn, with its stunning backdrop of Upper Wharfedale & Littondale, nestles in the Yorkshire Dales with the climbers' challenge, Kilnsey Crag, on the doorstep. The area is famous for walking & cycling with many footpaths, including the Dales Way, close by. At nearby Kilnsey you can book day fishing & food at The Kilnsey Park, or bar snacks at The Tennant Arms Hotel. Pony & Llama trekking & many other activities are also nearby. The barn provides warm, comfortable accommodation for walking, cycling, friends or family groups.

GROUPS ONLY

DETAILS

- **Open** - All year.
- **Beds** - 20: 2x2 (twin), 2x4, 1x8.
- **Price/night** - From £16 per person.

CONTACT:
Tel: 01756 636350
info@skirfarebarn.com
www.skirfarebarn.com
Kettlewell Rd, Kilnsey, North Yorkshire,
BD23 5PT

KETTLEWELL

HOSTEL

The Rose Award winning Kettlewell Hostel is a stylish Independent Youth Hostel in the heart of the Yorkshire Dales. Serving hearty, great value homemade meals & local beer in our large dining room. There's a cosy lounge with woodburner, a lovely garden, self-catering kitchen & big bike shed! Sleeps up to 42 in 11 bedrooms. Great walking and cycling routes on the doorstep.

  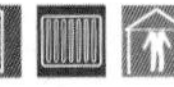      

DETAILS

- **Open** - All year. Reception 8-10.30am, 4-10pm.

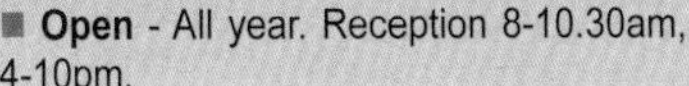

- **Beds** - 42: 1 x twin, 1 x double, 4x3, 2x4, 2x6, 1x5/6
- **Price/night** - Beds from £22, private rooms for 2 from £59. Sole use from £400/night.

CONTACT: Saul & Floss Ward
Tel: 01756 760232
saulward@hotmail.com
www.yha.org.uk/hostel/kettlewell
Whernside House, Kettlewell, Skipton, North Yorkshire, BD23 5QU

TOWN HEAD

BARN

175

Town Head Barn is a converted barn, located in Upper Wharfedale, in the small village of Buckden. The accommodation sleeps 13 in 4 rooms including a single leader's room with en suite facilities. Close (just 3.5 miles) to the village of Kettlewell with pubs and shops and with easy access to Buckden Pike which at 702m high is just waiting to be climbed.

This is the perfect location for groups or families wanting to get away from it all in the Yorkshire Dales National Park.

  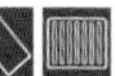      

DETAILS

- **Open** - All year. All day
- **Beds** - 13: 3x4,1x1
- **Price/night** - From £338 for two nights sole use. (Min booking 2 nights).

CONTACT: National Trust Holidays
Tel: 03443 351296
bunkhouses@nationaltrust.org.uk
www.nationaltrust.org.uk/holidays
Buckden, Skipton, North Yorkshire, BD23 5JA

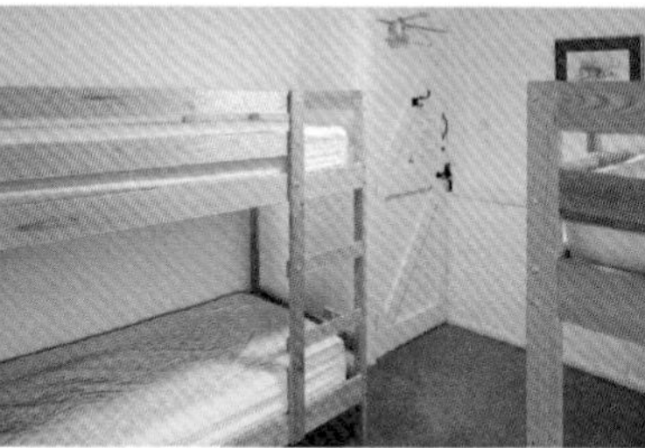

THE DALESBRIDGE

The Dalesbridge is just five miles from Ingleton and Settle in rural Yorkshire. In the grounds are cabins arranged around a camping field, with equipment storage, drying room, bar and conference rooms. Ideal for large groups. The Lodge B&B is furnished in a rustic mountain style with open fires. The bar, open at weekends, often serves breakfast and hosts a popular wood fired pizza night.

Ideal for visiting the Yorkshire Dales & Forest of Bowland, whether you are a family, a group or an individual.

DETAILS

- **Open** - All year
- **Beds** - 40: In Cabins + 8 B&B Rooms.
- **Price/night** - 4 bed cabin £55, 6 bed cabin £75.

CONTACT: Aimee & Ross
Tel: 01524 251021
info@dalesbridge.co.uk
www.dalesbridge.co.uk
Austwick, Nr Settle, LA2 8AZ

HORNBY LAITHE

BUNKHOUSE BARN

177l

Simple, comfortable accommodation in the Yorkshire Dales National Park, Hornby Laith Bunkhouse Barn occupies a secluded position within easy walking distance of the pretty village of Stainforth and the market town of Settle. It is within easy access of a wide variety of routes for walkers and climbers. Sleeping up to 50, there is a separate barn containing a recreational area, extra camping and space for a marquee for events/ weddings & ample parking. There's a self-catering kitchen and full catering can be organised by arrangement.

GROUPS ONLY

DETAILS

- **Open** - All year.
- **Beds** - 50
- **Price/night** - 36 people: £800 w/end. 50 people: £1,100 w/end. Enquire for prices for other party numbers.

CONTACT: Neil and Enid Caton,
Tel: 01729 822240
Hornby Laithe, Stainforth, Nr Settle,
North Yorkshire BD24 9PB

MALHAM TARN

BOTHIES

177r

Opening April 2019 on the National Trust Malham Tarn Estate in North Yorkshire, Ragged Robin Bothy and Meadowsweet Bothy will each sleeps 6 people on bunk bed platforms. Like camping but without the tent, you need to bring mats, sleeping bags and cooking equipment. There is one external toilet, cold water and no heating or lighting, so a perfect location for those who want to escape technology and enjoy dark skies. The bothys are right on the Pennine Way.

DETAILS

- **Open** - Opening April 2019. April to Oct.
- **Beds** - 12: Ragged Robin Bothy 6:1x6, Meadowsweet Bothy 6:1x6
- **Price/night** - £30 per bothy in low season, £40 in high season.

CONTACT: National Trust Holidays
Tel: 03443 351296
bunkhouses@nationaltrust.org.uk
www.nationaltrust.org.uk/holidays
Malham Tarn Estate, Waterhouses,
Settle, North Yorkshire, BD24 9PT

INGLETON YHA

GRETA TOWER

178l

On the edge of the Yorkshire Dales, surrounded by magnificent countryside with caves, waterfalls and mountains, Ingleton is dominated by Ingleborough, the best known of Yorkshire's Three Peaks (this is a great base for The Challenge). Known for its walking routes and waterfall trail, there is plenty here for walkers, climbers, mountain bikers and cavers. Licensed and serving tasty meals there is also a self-catering kitchen. Perfect for families and school trips.

DETAILS

- **Open** - All year (Sole use only Nov-Feb). Reception open 8am-noon, 5-10pm
- **Beds** - 64: 4x6, 7x4, 1x2, 2x5
- **Price/night** - Beds from £18, rooms from £39. Sole use bookings welcome

CONTACT: Manager
Tel: 015242 41444
ingleton@yha.org.uk
www.ingletonhostel.co.uk
Greta Tower, Sammy Lane, Ingleton, North Yorkshire, LA6 3EG

THE OLD SCHOOL

BUNKHOUSE

178r

Situated near Ingleton in the Yorkshire Dales, on the Yorkshire Three Peaks route. Old School Bunkhouse sleeps up to 30. It has a comfortable lounge, with TV, DVD & WiFi, a large kitchen diner, 4 bathrooms and a drying room with washing machine. Outside is parking for 12 cars and great views of Ingleborough and Whernside. The pub over the road is ideal for that celebratory drink.

     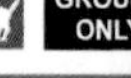

GROUPS ONLY

DETAILS

- **Open** - All year. 24 hours.
- **Beds** - 30: 5x6
- **Price/night** - Fri/Sat £350 per night (sole use) for up to 20 people + £18 per extra person. Min 2 nights at w/ends. Sun-Thurs £300 up to 20 + £15 per extra person. Max 30.

CONTACT: Debbie Bryant
Tel: 01931 714874 or 07884 260815
oldschoolbunkhouse@gmail.com
www.oldschoolbunkhouse.co.uk
Chapel-le-Dale, Ingleton, Carnforth, Lancs, LA6 3AR

BROADRAKE

BUNKBARN

179l

Broadrake Bunkbarn offers direct access to the Three Peaks Challenge Walk, Wainwright's Pennine Journey & The Dales High Way. This popular accommodation for 20 has an upstairs open-plan living space with excellent self-catering & communal facilities. It is perfect for special birthday celebrations, extended family reunions, cyclists, cavers and dark sky enthusiasts. Small groups welcome, especially mid-week.

DETAILS

- **Open** - All year. All day.
- **Beds** - 20: 1x8, 2x4, 2x twin.
- **Price/night** - Weekends (2 nights) £900. Bank Holiday WE (3 nights) £1350, or £25pppn. Mid-week £360 or £20pppn Week £2000. £5 bedding/towel hire.

CONTACT: Mike & Rachel Benson
Tel: 01524 241357
info@broadrake.co.uk
www.broadrake.co.uk
Broadrake, Chapel-le-Dale, Ingleton, LA6 3AX

GAUBER

BUNK BARN

179r

In the heart of Yorkshire's Three Peaks country right on the route between Pen-y-ghent & Whernside and close to the Dales Way, Dales High Way, Pennine Way and Pennine Bridleway. This warm comfortable bunk barn sleeps up to 13 in three bunk rooms. Living room with cosy wood burner, spacious well equipped kitchen & garden with stunning views. Group bookings only at weekends. Book by the bed or bunk room Sun-Thurs (not bank holidays.). Dogs & breakfast by arrangement. 4 bed annex also available

DETAILS

- **Open** - All year. All day.
- **Beds** - 17: Bunkhouse: 13: 2x4, 1x5 (dbl+3) ensuite. The Den 4: 1x4.
- **Price/night** - £21 inc fitted sheet & pillow. Duvet & towel one off charge of £5.

CONTACT: Jon Radda & Katie Hawkins
Tel: 01524 241150
gauberbunkbarn@gmail.com
www.gauberbunkbarn.co.uk
Ribblehead, Ingleton, Carnforth, LA6 3JF

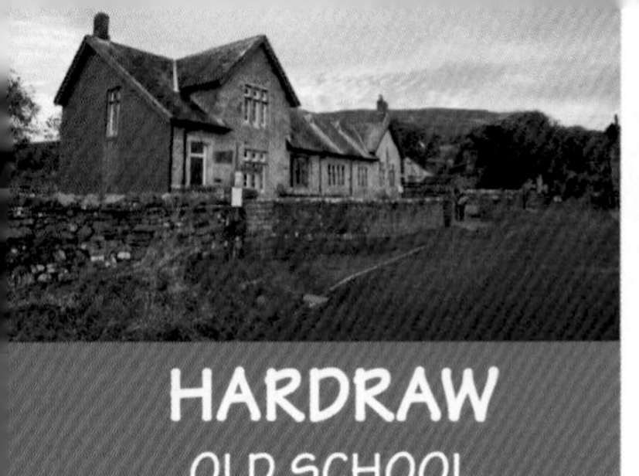

HARDRAW

OLD SCHOOL

180l

Next to the Pennine Way, in the village of Hardraw, The Old School Bunkhouse offers well appointed, practical accommodation for up to 26. The large hall (with games, table tennis, piano, log burner & sofas) and grounds are perfect for group activities. Hardraw has a café, inn and the famous Hardraw Force waterfall. The market town of Hawes is a 1.5 mile walk across fields. Instruction available in many outdoor activities.

DETAILS

- **Open** - All year. All day.
- **Beds** - 26:1x8,1x9,1x6,1x3 + 3 mattresses & 2 tent spaces
- **Price/night** - £15.50pp. Sole use £180-£315. Winter (Mid Nov to End Feb): min. 5 persons or min. charge of £65.

CONTACT: Helen
Tel: 01969 666034 or 07513 279899
enquiries@hardrawoldschoolbunkhouse.co.uk
www.hardrawoldschoolbunkhouse.co.uk
Schoolhouse, Hardraw, near Hawes, Wensleydale, North Yorkshire, DL8 3LZ

THE JONAS

CENTRE

180r

Twelve Scandinavian styled self-catering log cabins located at the hea of Wensleydale in the tranquil beauty the Yorkshire Dales,. Nine lodges are located in Elm Wood away from the ma complex & the other three are locatec near to Granary Barn, which has a shop, two lounges a meeting room an a kitchen for group use. The varied us of the centre means that facilities are comfortable rather than luxurious.

GROU ONL

DETAILS

- **Open** - All year. Office open from 9am 5pm Monday to Saturday.
- **Beds** - 60: 12 lodges each sleepin between 5 and 7 people.
- **Price/night** - See website for specia offers. Discounts for full site use.

CONTACT: Simon Eastwood
Tel: 01969 624900
stay@jonascentre.org
www.jonascentre.org
Redmire, Leyburn. North Yorkshire, DL 4EW

DALES

BIKE CENTRE

181l

Dales Bike Centre, Swaledale, is the centre of cycling in Yorkshire! Home of the Ard Rock Enduro, en-route of the 014 Tour de France Grand Depart, the 019 World Road Race Championship's route, the Yorkshire Dales Cycle Way and loads of great cycling & mountain biking. On-site café, bike shop, MTB, ad & e-bike hire, bike wash, workshop, drying room & lots of friendly advice. Close to 4 pubs & Reeth village.

DETAILS

- **Open** - All year. All day.
- **Beds** - 14: Old Barn 1x4, 1x2. New Barn 1x4, 2x2,
- **Price/night** - Single room £39, 2 bed bunkroom £58, 4 bed bunkroom £116, 3 people in 4 bed bunkroom £97. Inc b/fast.

CONTACT: Stu Price
Tel: 01748 884908
enquiries@dalesbikecentre.co.uk
www.dalesbikecentre.co.uk
Parks Barn, Fremington, Richmond, Yorkshire Dales DL11 6AW

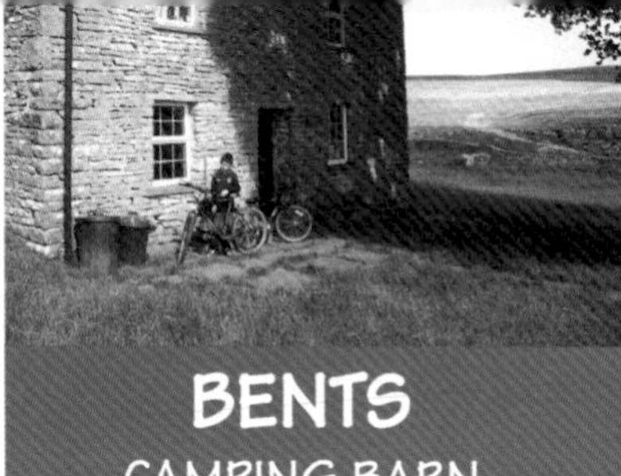

BENTS

CAMPING BARN

181r

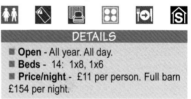

Bents Camping Barn, formerly a 17th century shepherd's cottage, is in the Yorkshire Dales National Park. There are 2 bunkrooms sleeping 14 in total (BYO sleeping bags), a well equipped kitchen and a dining area. Please bring £1 coins for the electric metre. The Coast to Coast path is nearby and the Howgill Fells, Wild Boar Fell and Crosby Garrett Common offer great fell walking. Smardale Gill Nature Reserve and Sunbiggin Tarn are also easily accessible.

DETAILS

- **Open** - All year. All day.
- **Beds** - 14: 1x8, 1x6
- **Price/night** - £11 per person. Full barn £154 per night.

CONTACT: Dorothy Ousby
Tel: 01768 371760, Booking: 01768 774301
info@bentscampingbarn.co.uk
www.bentscampingbarn.co.uk
Newbiggin-on-Lune, Kirkby Stephen, Cumbria, CA17 4NX

HOWGILLS

BARN

182

Howgills Barn offers a beautifully renovated self-catering barn in Sedbergh Yorkshire. Breathtaking views, plenty to see and do on the doorstep & set in a private location where the children can enjoy some freedom. A five minute walk into Sedbergh to nearby pubs, cafés and restaurants. Dogs welcome too. Hot tub available. Five stars on Trip Advisor from over 100 reviews gives a flavour of the quality of the accommodation.

DETAILS

- **Open** - All year. All day.
- **Beds** - 35: 6x4 1x5 1x6 (all en suite) plus camping
- **Price/night** - From £30pp inc. breakfast. Duvet £6 sgle, £9 dbl. Please enquire for hot tub rates. Camping £12pp.

CONTACT:
Tel: 08008 321632 or 07973 947753
info@howgillsaccommodation.co.uk
www.howgillsaccommodation.co.uk
Castlehaw Farm, Castlehaw Lane,
Sedbergh, Cumbria LA10 5BA

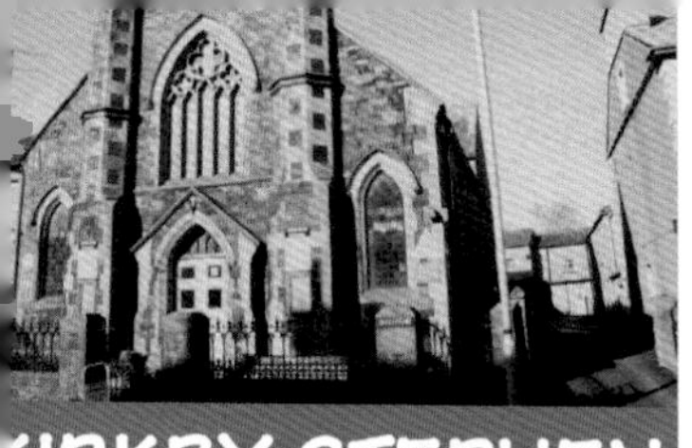

KIRKBY STEPHEN

HOSTEL

183l

ormer Methodist Church with a range of ccommodation for individuals, families nd groups amongst beautiful authentic features; stained glass, arches and panels. There's a large dining room & tchen and a quiet lounge in the gallery. Kirkby Stephen is a market town in the upper Eden valley. On Wainwright's Coast to Coast path with easy access the Pennine Journey, the W2W cycle route, the Howgill Hills, the Yorkshire Dales and the Lake District.

DETAILS

- **Open** - All year. Please arrive after 5pm (or ring to arrange arrival).
- **Beds** - 38: 1x8, 3x6, 2x4, 1x2, 1x2 en suite.
- **Price/night** - £20pp. Group rates.

CONTACT: Denise
Tel: 07812 558525
kirkbystephenhostel@btconnect.com
www.kirkbystephenhostel.co.uk
Market Street, Kirkby Stephen, Cumbria, CA17 4QQ

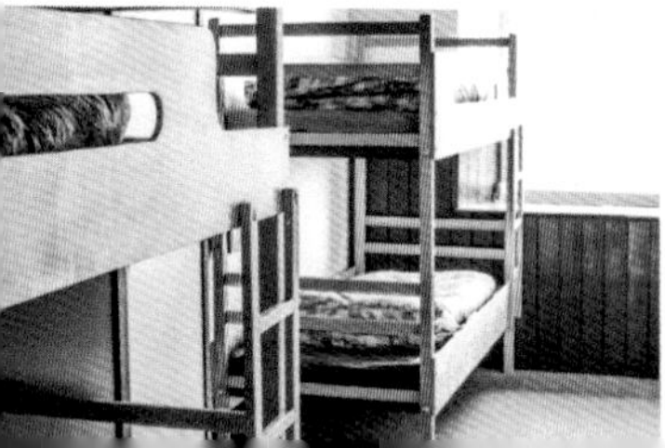

NEW ING

LODGE

183r

This 10-bedroom, 10-bathroom B&B & hostel offers comfortable, friendly, accommodation with delicious food. Shap is in the Eden Valley, just off the M6, on the edge of the Lake District National Park. The Howgills & the Pennine Fells are close by. On Wainwright's Coast to Coast, the Westmorland Way & the Miller's Way it's perfect for large groups or individuals.

DETAILS

- **Open** - All year.
- **Beds** - 30: 4xdbl, 2xfamily (dbl + 2 singles), 2xtriple, 2x4-bedded dormitory
- **Price/night** - £20pp dorm. B&B (private rooms) from £55pp. Discounts for larger groups/longer stays. Sole use from only £600.

CONTACT: Scott
Tel: 01931 716719
info@newinglodge.co.uk
www.newinglodge.co.uk
New Ing Lodge, Main Street, Shap, Penrith, Cumbria, CA10 3LX

GREENGILL
BARN

184

A converted traditional barn on the edge of Morland in Cumbria's rolling Eden Valley. Close to the Lake District and handy for the M6. Great for gatherings of family or friends wanting to visit the Lake District, the Pennines, the Yorkshire Dales and the Borders. There is a large, fully equipped kitchen/dining room and a large, two-storey games room. On NCR 71 and Wiggo's Loop on C2C. Good local walking and easy access to lakes & fells. Local café and pub for meals & ale.

   GROUPS ONLY

DETAILS

- **Open** - All year.
- **Beds** - 16: 2x8
- **Price/night** - Min 2 nights: £600 then £160 per night. Own sleeping bags free, or duvet, pillow, towel £10. Dogs £20.

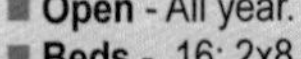

CONTACT: Freddy Markham
Tel: 01931 714244 or 07831 428541
freddy@greengillholidays.co.uk
www.greengillholidays.co.uk
Greengill Barn, Strickland Road,
Morland, Penrith, Cumbria CA10 3AX

YEALAND

OLD SCHOOL

185l

Yealand Old School Hostel, reopening in May 2019, is a stroll from Warton Crag for views across the sands of Morecambe Bay. In early summer hunt out a host of wild flowers on the mestone scenery at nearby Gaitbarrows NNR and Hutton Roofs crags. Kids will enjoy Lakeland Wildlife Oasis, a small zoo close by. The New Inn is only 300m away. Relax in the grounds of the djacent Quaker Meeting House. Groups only at weekends, except last minute.

GROUPS ONLY

DETAILS

- **Open** - Closed until May 2019
- **Beds** - 25: 3x2 plus 20 on mattresses.
- **Price/night** - £15pp, £7.50 children 5+, Min charge £100 for group Friday/Sat, £50 during week.

CONTACT: Sue Tyldesley
Tel: 01524 732336
yealandwarden@lancsquakers.org.uk
www.lancsquakers.org.uk/simple-hostel.php
'ealand Rd, Yealand Conyers, Carnforth, LA5 9SH

WITHERSLACK

CYCLE BARN

185r

Located between Grange Over Sands and Beck Head on the northern shore of Morecambe Bay. This new bunkhouse is within the beautiful Whitbarrow Nature Reserve. Built with cyclists and walkers in mind with drying room, locked cycle storage and laundry as well as kitchen and communal areas. Perfect for groups, families and individuals it is just 500m from the Morecambe 'Bay Cycle Way', the Lakes & Dales Loop and NCN 700 & 70 E-bike hire is available on site.

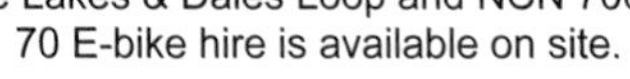

DETAILS

- **Open** - All year. All day
- **Beds** - 14: 2x2(twin) 1x4(family), 1x6.
- **Price/night** - From £20. £2 towel hire Food on request.

CONTACT: Steph Fry
Tel: 01539 552223 or 07876 576874
info@beckhead.co.uk
www.witherslackcyclebarn.co.uk
Beck Head Farm, Beck Head, Witherslack, Grange Over Sands. Cumbria, LA11 6SH

ROOKHOW

CENTRE

186

In the Rusland Valley, surrounded by glorious woods where bonfires/BBQs are permitted, near Coniston, Windermere & Grisedale Forest. Rookhow is the perfect base for walking, orienteering, mountaineering, biking and other outdoor activities or quiet retreat. A small, cosy hostel converted from stables of the nearby Quaker Meeting House (available for group activities). The sleeping areas can be rented as private/family rooms.

GROUPS ONLY

DETAILS

- **Open** - All year. All day.
- **Beds** - 16: in 3 rooms. Camping also available.
- **Price/night** - £250 (minimum 2 nights). £50 for extra meeting room. Camping: £10 adult, £5 child.

CONTACT: Warden
Tel: 07787 742680
contactrookhow@gmail.com
www.rookhowcentre.co.uk
Rusland Valley, nr Grizedale, Ulverston, Cumbria, South Lakeland, LA12 8LA

LOWICK SCHOOL

BUNKHOUSE

Within the old primary school at Lowick Green, nestled between Coniston (4 miles) and Ulverston, the bunkhouse has a lounge with wood-burning stove, large kitchen/dining room, great views of the mountains and an outdoor area with campfire. River Deep Mountain High Activity Centre provides a wide variety of outdoor activities. Group and family packages include activities in the price.

DETAILS

- **Open** - All year.
- **Beds** - 20: 2x8, 1x4 (one 8 bed can be expanded to 10)
- **Price/night** - Sole use from £600 at weekends (Club scheme), from £220 per night Mon-Thurs. £250 damage deposit. Family holiday packages.

CONTACT: Emma Hoving
Tel: 01539 528666
info@riverdeepmountainhigh.co.uk
riverdeepmountainhigh.co.uk/group-accommodation
Lowick Green, Ulverston LA12 8EB

FELL END

CAMPING BARN

188l

Fell End is a traditional 18th century Lakeland stone barn, located within its own grass courtyard approximately ½ mile from the farm. It is within easy distance of Coniston (6 miles) and the Duddon Valley (5 miles). Come and stay and witness the star filled skies, a truly breathtaking sight. Experience the magical sound of silence in the tranquil and calming Fell End Barn. Bring your own cooking equipment, torches, bedding and mat.

DETAILS

- **Open** - All year, All day.
- **Beds** - 12: 1x12
- **Price/night** - £11 per person.

CONTACT: Office or Jean Jackson
Tel: Office 01768 774301 Farm 01229 716340
info@lakelandcampingbarns.co.uk
www.lakedistrictcottages.co.uk
Thornthwaite Farm, Woodland, Broughton in Furness, Cumbria, LA20 6DF

HIGH WALLABARROW

CAMPING BARN

188r

High Wallabarrow is a traditional hill farm in the Duddon Valley, the Lake District's quiet corner. The well equipped camping barn, an old farmhouse, sleeps 10 upstairs. Downstairs there's a large living area with woodburning stove and fully equipped kitchen. Mattresses provided BYO sleeping bags/pillows. Toilet just outside and shower nearby. 15 mins' walk to pub, 10 mins to climbing crag. Not suitable for rowdy groups.

DETAILS

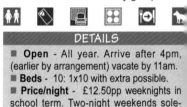

- **Open** - All year. Arrive after 4pm, (earlier by arrangement) vacate by 11am.
- **Beds** - 10: 1x10 with extra possible.
- **Price/night** - £12.50pp weeknights in school term. Two-night weekends sole-use £125/night. £1.50 per dog per night..

CONTACT: Chris Chinn (9am to 9pm)
Tel: 01229 715011
camden.chinn@gmail.com
www.wallabarrow.co.uk
High Wallabarrow, Ulpha, Broughton-in-Furness, Cumbria, LA20 6EA

HIGH WRAY

BASECAMP

189

Situated in the heart of South Lakeland, in secluded woodland, just 4 miles from the popular tourist village of Ambleside, High Wray Basecamp provides an ideal base for groups wishing to explore the Lake District. Local attractions include ambling, fell walking, climbing and water ports. The Basecamp ranger will happily assist with information on local walks and activities. The Longland block has two dormitories each sleeping 8, while the Acland block has two dormitories sleeping 10 each.

GROUPS ONLY

DETAILS

- **Open** - All year. All day.
- **Beds** - 16 + 22
- **Price/night** - Prices from £11 per person (minimum 8 persons booking)

CONTACT: Philippa Barber
Tel: 01539 434633
Philippa.barber@nationaltrust.org.uk
www.nationaltrust.org.uk/holidays
High Wray, Ambleside, Cumbria, Lake District. LA22 0JE

LAKE DISTRICT
BACKPACKERS

190l

In the heart of Windermere, close to shops, cafés and pubs, 2 minutes from the train & bus station and opposite the TIC and tour offices. Easy access to the National Park by the 555 bus, 25 minute walk to the lake with steamer trips and boat hire and access to the fells from our door. Maps and guides available in this friendly, cosy hostel.

DETAILS

- **Open** - All year. 24 hours with key code for front door.
- **Beds** - 20:- 1x6, 2x4, 2 x double with single above.
- **Price/night** - From £16.95pp dorms, £19.95pp private rooms. £2pn discount for stays of 3+ nights (Nov-Mar) inc self serve continental b-fast & free tea/coffee.

CONTACT: Paul
Tel: 01539 446374
info@lakedistrictbackpackers.co.uk
www.lakedistrictbackpackers.co.uk
High Street, Windermere, Cumbria, LA23 1AF

KENDAL
HOSTEL

190r

Kendal Hostel, a Georgian townhouse in the historic market town of Kendal, is next to the well known Brewery Arts Centre and only a stone's throw from the town centre. Facilities include 13 bedrooms for up to 66 guests, kitchen, lounge, dining room, bike shed and FREE WiFi. Single/double/family/group rooms plus mixed & single sex dorms.

DETAILS

- **Open** - All year. 8-11.30am, 4-8.30pm and by arrangement.
- **Beds** - 66: 1x12, 1x8, 2x7(fam), 2x6, 1x5(fam), 1x4, 1x3, 3x2, 1xdbl. Family rooms have a private shower room & double bed. Single rooms available also.
- **Price/night** - £20 Sun -Thurs, £22 Fri & Sat. Sole use from £700 per night.

CONTACT: Jan or Kristina
Tel: 01539 724066
kristina@kendalhostel.co.uk
www.kendalhostel.com
118-120 Highgate, Kendal, Cumbria, LA9 4HE

DACRES STABLE

CAMPING BARN

191l

A short drive from Kendal, Dacres Stable Camping Barn is on the eastern edge of the Lake District National Park. On a gated road away from the main A6 it is a perfect base for exploring the Yorkshire Dales, the Lake District and the Eden Valley.

Great too for mountain biking, walking, & cycling on quiet tracks and lanes. The camping barn comfortably sleeps 8 on a sole use, self-catering basis.

DETAILS

- **Open** - March to November inclusive
- **Beds** - 8: 1x2 1x6.
- **Price/night** - Sole use of the building. Ground floor only (sleeps 2 + 1) £60. Ground floor plus upper bunk room £80. Minimum 2 nights' stay.

CONTACT: Hilary Fell
Tel: 01539 823208 or 07788 633936
dacresstablecampingbarn.blogspot.co.uk
Grisedale Farm, Whinfell, Kendal, Cumbria, LA8 9EN

RYDAL HALL

YOUTH CENTRE

191r

Situated next to Rydal Beck in the heart of the Lake District, Rydal Hall Youth Centre provides accommodation for groups of up to 29 in four dormitories plus a large common room, drying room & a fully equipped stainless steel kitchen. There is also a quiet campsite for individuals and families, eco-pods in the grounds and en suite accommodation for up to 50 in the main hall and a tea shop.

DETAILS

- **Open** - All year. All day.
- **Beds** - Youth Centre 29: 1x10, 1x9, 1x6, 1x4. Plus campsite, eco-pods, accommodation for 50 in the main hall.
- **Price/night** - Youth Centre £315. Discounts & late deals possible. Pods £47.50, £42pn 2+ nights, £37pn 4+ nights.

CONTACT: Bookings Office
Tel: 01539 432050
groupbookings@rydalhall.org
www.rydalhall.org
Rydal Hall, Ambleside, Cumbria, LA22 9LX

ELTERWATER

HOSTEL

192

Located in the peaceful village of Elterwater, in the Langdale valley, 15 mins' drive from Ambleside. The area has many walks for people of all abilities, from gentle riverside meanders to the challenge presented by the Langdale Pikes, Bowfell and Scafell. Pubs, shops and other amenities are nearby. The area is popular for both on and off-road cycling, rock climbing and other outdoor activities. An ideal overnight stop on the Cumbria Way.

DETAILS

- **Open** - All year (Nov-Feb groups only). Access 7.30am-11.30pm. Reception open 7.30-10am and 5-10.30pm.
- **Beds** - 38 : 6x2, 1x4, 1x4 ensuite, 3x6
- **Price/night** - From £25pp, £21 in low season. For exclusive hire please call.

CONTACT: Nick Owen
Tel: 01539 437245
enquiries@elterwaterhostel.co.uk
www.elterwaterhostel.co.uk
Elterwater, Ambleside LA22 9HX

GREAT LANGDALE
BUNKHOUSE

Great Langdale Bunkhouse is situated amidst some of the finest mountain scenery in England with access to mountain biking, cycling, walking, fell running and climbing. The newly renovated bunkhouse has 20 single beds divided into 3 twin rooms, one room of 6 and one room of 8 (all bunk beds). The rooms are simple but comfortable and each room has a double plug socket. The bunkhouse has biomass central heating throughout so its toasty warm with an endless supply of hot water with powerful showers.

DETAILS

Open - All year. All day.
Beds - 20: 3x2, 1x6, 1x8 all bunkbeds.
Price/night - From £15 per person.

CONTACT: Ben or Sabrina
Tel: 01539 437725
langdale.bunkhouse@gmail.com
www.greatlangdalebunkhouse.co.uk
Great Langdale, Ambleside, Cumbria, LA22 9JU

THORNEY HOW

194

Thorney How offers clean, comfortable accommodation in Grasmere. Family-run and welcoming it provides en suite, simple B&B and self-catering. Close to the Coast to Coast path, local village and lake.Your perfect Lake District base. A bar, restaurant and spacious grounds complete the experience.

DETAILS

- **Open** - All year. Closed 10.30am to 3.30pm check in 3.30-10.30pm.
- **Beds** - 42: Main House 26, 2xdbl, 1xtwin, 2x4, 2x6. Bunkhouse 16
- **Price/night** - Dble en suite B&B from £82. Family en-suite B&B from £100. 4 person budget rooms from £80. Larger catered groups please enquire.

CONTACT: Taylor Nuttall
Tel: 01539 435597
enquiries@thorneyhow.co.uk
www.thorneyhow.co.uk
Thorney How, Off Helm Close & Easedale Rd, Grasmere, Cumbria, LA22 9QW

SHEPHERDS
CROOK

Noran Bank Farm is near Ullswater just through Patterdale in Cumbria, just 5 minutes' walk away from the Coast to Coast route and The Westmorland Way. Shepherd's Crook Bunkhouse is a barn converted to a very high standard and sleeps 8. Duvets, linen and towels are provided. DIY breakfast and packed lunches can be pre-booked. It is very popular with Coast to Coasters, walkers, cyclists and for family/friends get-togethers.

DETAILS

- **Open** - All year.
- **Beds** - 8: 1x6, 1x2 + B&B.
- **Price/night** - £15pp (6 bed room), £20pp (double room). Sole use £120. Farmhouse B&B £30pp.

CONTACT: Mrs Heather Jackson
Tel: 01768 482327 or 07833 981504
heathernoranbank@gmail.com
www.noranbankfarm.co.uk
Noran Bank Farm, Patterdale, Penrith, Cumbria, CA11 0NR

FISHER-GILL
CAMPING BARN

Situated in Thirlmere at the foot of the Helvellyn mountains, close to Sticks Pass and the spectacular Fisher-Gill waterfall, the camping barn offers you direct access to numerous walks, hill and rock climbing. It is just off the A591 with local and national bus stops at the end of the lane. Accommodation consists of two rooms; a kitchen/diner with all the basic equipment and a 10 bed bunkroom (sleeping bags/liners are required). A pub serving meals is within walking distance. Perfect for quite country retreats, it is not suitable for late night drinking parties

DETAILS

- **Open** - All year. Check in by 9pm.
- **Beds** - 10
- **Price/night** - £16pp. Sole use £160.

CONTACT: Mrs Jean Hodgson
Tel: 017687 74391 or 017687 73232
stybeckfarm@btconnect.com
www.stybeckfarm.co.uk
Stybeck Farm, Thirlmere, Keswick, Cumbria CA12 4TN

ST JOHNS IN THE VALE CAMPING BARN

197

St John's-in-the-Vale Camping Barn, a renovated 18th century stable on a eaceful hill farm, has stunning views to Blencathra, Helvellyn and Castle Rock. The Barn has a sleeping area upstairs nattresses provided) and a sitting/dining area below. A separate toilet, shower and cooking area (BYO equipment) are ithin the building. A wood-burning stove nakes it nice and cosy. Outside there is BBQ area. As there is no light pollution, the star-filled night skies are magical. Northern Lights have been seen too!

- **Open** - All year. All day.
- **Beds** - 8 : 1x8
- **Price/night** - £11.00 per person.

CONTACT: Graham or Sarah
Tel: 017687 79242 (Bookings 017687 74301)
info@campingbarn.com
www.campingbarn.com
Low Bridge End Farm, St John's-in-the-Vale, Keswick, CA12 4TS

CARLISLE DIOCESAN YOUTH CENTRE

198l

Near St John's-in-the-Vale and just four miles from Keswick. The centre offers self-catering accommodation for groups with en suite bunkrooms and a recently refurbished common room with wood-burner. With amazing views and fell walking, climbing, orienteering and cycling on the doorstep. Perfect for a group retreat, large family get-together or field trips. BYO sleeping bag, pillowcase and towel.

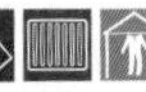

GROUPS ONLY

DETAILS

- **Open** - All year. 24 hours.
- **Beds** - 39: School 25: 1x6,1x5,3x4,1x2, Chapel 14: 3x4,1x2.
- **Price/night** - £18pp. Charity groups with children (eg scouts, schools and church groups) 14pp.

CONTACT: Warden
Tel: 07530 968219
carlisledyc@gmail.com
www.cdyc.org.uk/
St John's-in-the-Vale, Keswick, Cumbria,CA12 4UB

ROOKIN HOUSE CAMPING BARN

198r

Rookin House Farm Camping Barn sleeps up to 24 with central heating, fully equipped kitchen and inside toilets & showers (BYO bedding). The centre also has luxury self catering group accommodation and provides outdoor activities. At the heart of the Lake District surrounded by some of the best walking country and close to C2C cycle route.

GROUP ONLY

DETAILS

- **Open** - All year. All day
- **Beds** - 65: Camping Barn 24: 2x6, 1x12. Barn 23. Blencathra View 18.
- **Price/night** - Camping Barn mid week £17.50pp (min of 4 people), weekends £400 for 2 night stay for 12 people plus £12.50pp for extra people. Additional nights £150 per night for up to 12 people.

CONTACT: Deb and Emma
Tel: 01768 483561
deborah@rookinhouse.co.uk
www.rookinhouse.co.uk
Rookin House Farm, Troutbeck, Ullswater,Penrith,Cumbria, CA11 0SS

THE WHITE HORSE

INN BUNKHOUSE

The White Horse Inn has 2 bunkhouses in the converted stables of this traditional Lake District inn at the foot of Blencathra. Guests are welcome in the Inn which has great pub food, open fires, local ales and is open from 11am to 11pm. Each bunkhouse has a basic kitchen, dining area and bunkrooms sleeping between 4 and 6. Paths to the mountains from the garden & the C2C route passes the door.

DETAILS

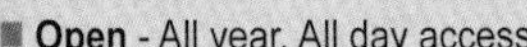

- **Open** - All year. All day access.
- **Beds** - 50:1x8,3x6,6x4 (2 bunkhouses)
- **Price/night** - £12pp. Private rooms: 4 bed £48, 6 bed £72, 8 bed £96. Sole use of 24 bed bunkhouse £260. Sole use of 26 bed bunkhouse £280. Bedding £5/stay. Enquire for Xmas/New Year.

CONTACT: Phil or Cozmin
Tel: 017687 79883
info@thewhitehorse-blencathra.co.uk
www.thewhitehorse-blencathra.co.uk
The White Horse Inn, Scales, Nr
Threlkeld, Keswick, CA12 4SY

BLAKEBECK FARM

CAMPING BARN

200l

At the foot of Souther Fell, within easy reach of Blencathra, Blakebeck Farm is set amidst the wildflower meadows of Mungrisdale. On the C2C cycle route and the Cumbrian Way. Perfect as a weekend break for walkers and families. The large upstairs room has bunk beds for 10 people (BYO sleeping bags) and a large farmhouse table. The kitchen has all you need to cook a simple meal. DIY breakfast & pack lunches can be pre-booked. One dog welcome with sole use. Not suitable for parties.

DETAILS

- **Open** - All year. All day
- **Beds** - 10: 1x10 + holiday cottages
- **Price/night** - £11 per person. Sole use £110. Dog £10 per stay.

CONTACT: Judith
Tel: Booking Office 017687 74301 Farm 017687 79957 Mob 07789 287121
j.egan001@btinternet.com
wwwblakebeckfarm.co.uk
Blakebeck, Mungrisdale, CA11 0SZ

BASSENTHWAITE

PARISH ROOM

200r

Refurbished to a very high standard, the Parish Room is a great base for outdoors enthusiasts to explore Skiddaw the Northern Lakes, Keswick and the Cumbrian coast. There is a modern well equipped kitchen, large hall, meeting room with sofa and large Freeview TV. There is also disabled access throughout. Separate male/female toilets and two shower rooms. Bring your own beds, bedding and towels. Free WiFi. Sorry no stag/hen parties.

GROUP ONLY

DETAILS

- **Open** - All year
- **Beds** - 18 (BYO beds/bedding/towels)
- **Price/night** - £180 for 18 people (larger and smaller groups please get in touch for price). Two night minimum stay.

CONTACT: Louise
Tel: 07786 434411
bookbassenthwaiteparishroom@gmail.com
www.bassenthwaite.org.uk/the-parish-room.html
School Road, Bassenthwaite, Keswick, CA12 4QJ

THE COACH HOUSE

AT OLD WINDEBROWE

Situated on the outskirts of Keswick. the dog friendly Coach House sleeps up to 14 people in 2 dormitories and incorporates a kitchen, dining area and lounge. To the front there is parking and an outside south-facing seating area in the cobbled area and to the rear a shared utility room with washing machine, tumble dryer and drying racks. All the amenities of Keswick are 5 minutes away by car, or 20 minutes by foot. Bed linen & mattresses provided.

DETAILS

- **Open** - All year
- **Beds** - 14
- **Price/night** - £162 per night for sole use, with a minimum stay of 2 nights.

CONTACT: Reception at the Lake District Calvert Trust
Tel: 017687 72255
enquiries@calvertlakes.org.uk
www.calvertlakes.org.uk
Coach House, Old Windebrow, Keswick, CA12 4NT

SKIDDAW HOUSE

HOSTEL

2021

The highest hostel in Britain! Escape the crowds at this remote mountain hostel. No roads, no other buildings, no phone signal, just views of beautiful mountain wilderness. But there's no need to compromise on comfort, with wood burning stoves, hot showers, a well-stocked bar and full bedding provided. An easy walk or mountain bike ride from Keswick or Threlkeld.

DETAILS

■ **Open** - March-Oct. Winter groups only. Check in from 5pm, check out by 10am.
■ **Beds** - 22 : 1 x 8, 2 x 5, 1 x 4
■ **Price/night** - Dorm from £20 (adult), £13 (U18). Private rooms from £50. Camping from £10. £3 discount for YHA members. Cards not accepted.

CONTACT: Martin or Suzy
Tel: 07747 174293
info@skiddawhouse.co.uk
www.skiddawhouse.co.uk
Bassenthwaite, Keswick, Cumbria, CA12 4QX

DENTON

HOUSE

202r

Denton House is a purpose built hostel and outdoor centre in the Lake District offering bunkhouse accommodation. Warm and well equipped for self-catering, the centre was designed for groups with parking for 40 cars. A variety of outdoor activities can be arranged on site. There is equipment storage and access to the River Greta across the road.

DETAILS

■ **Open** - All year (including Christmas). Office hours 9am - 8pm.
■ **Beds** - 56: 1x4, 2x6, 1x8, 2x10, 1x12.
■ **Price/night** - £17 midweek, £22 weekend. Sole use £900 (midweek). Breakfast £6. Pack lunch £6. Dinner £10. Activities £30/half day.

CONTACT: Libby Scott
Tel: 01768 775351
keswickhostel@hotmail.co.uk
www.dentonhouse-keswick.co.uk
Penrith Road, Keswick, Cumbria, CA12 4JW

DERWENTWATER

INDEPENDENT HOSTEL

Family run and friendly, Derwentwater Independent Hostel is a Georgian mansion in 17 acres of grounds with stunning mountain views. Just 2 miles from Keswick, close to the Coast to Coast route and the delights of Borrowdale, it makes a great base for individuals, families, groups and conferences. The hostel has plenty of space in & out for you to use and relax in. Home-made food is available.

DETAILS

- **Open** - All year. 7am - 11pm.
- **Beds** - 88: 1x4, 2x5, 3x6, 3x8, 1x10, 1x22
- **Price/night** - From £22.00 (adult), £17.00 (child). Family rooms from £76 (for 4). Ask if you want a room for 2 or 3.

CONTACT:
Tel: 01768 777246
reception@derwentwater.org
www.derwentwater.org
Barrow House, Borrowdale, Keswick, Cumbria, CA12 5UR

HAWSE END
CENTRE

204

Hawse End Centre sits at the head of the magnificent Borrowdale Valley on the shores of Derwentwater with easy access to Keswick via launch or lakeside walk. The house is a large, comfortable, country mansion, ideal for large groups, while the Cottage is more suited to smaller group, families and individuals. For the more adventurous there are two yurts with stunning views and transparent domes for star gazing. Catering & outdoor activities with instruction can be booked in advance.

DETAILS

- **Open** - All year.
- **Beds** - House 49: (9 rooms). Cottage 24: (6 rooms). Yurts: 24 (2x12)
- **Price/night** - Enquire for prices.

CONTACT:
Tel: 01768 812280
cumbriaoutdoors.enquiries@cumbria.gov.uk
www.cumbria.gov.uk/cumbriaoutdoors
Hawse End Centre, Portinscale,
Keswick, Cumbria, CA12 5UE

BOWDERSTONE

BUNKHOUSE

205l

Bowderstone Bunkhouse is situated along the Borrowdale Valley by the famous Bowderstone – a massive boulder that has lain precariously on one side for the last 10,000 years! It has a kitchen, accessible shower room and communal area, plus running water, electricity and drainage, but linen and mattresses not provided. Please note, Bowderstone Bunkhouse is only for use by clubs, educational groups or other organisations such as the Scouts, as it is on National Trust land and has certain restrictions to its use.

GROUPS ONLY

DETAILS

- **Open** - All year.
- **Beds** - 12
- **Price/night** - £100 per night

CONTACT: Reception at the Lake District Calvert Trust
Tel: 017687 72255
enquiries@calvertlakes.org.uk
www.calvertlakes.org.uk
Grange, Keswick, CA12 5XA

DINAH HOGGUS

CAMPING BARN

205r

Dinah Hoggus Camping Barn lies on the old Packhorse route to Watendlath on the edge of the village of Rosthwaite in the Borrowdale valley. For walkers it is perfectly located right on the Cumbria Way and the Coast to Coast walk. It sleeps 12 on mattresses (BYO sleeping bag) & has a cooking/dining area. Basic cooking equipment is provided and there's an electric shower. The pub and village shop are just 300m away.

DETAILS

- **Open** - All year.
- **Beds** - 12 : 1 x12
- **Price/night** - £11 pp. Electricity is charged extra by meter reading.

CONTACT:
Tel: Bookings 017687 74301 Farm 017687 77689
info@lakelandcampingbarns.co.uk
www.lakelandcampingbarns.co.uk/barns/dinah-hoggus-camping-barn
Stonecroft, Borrowdale, Keswick, Cumbria, CA12 5XB

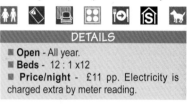

WATENDLATH

BOTHY

206

Watendlath Bothy sits next to the tarn in the quiet, picturesque hamlet that shares its name. High in a beautiful valley, it offers superb access to the surrounding fells. Visitors should treat the Bothy as a stone tent, BYO equipment as for camping, such as cutlery, plates, sleeping bags & mats, matches, etc. The perfect choice for people looking to escape to one of the most remote-feeling places in the Lake District.

DETAILS

- **Open** - Mid March- Mid October
- **Beds** - 6: BYO mats and sleeping bags
- **Price/night** - Low season: £60/night High season: £70/night. Minimum 3 nights.

CONTACT: Watendlath Bothy at National Trust Holidays
Tel: 015394 32733
lakescampsites@nationaltrust.org.uk
www.nationaltrust.org.uk/holidays/
Watendlath, Borrowdale, Cumbria, CA12 5UW

HIGH HOUSE

207l

High House in Seathwaite, at the head of the beautiful valley of Borrowdale, offers comfortable bunkhouse/hostel accommodation. Popular with walking and climbing clubs and educational groups, early booking is advised. Two dorms are available each with toilet, washbasin and shower. There is a third dorm reserved for K Fellfarers members and club members may use this room during your stay. If you wish to have exclusive use, including this Members Room, there's a £25 supplement per night.

DETAILS

- **Open** - All year. All day.
- **Beds** - 26: 1x18, 1x8
- **Price/night** - £160 or £185 if exclusive occupancy required.

CONTACT: Hugh Taylor
Tel: 01524 762067
jhugh.taylor@btinternet.com
highhouseborrowdale.co.uk
Seathwaite, Borrowdale, Keswick.

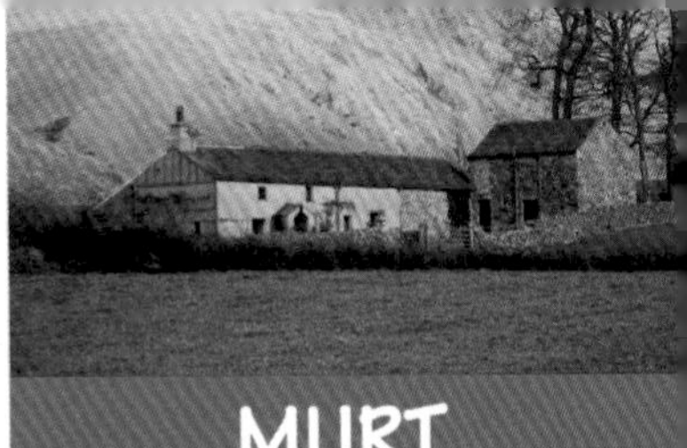

MURT

CAMPING BARN

207r

Nestling in the wild and remote Wasdale valley, Murt Camping Barn is ideally situated for high fell walks in the Lake District including Scafell Pike, Mosedale Horseshoe and Great Gable. Converted from a hay loft and byre, it sleeps 8, with WC, shower & hot water in the same building. Pubs in the village of Nether Wasdale are just a 10 minute walk away and nearest shops are within 5 miles. Waswater & its YHA are half mile down road, towards the Scafell range of mountains.

DETAILS

- **Open** - All year.
- **Beds** - 8: 1x8
- **Price/night** - £11.00 per person. Sole use bookings only at week ends

CONTACT:
Tel: Booking office 01768 774301
info@lakelandcampingbarns.co.uk
www.murtbarn.co.uk
Murt, Nether Wasdale, Seascale, Cumbria, CA20 1ET

CRAGG

CAMPING BARN

Cragg Camping Barn, with stunning views of the Buttermere Fells, is a great base for all outdoor enthusiasts with great walking, climbing and mountain biking close by. Sleeps 8 with a kitchen and seating area, hot shower on a meter and toilet/ washbasin with hot and cold water. BYO sleeping bag and stove/ eating utensils if you wish to self-cater. Under-5's and dogs welcome (sole occupancy only). Cragg House Farm also has a holiday cottage sleeping two.

DETAILS

- **Open** - All year. Arrival from 4pm, late arrivals by arrangement.
- **Beds** - 8: 1 x 8
- **Price/night** - £11 per person.

CONTACT: John and Vicki Temple
Tel: Camping Barn 01768 774301 Farm and Cottages 01768 770204
info@lakelandcampingbarns.co.uk
www.buttermerecottage.co.uk
Cragg House Farm, Buttermere, Cockermouth, Cumbria, CA13 9XA

.OW GILLERTHWAITE FIELD CENTRE

209l

In the Ennerdale Valley, one of the nost beautiful, least spoilt and quietest in the Lake District, Low GIllerthwaite ield Centre sits at the foot of Pillar and Red Pike. Well equipped for groups it is the perfect base for fell walking, ock climbing, bird & wildlife watching, ountain biking, orienteering, canoeing. The centre generates its own hydro-electricit. Vehicle access is by forest rack and a BT payphone is on site as most mobiles do not work here.

DETAILS

- **Open** - All year (except Christmas and Boxing Day). 24 hours.
- **Beds** - 40: 2x4, 1x8, 1x10, 1x14.
- **Price/night** - From £11.50 per person children and students), £15.50 (adults), camping is £5 per person.

CONTACT: Ellen or Walter
Tel: 01946 861229
Warden@lgfc.org.uk
www.lgfc.org.uk
Ennerdale, Cleator, CA23 3AX

THE WILD WOOL BARN

209r

Nestled in the peace of the Ennerdale Valley, overlooking Ennerdale Water, The Wild Wool Barn provides luxury bunkhouse accommodation for 6 (plus up to 4 camping). Traditional wood-burning stove, electric heating, cooker and shower marry tradition with luxury. With no mobile signal or WiFi The Wild Wool Barn is a true chance to get away from it all and explore the rarely visited Western Lake District.

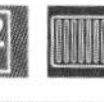

DETAILS

- **Open** - All year. Easter-Oct groups only.
- **Beds** - 6: 1x6 + 4 camping
- **Price/night** - High season sole use: from 1 night £120 to 7 nights £380. Bank hols min 3 nights. Low season: £30pp, min booking £60. Camping £10pp

CONTACT: Susan Denham-Smith
Tel: 01946 861270
susan@wildwoolworkshop.co.uk
www.wildwoolbarn.co.uk
Routen Farm Cottage, Ennerdale, CA23 3AU

SUMMERGROVE

HALLS

210

Close to the start of the Coast to Coast Walk at Whitehaven and within easy access to the Cumbrian coast and Lake District. Summergrove Halls offer en suite self-catering accommodation in rooms with small double (3/4 size) beds. Bed linen and towels are provided along with basic toiletries. Self-cater or choose from the popular dinner menu in the Terrace Bar and Grill. Breakfast is also available. Communal areas include a TV room. Nestled in attractive grounds there are nature and cycle trails from the door, as well as an on-site gym.

DETAILS

- **Open** - All year. All day
- **Beds** - 131
- **Price/night** - From £27.60

CONTACT: Reception
Tel: 01946 813328
info@summergrovehalls.co.uk
www.summergrovehalls.co.uk
Hensingham, Whitehaven, Cumbria,
CA28 8XZ

HOLME WOOD

BOTHY

Holme Wood Bothy offers basic accommodation in a spectacular ecluded location, right on the shore of Loweswater. This stone tent provides a roof, kitchen area and sleeping latform. Visitors must bring all camping equipment including plates, matches, leeping mats, sleeping bags, food and ater. If you are looking for a remote and basic getaway with easy access to the lake, this bothy is your perfect choice. Great for accessing the lakes and canoeing on Loweswater.

DETAILS

- **Open** - All year. All day.
- **Beds** - 6- BYO mats and sleeping bag.
- **Price/night** - Low season: £60/night High season: £70/night

CONTACT: National Trust Holidays
Tel: 01539 432733
lakescampsites@nationaltrust.org.uk
www.nationaltrust.org.uk/holidays
Watergate Farm, Loweswater,
Cockermouth, Cumbria, CA13 0RU

SWALLOW BARN

CAMPING BARN

212l

In the picturesque Loweswater Valley, Swallow Barn is part of a set of buildings dating back to 1670 on a working beef and sheep farm. Sleeping 18 on mattresses (BYO sleeping bags), there is a cooking and eating area, metered showers & plug socket and 2 toilets. Perfect for exploring the Western Fells on both high and low level walks with spectacular views, or enjoying the peace and tranquillity of the valley. On the C2C cycle route. The Kirkstyle pub (1 mi) serves food, Cockermouth (8 mi).

DETAILS

- **Open** - All year. All day.
- **Beds** - 18: 1x9, 3x3
- **Price/night** - £11 per person.

CONTACT: Kath Leck
Tel: Booking office 017687 74301 Farm 01946 861465
info@lakelandcampingbarns.co.uk
www.lakelandcampingbarns.co.uk
Waterend Farm, Loweswater, Cockermouth, Cumbria, CA13 0SU

HILLSIDE FARM

BUNKBARN

212r

A Georgian farmstead, still a working farm, right on Hadrian's Wall National Trail and Cycleway near the Solway Coast AONB. Stunning views over the Solway Firth marshes towards Scotlan Bunkbarn or B&B rooms available. Th bunkbarn, in a converted stable block, has cooking facilities & hot showers. Towels and sleeping bags can be hire The bunk barn is heated with a bio mas boiler. Breakfast or bacon sandwiches available with notice. Walking, cycling and family groups are most welcome.

DETAILS

- **Open** - All year. 10am to 9pm.
- **Beds** - 12
- **Price/night** - £13pp inc shower. £4 ful english, £2.50 hot sandwiches.

CONTACT: Mrs Sandra Rudd
Tel: 01228 576398
ruddshillside1@btinternet.com
www.hadrianswalkbnb.co.uk
Hillside Farm, Boustead Hill, Burgh-by Sands, Carlisle, Cumbria, CA5 6AA

WAYFARERS

INDEPENDENT HOSTEL

213l

lose to Penrith town centre and perfect for the C2C cycle route.

xcellent value accommodation for those isiting Penrith, the Eden Valley and the North Lake District National Park. Bike leaning and maintenance facilities and ike hire on site. Full kitchen and dining facilities, en suite rooms with made up eds, lockers, bedside lights. Individuals, small parties and groups welcome.

DETAILS

- **Open** - Feb-Dec. Reception open 8-11am, 4-9pm.
- **Beds** - 18: 2x2 (twin), 1x6, 2x4.
- **Price/night** - From £23pp (dorm room bed). Sole use from £370pn. Family room: Sun-Thurs from £60. B/fast: £4.Towel: £1.

CONTACT: Mark Rhodes
Tel: 01768 866011
guests@wayfarershostel.com
www.wayfarershostel.com
9 Brunswick Square, Penrith, Cumbria, CA11 7LR

CARLISLE

CITY HOSTEL

213r

Carlisle's only independent hostel. Located on picturesque Abbey Street, the building is an old Georgian terrace accommodating up to 20 guests. There is a communal kitchen, lounge with TV, DVDs and book swap and a dining room. Free tea, coffee and WiFi in communal areas. Prices include basic breakfast. A great place from which to explore Carlisle, The Tuille House Museum,The Eden Valley, Hadrian's Wall and more The staff look forward to welcoming you as their guest to the hostel and the city.

DETAILS

- **Open** - All year. Check in between 3pm- 8pm ONLY (Sunday 4pm-8pm).
- **Beds** - 20 : 2x6, 2x4.
- **Price/night** - £18 to £26 pp. Groups of over 8 by pre-arrangement only.

CONTACT: Jonathan Quinlan
Tel: 07914 720821
info@carlislecityhostel.com
www.carlislecityhostel.com
36 Abbey Street, Carlisle, CA3 8TX

HAGGS BANK

BUNKHOUSE & CAMPING

214

In the stunning North Pennines AONB, England's last wilderness, perfect for lovers of the great outdoors such as walkers and cyclists. Isaac's Tea Trail passes through the site, directly on the C2C and with bicycle hire (including electric bikes) available nearby. Pre-booked breakfast and evening meals can be provided for larger groups. The campsite has tiered pitches to enhance the views across the Nent valley. Electric hook-ups available in the car park.

DETAILS

- **Open** - All year. All day access.
- **Beds** - 24: 1x4/5, 1x9, 1x10.
- **Price/night** - £20pp. Sole use £380, £1080 (3 nights). Camping: £12, U15, £7. Motorhomes/caravans £25 up to 2 people

CONTACT: Danny Taylor
Tel: 07919 092403/ 01434 382486
info@haggsbank.com
haggsbank.com
Haggs Bank Bunkhouse, Nentsbury, Alston, Cumbria, CA9 3LH

NINEBANKS

YOUTH HOSTEL

Book a bed, a room, a Chalet room or the whole hostel. Ninebanks 4* Hostel, in stunning rural Northumberland, has en-suite bedrooms, a sitting room with log-burner and a spacious dining room. In the Chalet are two high quality studio rooms, fully self-contained and separate from the hostel. Dogs welcome with prior notice on sole use or in the chalet. In the North Pennines close to Hadrian's Wall and on Isaac's Tea Trail.

DETAILS

- **Open** - All year. All day. Office 5-10pm.
- **Beds** - Hostel 28: 2x2/3, 2x4, 1x6, 1x8. Chalets 1 x double, 1 x double plus bunk.
- **Price/night** - Beds from £17, rooms from £39, whole hostel from £200. Chalet from £60. Dogs incur a cleaning fee

CONTACT: Pauline or Ian
Tel: 01434 345288
contact@ninebanks.com
www.ninebanks.org.uk
Orchard House, Mohope, Hexham,
Northumberland NE47 8DQ

ALSTON
YOUTH HOSTEL

216l

On the very eastern edge of Cumbria, nestled in the North Pennines and within the historic town of Alston, is Alston Youth Hostel. Not only is the hostel about halfway on the very popular Coast to Coast (C2C) cycle route but it is also located directly on the Pennine Way! The perfect stop-over for walkers and cyclists. You'll receive a warm welcome (as warm as our large drying room!!) and hopefully see the resident red squirrels!

DETAILS

- **Open** - All year. 8-10am, 5-10pm
- **Beds** - 30: 2x2, 2x4, 3x6
- **Price/night** - From £21pp (adult), discount for YHA members. Private rooms from £40. Sole use from £500 for 2 nights midweek, £700 for 2 nights Fri-Sat.

CONTACT: Linda, Neil or Jenny
Tel: 01434 381509
alston@yha.org.uk
alstonyouthhostel.co.uk/
Firs Edge, The Firs, Alston, Cumbria, CA9 3RW

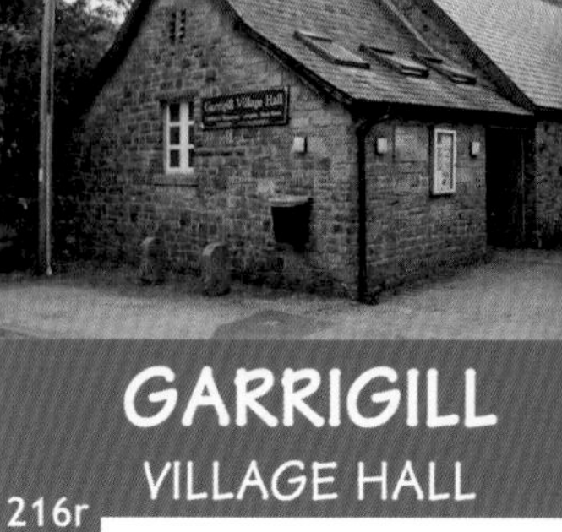

GARRIGILL
VILLAGE HALL

216r

Perfect for the Pennine Way or C2C cycle route. In the lovely village of Garrigill, the bunkroom above the villag hall sleeps 8 with bedding hire availabl Larger groups can BYO bedding and us the hall itself where some camp beds are available. There is a well equippe kitchen, showers and drying room so th perfect long distance walk stop over.

DETAILS

- **Open** - All year. All day
- **Beds** - 14: 1x8 (bunks) + 6 camp beds and space for up to 20 on the floor downstairs
- **Price/night** - £15pp. Bedding hire (if required) £5 pp per stay. Camping £5 pp (£3.50 Dof E or other youth activity groups).

CONTACT: Booking Secretary
Tel: 01434 647516
bookings@garrigillvh.org
www.garrigillvh.org.uk
Garrigill Village Hall, Garrigill, Alston, Cumbria, CA9 3DS

ALLENHEADS

LODGE

217l

Situated in the heart of the North Pennines, Allenheads Lodge is an excellent venue for outdoor activities or relaxing in the peaceful countryside.

An ideal accommodation stop on the Coast 2 Coast (C2C) cycle route, just 7 miles from the North Sea coast. With 24 beds in four rooms, central heating, individual toilet and showers and a large kitchen/dining room, the lodge also boasts hot showers, drying facilities, bed linen and secure bike storage.

DETAILS

- **Open** - All year. All day.
- **Beds** - 24
- **Price/night** - Bed only: £19.50pp. B&B: £25pp. Ask for group discounts.

CONTACT: Andrea Cowie
Tel: 01915 155300
acowie@springboard-ne.org
www.allenheadslodge.com
Allenheads Lodge, Allenheads, Northumberland NE47 9HW

BARRINGTON

BUNKHOUSE

217r

Situated in the peaceful village of Rookhope, Weardale, Barrington Bunkhouse accommodates 15 people. There's room for 13 in the bunkhouse, whilst the adjacent caravan sleeps two. Camping space is also available. The kitchen is equipped with two toasters, a kettle, a microwave, and a fridge, whilst The Rookhope Inn serves fine food and good drinks and is located just next door. All are welcome; cyclists, walkers and family groups.

DETAILS

- **Open** - All year, All day.
- **Beds** - 12 (+1): 1 x 12 + 1 fold up bed
- **Price/night** - £24pp incl. snack b/fast. Camping £14 with b/fast, £10 without. Sole use rates negotiable.

CONTACT: Valerie Livingston
Tel: 01388 517656
barrington_bunkhouse@hotmail.co.uk
www.barrington-bunkhouse-rookhope.com
Barrington Cottage, Rookhope, Weardale, Co. Durham, DL13 2BG

EDMUNDBYERS YHA

AT LOW HOUSE HAVEN

218

Edmunbyers hostel lies in moorland, close to the Northumberland/County Durham boundary, with fine views. It's just two miles from Derwent Reservoir, for sailing & fishing. Ideal for walking holidays, it's also on the Coast to Coast (C2C) cycle route & is close to Hadrian's Wall & Beamish outdoor museum. Cosy & comfortable with optional home cooked evening meals & breakfasts.

DETAILS

- **Open** - All year (camping Apr-Oct). Check in 5-10pm, check out 8-10am.
- **Beds** - 28: 2x6, 2x5,1x4,1x3. 8 pitches for camping.
- **Price/night** - From £23 (adult), £19 (under 18). Discounts for YHA members: Room for 3:£60, 4:£70, 5:£80, 6:£90.

CONTACT: Debbie Clarke
Tel: 01207 255651 Mob: 07884 969725
info@lowhousehaven.co.uk
www.lowhousehaven.co.uk
Low House, Edmundbyers, Consett, Durham,DH8 9NL

ALLENDALE
BUNKHOUSE

219l

The Allendale Bunkhouse sits on the Market Square overlooking the hustle nd bustle of this small country town and the fells and River East Allen beyond. An oasis for walkers, cyclists, horse riders, families, groups of friends and youth & school groups alike. Book a bunk, a room, a floor (up to 18) or the whole bunkhouse (up to 38). Allendale s well served with tea rooms, the Forge art gallery & café, a quirky gift shop, pharmacy, and three wonderful country pubs, all serving food and family & dog friendly.

  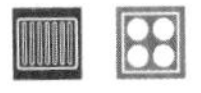    

GROUPS ONLY

DETAILS

- **Open** - All year. 8am-8pm.
- **Beds** - 38:1x2, 1x3, 2x4, 1x5, 2x6, 1x7
- **Price/night** - From £14 - £40pp.

CONTACT: Linda Beck
Tel: 01434 618579
info@allendalebunkhouse.co.uk
www.allendalebunkhouse.co.uk
Market Place, Allendale, Hexham, NE47 9BD

BIRDOSWALD
BUNKHOUSE

219r

Birdoswald Bunkhouse is a 17th century farmhouse built into the remains of Birdoswald Roman Fort on the best preserved stretch of Hadrian's Wall. Set within an English Heritage estate overlooking the magnificent Irthing Gorge, the bunkhouse is an ideal base for wild walks with breathtaking views and discovering the area's Roman heritage. The bunkhouse provides group accommodation for up 37 people, with seven bedrooms & bathrooms, a large farmhouse kitchen and a dining room with views over the fort.

GROUPS ONLY

DETAILS

- **Open** - All year
- **Beds** - 37: in 7 rooms
- **Price/night** - Enquire for prices.

CONTACT: Reservations team
Tel: 03703 331187
accommodation@english-heritage.org.uk
www.english-heritage.org.uk
Birdoswald Roman Fort, Gilsland, Brampton, Cumbria, CA8 7DD

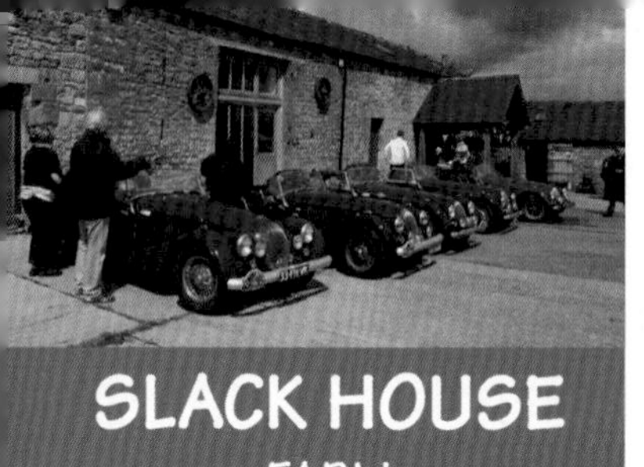

SLACK HOUSE
FARM

220

Slack House Farm is an organic dairy farm overlooking Birdoswald Roman Fort on Hadrian's Wall. It is on the NCN 72 cycle route and is only 0.5km from the Hadrian's Wall National Trail. The bunkbarn is next to Gladje in the Scypen café and farm shop (Birdoswald cheese is made on-site). The bunkbarn is warm and cosy and has basic self-catering facilities. Breakfasts, farmhouse suppers and packed lunches can be provided.

DETAILS

- **Open** - All year. Check in from 5pm, check out by 10am.
- **Beds** - 18: 1x10, 1x5, 1x3 (family)
- **Price/night** - Beds £15pp. Camp bed loft £12pp. Sole use: 5 bed room £60, family £45, private 10 bed dorm £80.

CONTACT: Dianne Horn
Tel: 01697 747351 Mob: 07900 472342
slackhouseorganicfarm@gmail.com
www.slackhousefarm.co.uk
Slack House Farm, Gilsland Brampton, Cumbria, CA8 7DB

GREENHEAD

BUNKHOUSE

221l

Situated in the village of Greenhead on Hadrian's Wall, the bunkhouse is ideal for walking the Pennine Way or The Wall or for exploring the nearby Roman heritage sites. It has a self-catering kitchen big enough for large groups. The flexible accommodation can be booked by the bed, the room or for sole use. Greenhead hostel/ bunkhouse is run by Greenhead Hotel just over the road.

DETAILS

- **Open** - All year. All day. Groups only in winter, please enquire.
- **Beds** - 45: Hostel 40: 4x6. Flat 5: 2dbl, 1 single.
- **Price/night** - Bunkhouse: From £15.50pp, sole use £600. Flat (sleeps 5) £85.

CONTACT: Greenhead Hotel
Tel: 01697 747411
enquiries@greenheadhotelandhostel.co.uk
www.greenheadhotelandhostel.co.uk
Greenhead Hotel, Greenhead, Brampton, Cumbria, CA8 7HG

FLORRIE'S

BUNKHOUSE

221r

Located right on the Hadrian's Wall National Trail this newly converted bunkhouse is aimed at walkers or cyclists. With drying room and cycle storage this is the perfect stop-over on the trail. Open for individuals from April to October, Florrie's provides a comfortable bed, breakfast and evening meals plus the opportunity to socialise with other guests at the bar. From October 2019 the bunkhouse will be open to groups in the winter season with self-catering.

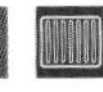   

DETAILS

- **Open** - April to October. (Sole use for groups available in the winter season).
- **Beds** - 16 (17) : 3x4, 1x4 (or 5 if family)
- **Price/night** - B&B £25pp. Private rooms available. Ask for group rates.

CONTACT: Rebecca & Joss
Tel: 01697 741704
hello@florriesonthewall.co.uk
florriesonthewall.co.uk
Florrie's on the Wall, Kingbank, Walton, Cumbria, CA8 2DH

GIBBS HILL

FARM HOSTEL

Gibbs Hill Farm Hostel is on a working hill farm near Once Brewed on Hadrian's Wall and close to the Pennine Way. Designed to reduce energy consumption it is centrally heated throughout. Comprising 3 bunkrooms, 2 shower rooms, 2 toilets, a well equipped kitchen, a comfortable communal area and a large deck where you can enjoy the evening sun. Ideal for families who can book a whole room with private facilities. Study groups welcome.

DETAILS

- **Open** - All year. Hours flexible but no check in after 9pm.
- **Beds** - 18: 3x6
- **Price/night** - £18 adult, £12 child (under 12), including bedding.

CONTACT: Valerie Gibson
Tel: 01434 344030
val@gibbshillfarm.co.uk
www.gibbshillfarm.co.uk
Gibbs Hill Farm, Bardon Mill, Nr Hexham, Northumberland, NE47 7AP

DEMESNE FARM

BUNKHOUSE

223l

This bunkhouse is on a working hill farm in the centre of Bellingham and near to Northumberland National Park. Situated on the Pennine Way, Route 68, and the Reivers & Sandstone Way cycle routes, it is an ideal base for exploring Northumberland, Hadrian's Wall, Kielder Water and many climbing crags. The bunkhouse is very well appointed with quality bunks, a well equipped kitchen, a farmhouse table to seat 15 and a large comfortable communal area.

DETAILS

- **Open** - All year. Hours flexible but no check in after 9pm.
- **Beds** - 15: 1x8, 1x4, 1x3.
- **Price/night** - £22 per person, £16 under 18's (including linen).

CONTACT: Robert Telfer
Tel: 01434 220258 or 07967 396345
stay@demesnefarmcampsite.co.uk
www.demesnefarmcampsite.co.uk
Demesne Farm, Bellingham, Hexham, Northumberland, NE48 2BS

EURO HOSTEL

NEWCASTLE

223r

With its brilliant city centre location and recently refurbished bedrooms, Euro Hostel offers comfortable, convenient and cost effective accommodation in the heart of Newcastle. Guests enjoy spacious bedrooms including large screen, smart TVs and en-suite facilities in every room. There's also a TV lounge with bean bags, free guest laundry, luggage storage and a bar with meals, great tunes and cheap drinks & cocktails.

DETAILS

- **Open** - All year except Christmas week.
- **Beds** - 236. Singles, doubles, 2, 4, 6, 8 and 14 person rooms. All en suite.
- **Price/night** - From £16pp in a 10 bed room, £29 pp in private rooms, including a fabulous continental breakfast..

CONTACT: Reception
Tel: 08454 900371
newcastle@eurohostels.co.uk
www.euro-hostels.co.uk
17 Carliol Square, Newcastle Upon Tyne, NE1 6UQ

HOUGHTON NORTH

FARM ACCOMMODATION

Houghton North Farm, partly built with stones from Hadrian's Wall is in the beautiful Northumberland countryside right on the Hadrian's Wall trail 15 miles from the start. This spacious new build is perfect for groups, individuals or families. The bunkrooms are located around the central courtyard. There is a self-catering kitchen (continental breakfast included). The TV lounge has a log fire and WiFi. Long-term parking, baggage transfer and packed lunches are available on request.

DETAILS

- **Open** - All year. Arrive after 3.30pm depart by 10am.
- **Beds** - 22: 1x5, 3x4, 1x3, 1x2.
- **Price/night** - B&B from £25-£40 (adult) Group discounts.

CONTACT: Mrs Paula Laws
Tel: 01661 854364
wjlaws@btconnect.com
www.houghtonnorthfarm.co.uk
Houghton North Farm, Heddon-on-the-Wall, Northumberland, NE15 0EZ

GIBSIDE

STABLES

225

This converted grade II listed stables in the heart of the National Trust Gibside Estate is now a comfortable, well equipped bunkhouse sleeping 25 in 4 rooms. Up to 2 dogs welcomed by arrangement. Enjoy the cafés and activities on the estate during the day ınd enjoy the whole park to yourselves n the evening. Within driving distance f the Northumberland coast, Newcastle,)urham and National Trust estates such as Cragside, Wallington and Souter Lighthouse.

DETAILS

- **Open** - All year. All day
- **Beds** - 25 1x10, 1x11, 2x2
- **Price/night** - from £700 for (min) 2 nights. Bedding provided, BYO Linen.

CONTACT: National Trust Holidays
Tel: 03443 351296
bunkhouses@nationaltrust.org.uk
www.nationaltrust.org.uk/holidays/Nr
Rowlands Gill, Gateshead, Tyne & Wear,
NE16 6BG

TARSET TOR

BUNKHOUSE & BOTHIES

In the heart of the Northumberland International Dark Sky Park and close to the Pennine Way. These striking timber eco-buildings integrate into their natural surroundings making the most of this remarkable location and providing the perfect base for outdoor adventures.

The bunkhouse & bothies provide stylish, modern, versatile & comfortable self-catering accommodation which can be used for events, conferences & parties.

DETAILS

- **Open** - Mid January - December.
- **Beds** - 44: Bunkhouse:16-20. Bothies: 4x8. 3 camper van bays.
- **Price/night** - Bunkhouse: £352 to £400. Bothies: £176 to £200.

CONTACT: Robert and Claire Cocker
Tel: 01434 240980
info@tarset-tor.co.uk
www.tarset-tor.co.uk
Greystones, Lanehead, Tarset, Hexham, NE48 1NT

WALLINGTON

BUNKHOUSE

Situated in the heart of the National Trust Wallington Estate, visitors to the bunkhouse will have and free access to the mansion, it's shops and café, and everything the estate has to offer. Perfect for groups of families with lots of on-site activities including cycling and play areas or for walkers wanting a base from which to visit the Cheviots and Hadrian's wall, both within an hour's drive. The bunkhouse is perfect for self-catering groups with a large well-equipped kitchen and large living/dining area. It sleeps 20 in four rooms.

DETAILS

- **Open** - All year. All day.
- **Beds** - 20: 2x8, 2x2
- **Price/night** - From £360 for two nights.

CONTACT: National Trust Holidays
Tel: 0344 335 1296
bunkhouses@nationaltrust.org.uk
www.nationaltrust.org.uk/holidays/
Wallington, Cambo, Morpeth,
Northumberland, NE61 4AR

TOMLINSONS

BUNKHOUSE

228

Located in the historic town of Rothbury overlooking the River Coquet, Tomlinson's is a one-stop shop for low-cost accommodation, homemade meals and cycle hire. There's also a function room for hire. Rothbury is becoming the Northumberland National Park's cycling hub and the bunkhouse is just metres from a string of off-road cycle tracks and public footpaths. The bunkhouse has a fleet of mountain bikes available to hire and instructors to lead cycle groups of all ages. Perfect for families and groups.

DETAILS

- **Open** - All year. All day.
- **Beds** - 21: 1x8, 1x6 1x6 x 1 double
- **Price/night** - Dorms £25pp. Double room £60. Whole bunkhouse from £400.

CONTACT: Jackie
Tel: 01669 621979
info@tomlinsonsrothbury.co.uk
www.tomlinsonsrothbury.co.uk
Bridge Street, Rothbury,
Northumberland, NE65 7SE

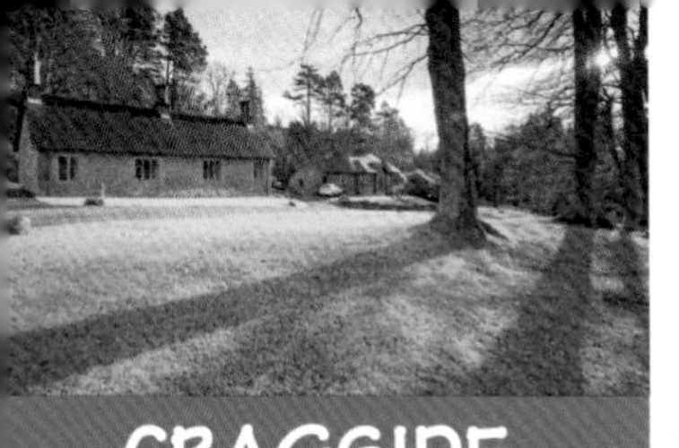

CRAGSIDE

BUNKHOUSE

A traditional conversion of Victorian workers cottages in the centre of the National Trust Cragside Estate with abulous views overlooking the lake and surrounding hills.

Cragside bunkhouse sleeps 16 in 4 ooms with a well equipped self-catering kitchen, making it the perfect base for families or other groups wanting to explore this stunning part of the UK Located in the heart of Northumberland within an hours' drive of the coast, the Cheviots and Hadrian's Wall.

GROUPS ONLY

DETAILS

- **Open** - All year. All day
- **Beds** - 16: 1x6, 1x4, 3x2
- **Price/night** - Sole use: 2 nights from £380.

CONTACT: National Trust Holidays
Tel: 03443 351296
bunkhouses@nationaltrust.org.uk
www.nationaltrust.org.uk/holidays
Cragside, Rothbury, Morpeth, Northumberland, NE65 7PX

ALNWICK

YOUTH HOSTEL

This family friendly 4* hostel has en suite rooms, cosy lounge, games room and a spacious dining room. Located in the centre of town, it is ideal for Alnwick Castle, (of Downton Abbey and Harry Potter fame) and Alnwick Garden. The coast, with castles at Dunstanburgh and Bamburgh, Farne Isles, magical Holy Island and glorious sandy beaches is just a 15 drive. While inland there's the Cheviot Hills & Hadrian's Wall.

DETAILS

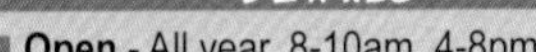

- **Open** - All year. 8-10am, 4-8pm
- **Beds** - 56: 1xdbl, 2x2, 1x3, 6x4,1x5, 3x6
- **Price/night** - Dorm from £20, under 18 from £15. 2 bedded rooms from £49. 4 bedded rooms from £69.

CONTACT: Anthony Sewell
Tel: 01665 660800
info@alnwickyouthhostel.co.uk
www.alnwickyouthhostel.co.uk
34 - 38 Green Batt, Alnwick,
Northumberland, NE66 1TU

CALICO BARN

BUNKBARN

On the Northumberland Coast close to Amble and Warkworth, Calico Barn is perfect for walkers and cyclists on NCN1 and Coast & Castles routes. The bunkhouse has a log burner and is lesigned to be a home from home. Fully quipped kitchen and dining area, private ind shared rooms with comfortable bunk eds. Cereal breakfast included and self-ook breakfast packs available. Veranda and paddock outside.

  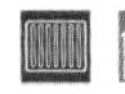      

DETAILS

- **Open** - All year. All day.
- **Beds** - 18: 2x2, 1x6, 2x4
- **Price/night** - Twin: £50. Quad: £100. 6-Bed £150. Beds in shared room £25. Whole Barn £450. Self-catering with cereals, tea & coffee provided

CONTACT: Alison
Tel: 01670 458118 or 07876 344509
hello@hemscotthill.com
www.hemscotthill.com/bunkbarn
Hemscott Hill Farm, Widdrington,
Morpeth, Northumberland, NE61 5EQ

MOUNTHOOLY
BUNKHOUSE

232

Nestled in the beautiful College Valley, North Northumberland, Mounthooly Bunkhouse is a perfect stop-off on the Pennine Way and St Cuthbert's Way. Dogs are welcome by arrangement. There is a well equipped kitchen and living area with log burner. Bedding is supplied. Cars need a permit to access the private valley which is provided on arrival. A haven for wildlife with red squirrels, otters and a thriving population of feral goats in the valley. The perfect wild get away from it all.

DETAILS

- **Open** - All year. All day.
- **Beds** - 24: 2x9 1x2 1x4
- **Price/night** - £17pp. Discount for concessions and sole use

CONTACT: Charlene Drysdale
Tel: 01668 216210
mounthooly@college-valley.co.uk
www.college-valley.co.uk/Mounthooly.htm
Mount Hooley, College Valley, Wooler, Northumberland, NE71 6TU

WOOLER

YOUTH HOSTEL

Wooler Youth Hostel & Shepherd's Huts are on the edge of the town and offer an ideal base for exploring the Northumberland National Park, the Cheviot Hills, local castles and fine sandy beaches. For walkers there's St Cuthbert's Way and for cyclists, Wooler cycle hub routes, Pennine Cycleway and the Sandstone Way. There are bridleways perfect for mountain biking and lots of bouldering and climbing.

DETAILS

- **Open** - April-Oct. (Group bookings Nov to March). Reception 8-10am and 5-9pm.
- **Beds** - 53: 3x2, 6x4, 1x6, 1x8. Shepherd's huts 3x2, 1x3 (family).
- **Price/night** - From £20 adult, £15 child. Group discounts available.

CONTACT: Hostel Manager
Tel: 01668 281365
wooler@woolerhostel.co.uk
www.woolerhostel.co.uk
30 Cheviot Street, Wooler,
Northumberland, NE71 6LW

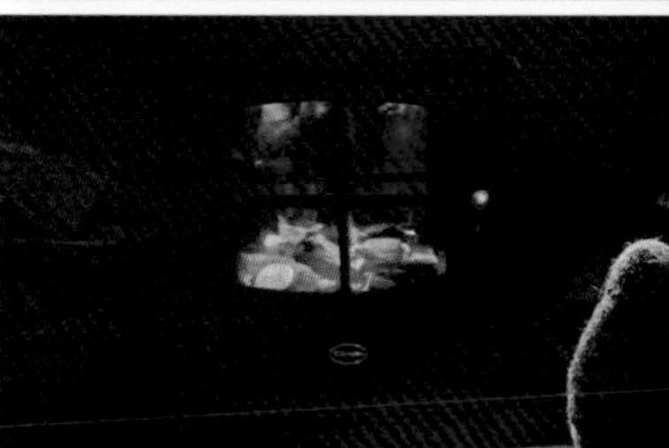

CHATTON PARK

BUNKHOUSE

234l

A former smithy converted into a self-catering bunkhouse on a mixed working farm.1/2 mile from Chatto, 8 miles from Northumberland's vast empty beaches and historic castles and 5 miles from the heather clad Cheviot Hills. Walking, water sports, climbing, fishing, golf and cycling are all nearby. The 2 dorms can be rented separately. There is a fully equipped kitchen, seating around the original blacksmith's fire & hot showers.

DETAILS

- **Open** - March to November. Flexible times but no check in after 9pm.
- **Beds** - 12: 2x6.
- **Price/night** - From £15. Group rates available. Teens must be led by a responsible adult. Dogs: £10/dog/stay.

CONTACT: Jane or Duncan
Tel: 01668 215247
jaord@btinternet.com
www.chattonparkfarm.co.uk
Chatton Park Farm, Chatton, Alnwick, Northumberland, NE66 5RA

BLUEBELL

FARM BUNKBARN

234r

Bluebell Farm Bunkbarn is within walkin distance of shops and pubs. It is ideally located for exploring Nothumberland's Heritage Coast, the Cheviot Hills and the Scottish Borders. The Bunkbarn sleeps 14, the Studio 4. Plus 2 studio apartments and 5 self-catering cottages There is a shared modern toilet block. BYO sleeping bags/towels or hire. Studi apartments & cottages have bed linen.

DETAILS

- **Open** - All year. Check in by 9 pm, departure by 10 am.
- **Beds** - Bunkbarn 14: 1 x 8, 1 x 6. Studio 4: 1 x 4.
- **Price/night** - Bunkbarn: £15 under 16s £8. Studio: £20 under 16s £10. Linen and towel hire £8pp. Sole use rates available.

CONTACT: Phyl
Tel: 01668 213362
corillas@icloud.com
www.bluebellfarmbelford.com
Bluebell Farm Caravan Park, Belford, Northumberland, NE70 7QE

THE HIDES

235

ocated in Seahouses with an easy walk to St Aidan's beach. The Hides provide affordable accommodation on the magnificent Northumbrian Coast.

Perfect for groups, families or independent travellers. Each Hide is an en-suite room sleeping 4 in beds & bunks. The rooms open onto a communal courtyard with access to the vell equipped, self-catering kitchen, bike storage, drying room & laundry.

DETAILS

- **Open** - All year.
- **Beds** - 20: 5x4
- **Price/night** - £25 minimum 2 night stay. Children £22. Dogs £5

CONTACT: Kerry
Tel: 01665 720645
info@the-hides.co.uk
www.the-hides.co.uk
146 Main Street Seahouses
Northumberland NE68 7UA

SEAHOUSES

HOSTEL

Within easy walking distance of Seahouses, this recently refurbished hostel offers affordable, spacious & comfortable accommodation. A perfect base for visiting the beaches and castles of the Northumbrian Coast. Particularly popular with divers, families, cyclists, walkers, school, church and youth groups, parties of all sizes welcome, sole use also available. Booking is essential.

DETAILS

- **Open** - All year. Arrive after 4pm, depart by 10am unless otherwise agreed.
- **Beds** - 42: 1x8, 2×2 (en-suite), 1x6 (en-suite wet room), 2x4, 1x6, 1×10
- **Price/night** - £19-£25pp. Children, recognised youth groups & leaders £16pp. Under 5s free. Min 2 nights.

CONTACT: Karen Leadbitter
Tel: 07531 305206
seahouseshostel@outlook.com
www.seahouseshostel.org.uk
157 Main Street, North Sunderland, Seahouses, Northumberland NE68 7TU

SPRINGHILL
BUNKHOUSE

Springhill's Lookout & Wigwams offer great value, comfortable accommodation which can be booked as a whole or on a per bed/night basis. Ideal for groups, families or couples. Superbly located on the Northumberland Heritage Coastline there are stunning views towards the Farne Islands and Cheviot Hills while Seahouses and Bamburgh are within very easy reach.

GROUPS ONLY

DETAILS

- **Open** - All year. Arrive 3-6pm, departure by 10am. Cleaning noon-4pm.
- **Beds** - The Lookout 32: 8x4. Wigwams 40: 5x8. Wigwam Ensuite 8: 2x4.
- **Price/night** - The Lookout £480 sole use per night. Wigwams £21.50 pppn. En-suite Wigwams £27.50 pppn.

CONTACT: Springhill Accommodation
Tel: 01665 721820
enquiries@springhill-farm.co.uk
www.springhill-farm.co.uk
Springhill Farm, Seahouses,
Northumberland NE68 7UR

MAUGHOLD

VENTURE CENTRE

238l

Maughold Venture Centre Bunkhouse overlooks farmland with views out to sea. The popular beach of Port e Vullen is just 10 min's walk away. Enjoy self-catering accommodation, with en suite, centrally heated rooms. Tasty meals are available from the neighbouring Venture Centre, where you can also book kayaking, abseiling, air rifle shooting, archery, gorge walking, dinghy sailing & team events. With its own stop, Lewaigue Halt, on the Manx Electric Railway you have easy access to Douglas, Ramsey, mountains & tranquil glens.

DETAILS

- **Open** - January - December. 24 hours.
- **Beds** - 52: 2x2, 1x5, 4x8, 2x10.
- **Price/night** - £12-£15 per person.

CONTACT: Simon Read
Tel: 01624 814240
contact@adventure-centre.co.uk
www.adventure-centre.co.uk
The Venture Centre, Maughold, Isle of Man, IM7 1AW

KNOCKALOE BEG

FARM BUNKHOUSE

238r

A working farm nestled under Peel Hill, Isle of Man, Knockaloe Beg offers B&B, cottages, bunkhouse, bothy & glamping The bunkhouse sleeps 8; with beds at one end of the room, dining and seating at the other. The bothy is a cosy, twin bed room. Washing facilities are a short step outside, below the rooms. In the orchard there are two deluxe, en suite glamping cabins each sleeping four.

DETAILS

- **Open** - Bunkhouse: 1 April-30 September. Bothy: all year.
- **Beds** - 18: Bunkhouse 8. Bothy 2. Cabins 8: 2x4
- **Price/night** - Bunkhouse: £15pp; min 2 people. TT/Classic TT fortnight: £120pn sole use (max 8). Bothy: £20 pp, min 2 people. Breakfast (when available): £10pp

CONTACT: Fiona and John Anderson
Tel: 01624 844279
info@knockaloebegfarm.com
www.knockaloebegfarm.com/
Patrick, Isle of Man, IM5 3AQ

CASTLE WARD

BUNKHOUSE

In the heart of the National Trust's Castle Ward Estate in Northern Ireland, this bunkhouse is the perfect base to explore the park and gardens or visit the beautiful shores of Stangford Lough. The bunkhouse sleeps up to 14 in three rooms making it a great choice for groups or family get-togethers. The estate is criss-crossed with footpaths and cycle trails and has a number of play areas making this a particularly family friendly location. The bunkhouse and estate are also great for team building weekends or groups holidaying together.

DETAILS

- **Open** - All year. All day
- **Beds** - 14: 2x6, 1x2
- **Price/night** - 2 nights from £320

CONTACT: National Trust Holidays
Tel: 03443 351296
bunkhouses@nationaltrust.org.uk
www.nationaltrust.org.uk
Castle Ward, Strangford, Down,
BT30 7LS, **Northern Ireland**

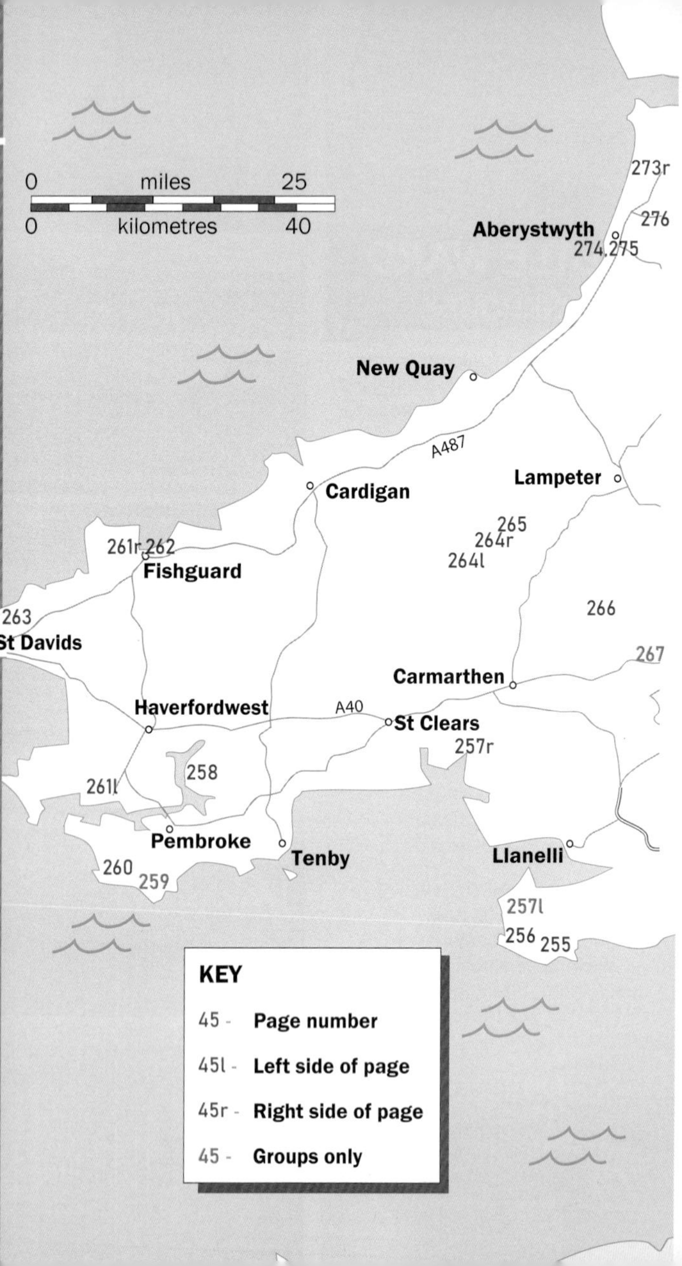

0 miles 25

0 kilometres 40

Aberystwyth 274,275

273r

276

New Quay

A487

Cardigan

Lampeter

265

264r

264l

261r,262

Fishguard

263

St Davids

266

267

Carmarthen

Haverfordwest

A40

St Clears

257r

258

261l

Pembroke

Tenby

Llanelli

260

259

257l

256

255

KEY

45 - **Page number**

45l - **Left side of page**

45r - **Right side of page**

45 - **Groups only**

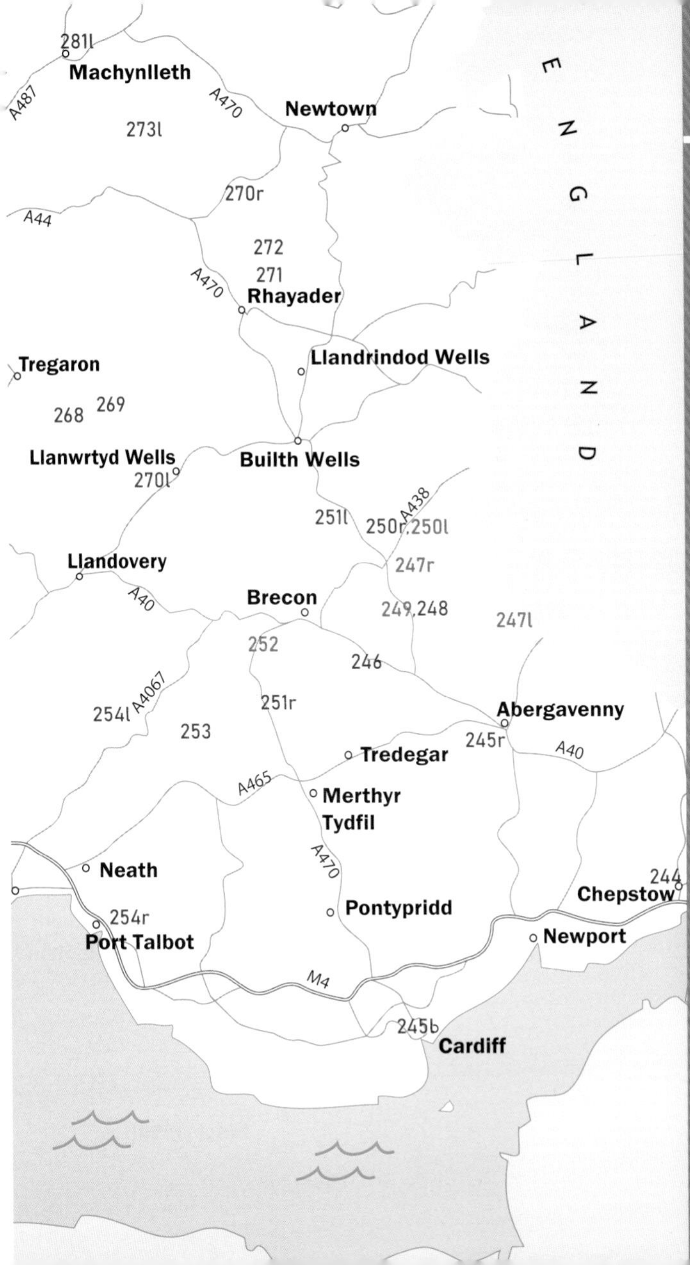

281l
Machynlleth
A487
A470
Newtown
273l
E N G L A N D
270r
A44
272
271
A470
Rhayader
Llandrindod Wells
Tregaron
268
269
Llanwrtyd Wells
270l
Builth Wells
A438
251l
250r,250l
Llandovery
247r
A40
Brecon
249,248
247l
252
246
A4067
254l
253
251r
Abergavenny
245r
A40
Tredegar
A465
Merthyr
Tydfil
A470
Neath
244
Chepstow
Pontypridd
254r
Port Talbot
Newport
M4
245b
Cardiff

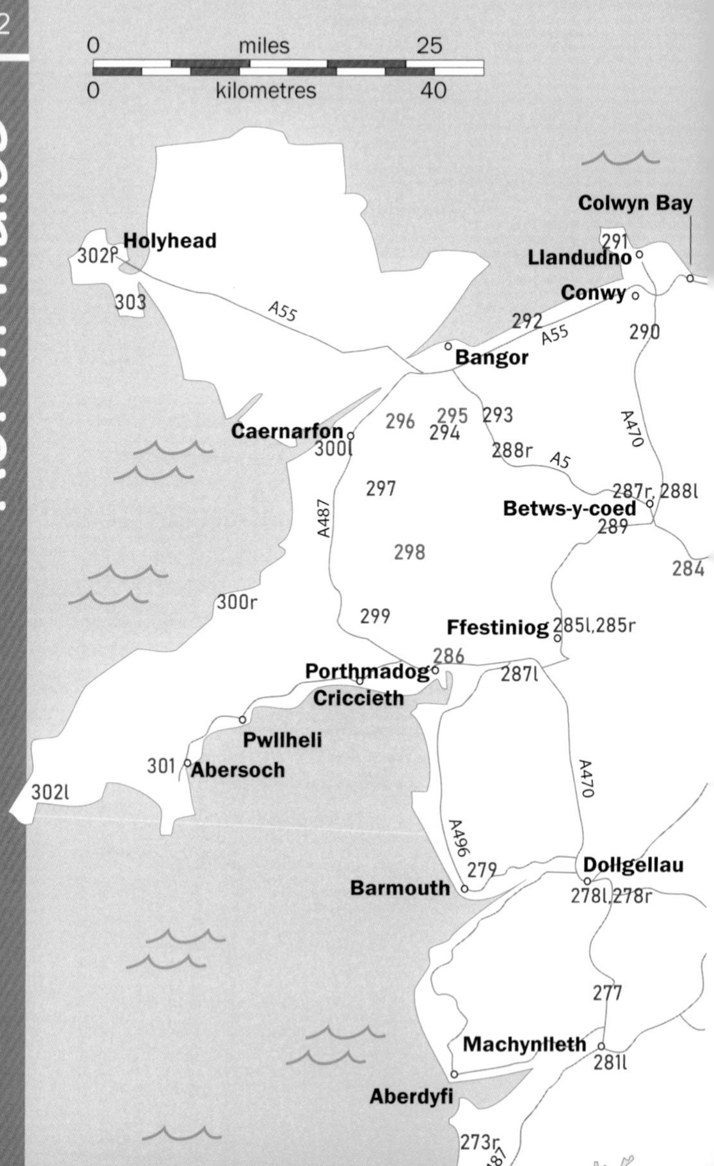
0
miles
25
0
kilometres
40
Colwyn Bay
Holyhead
302r
303
A55
291
Llandudno
Conwy
292
A55
290
Bangor
296
295
294
293
A470
Caernarfon
300l
288r
A5
297
287r, 288l
Betws-y-coed
289
A487
298
284
300r
299
Ffestiniog
285l,285r
286
Porthmadog
287l
Criccieth
Pwllheli
301
Abersoch
302l
A470
A496
279
Dollgellau
Barmouth
278l,278r
277
Machynlleth
281l
Aberdyfi
273r

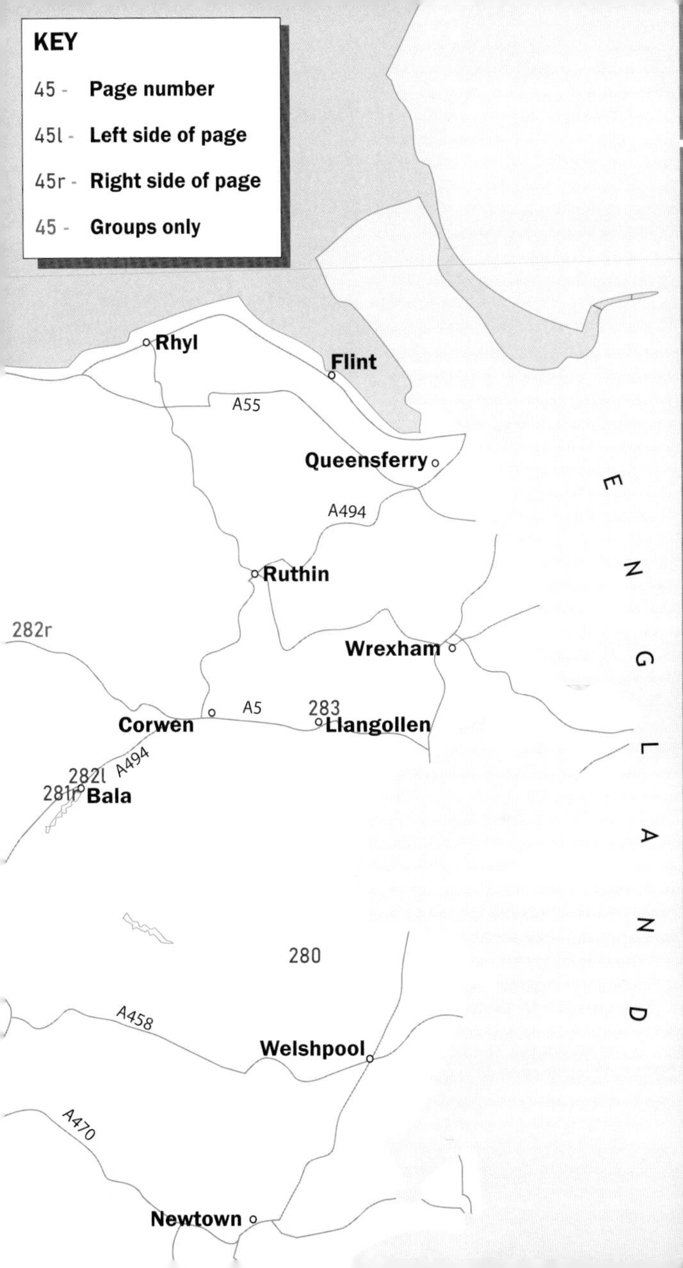

KEY

45 - **Page number**

45l - **Left side of page**

45r - **Right side of page**

45 - **Groups only**

Rhyl
Flint
A55
Queensferry
A494
Ruthin
E N G L A N D
282r
Wrexham
A5
283
Corwen
Llangollen
A494
282l
281r
Bala
280
A458
Welshpool
A470
Newtown

GREEN MAN

BACKPACKERS

244

Green Man Backpackers offers inspired accommodation in a Grade 2 building in the heart of Chepstow. Chepstow is the starting/finishing point for Offa's Dyke path, the Wales Coast Path, Gloucester Way and the Wye Valley Walk. The Land's End/John O'Groats route is just 1 mile away. The Forest of Dean & Wye Valley AONB are also nearby.

DETAILS

- **Open** - All year. All day. Except New Year's Eve/Day.
- **Beds** - 49: 28 in dorms of 6 or 4 beds, 5 en suite family / twin rooms.
- **Price/night** - Dorms from £22pp, family/4 bed rooms from £65 (en suite from £75), 5 bed from £75, family/double en suite (sleeps 3) from £55.

CONTACT: Mick and Ness
Tel: 07870 611979 or 01291 626773
info@greenmanbackpackers.co.uk
greenmanbackpackers.co.uk13
Beaufort Square, Chepstow, NP16 5EP
(Car park NP16 5LL)

RIVER HOUSE

HOSTEL

245l

This family run 4* hostel in the heart of Cardiff was voted number 1 in ostelworld's list of best hostels. Opened 2007 to rave reviews, the brother and sister team have made sure this will be e best hostel experience you will come across on your travels. With fabulous views of the world famous Millennium Stadium and River Taff and the central rain and bus stations just 5 mins' walk away. What's stopping you?

DETAILS

- **Open** - All year. 24 hours.
- **Beds** - 50: 2 bed private rooms, 4 bed dorms and 6 bed dorms.
- **Price/night** - From £15pp. Private (twin) rooms from £30 for two people. All prices include breakfast.

CONTACT: Reception
Tel: 02920 105590
info@riverhousebackpackers.com
www.riverhousebackpackers.com
59 Fitzhamon Embankment, Riverside, Cardiff, CF11 6AN

MIDDLE NINFA

BUNKHOUSE

245r

Middle Ninfa Farm, on the edge of the Blaenavon Industrial Landscape World Heritage Site in the Brecon Beacons, offers bunkhouse/cottage accommodation, camping and hands-on training in coracle making and willow sculpture. Sympathetically renovated to retain the rustic charm with fine views over the Usk Valley, the bunkhouse provides comfortable self-catering accommodation for up to 6 people. BYO food, sleeping bags, & pillowcases.

DETAILS

- **Open** - All year.
- **Beds** - 6: 1x4, 1x2 (dbl) plus camping.
- **Price/night** - From £10 per person. Weekly rate for 6 persons £300-360. Camping £5 pp + pitch fee of £5/£10.

CONTACT: Richard and Rohan Lewis
Tel: 01873 854662
bookings@middleninfa.co.uk
www.middleninfa.co.uk
Middle Ninfa Farm, Llanellen, Abergavenny, NP7 9LE

THE STAR
BUNKHOUSE

246

An ideal base for exploring the beautiful Brecon Beacons National Park. The bunkhouse is situated in the village of Bwlch alongside the Beacons Way long distance footpath. Expect a warm & comfortable stay in this dog friendly bunkhouse with spacious bedrooms, cosy lounge/dining areas, fully-equipped kitchen, outside BBQ area, hot showers, drying room and car park. Accommodation for up to 20 people in bunkbeds in 6 bedrooms. Private bedrooms or sole use available. Individuals, couples & groups welcome.

  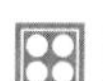    

DETAILS

- **Open** - All year. All day
- **Beds** - 20: 1×4 (en-suite), 3×4, 2×2
- **Price/night** - Standard rate £19pp

CONTACT: Emma & Pete Harrison
Tel: 01874 730080 or 07341 906937
info@starbunkhouse.com
www.starbunkhouse.com
Brecon Road (A40), Bwlch, Brecon, Powys, LD3 7RQ

THE WAIN HOUSE

247l

This old stone barn continues the tradition of 900 years when Llanthony Priory next door provided accommodation. Surrounded by the Black Mountains in the Brecon Beacons National Park, it is your ideal base for all mountain activities. There is a fully equipped kitchen, hot showers, heating throughout and a wood burning stove. Small or large groups are welcome with sole use and a minimum charge. Two pubs nearby offer real ale and bar food.

GROUPS ONLY

DETAILS

- **Open** - All year. All day. No restrictions.
- **Beds** - 16: 1 x 8; 1 x 4; 1 x 6.
- **Price/night** - £35 per person for a two-night weekend, with a minimum charge of £350. Mid-week reductions

CONTACT: Cordelia Passmore
Tel: 01873 890359
courtfarm@llanthony.co.uk
www.llanthonybunkbarn.co.uk
Court Farm, Llanthony, Abergavenny, Monmouthshire, NP7 7NN

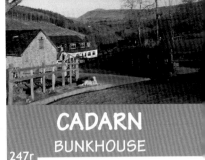

CADARN BUNKHOUSE

247r

On a small hill farm in the Brecon Beacons National Park, Cadarn Bunkhouse is surrounded by views of the Black Mountains and the Wye Valley. With easy access to the mountains it is perfect for walking, mountain biking and horse riding whist the River Wye is great for canoeing. Self-catered bunkhouse, with the pub in Felindre half a mile away. Close to Hay on Wye and Brecon. Pony trekking available on-site, plus bike and canoe hire available locally.

    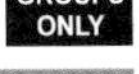

GROUPS ONLY

DETAILS

- **Open** - All year.
- **Beds** - 57: Large Bunkhouse 47 in 7 rooms, Small Bunkhouse 9: 3x3
- **Price/night** - From £16 pp.

CONTACT: Haydn Jones
Tel: 01497 847351
info@tregoydriding.co.uk
www.tregoydriding.co.uk
Tregoyd Mountain Riders, Lower Cwmcadarn Farm, Felindre, Three Cocks, Brecon, Powys, Wales LD3 0TB

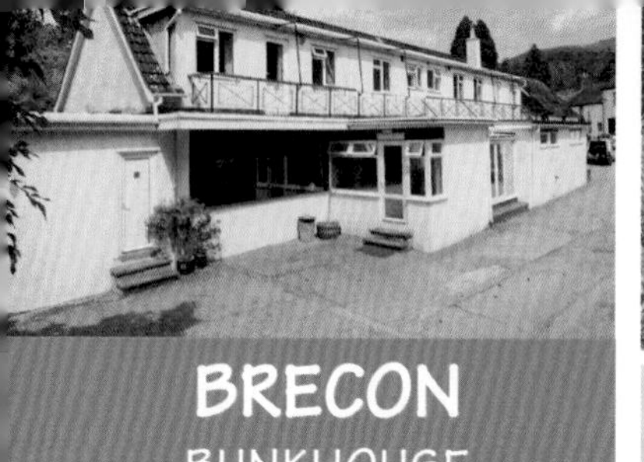

BRECON

BUNKHOUSE

Brecon Bunkhouse is a spacious, comfortable, bunkhouse in the Brecon Beacons. Offering great value self-catering accommodation with a big dining room and sitting room with wood-burner. In the Black Mountains, with mountain walks from the door, an ideal base for horse riding, mountain biking and canoeing. There is a riding centre on the farm and the bunkhouse has a drying room and storage/cleaning facilities for bikes and canoes. Camping available.

DETAILS

- **Open** - All year. All day.
- **Beds** - 28+3: 1x10,1x2,1x2,1x6,1x8. Plus extra 3 bed room available.
- **Price/night** - £20pp, minimum of 4 people. £300 for exclusive use.

CONTACT: Paul and Emily Turner
Tel: 01874 711500
breconbunkhouse@gmail.com
www.brecon-bunkhouse.co.uk
Brecon Bunkhouse, Cwmfforest Farm, Pengenfford, Talgarth, Brecon, LD3 0EU

THE DRAGONS
BACK

249

ne Dragons Back (formerly The Castle Inn) is a pub with B&B, camping & 3 bunkrooms in the Brecon Beacons lational Park. The bunkrooms are fully carpeted and centrally heated with en suite wet rooms, self-catering, drying icilities and secure storage. Stag/hens elcome. Dogs £5 pn in the bunkhouse. 'eals in the pub. Glamping is available n our Shepherds Hut and the Tardis !

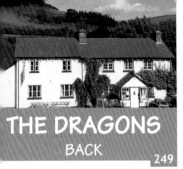

GROUPS ONLY

DETAILS

- **Open** - All year. Arrive after 2pm, depart efore 11 am.
- **Beds** - 42: Bunkhouse 28: 1x6, 1x10, 1x12. B&B: 10: 4 rooms. Glamping: 2x2
- **Price/night** - £16pp, £23pp with b/fast. Min of 5 people required for 6 bunk room, 7 for 10 b/room, or 9 for 12 b/room. Sole use £375, or £550 with breakfast.

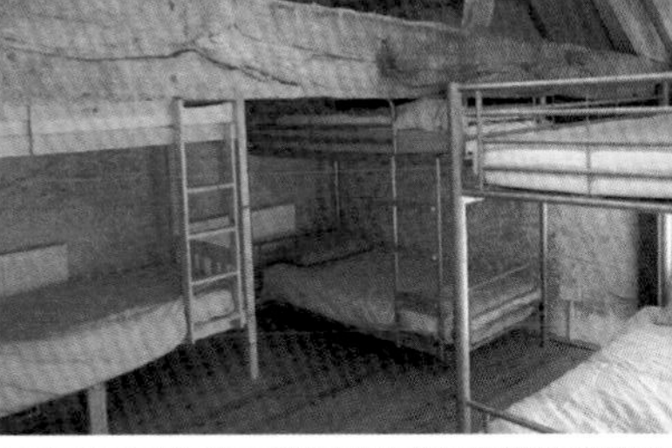

CONTACT: Jill Deakin
Tel: 01874 711353
info@thedragonsback.co.uk
www.thedragonsback.co.uk
Pengenffordd, LD3 0EP

WYE VALLEY CANOES

BUNKHOUSE

250l

In a converted Welsh Chapel, Wye Valley Canoes 5* award-winning Bunkhouse is a warm, modern space with huge sofas and a slide to reach the ground floor!

There's a small kitchen area but the River Café next door can cater for you. Enjoy the swanky bathrooms, power showers & designer furniture. Canoes, kayaks & mountain bikes can be hired & activities arranged. The beautiful market town of Hay on Wye is just 4 miles away.

- **Open** - All year. All day
- **Beds** - 14: 12x1 (pods), 1 x double
- **Price/night** - From £45 per person (max 8) weekdays. From £1370 for a 2 night weekend (Friday/Saturday)

CONTACT: Jane Hughes
Tel: 01497 847213 or 01497 847007
info@wyevalleycanoes.co.uk
www.wyevalleycanoes.co.uk
The Boat House, Glasbury-On-Wye, Herefordshire, HR3 5NP

WOODLANDS

BUNKHOUSE

250r

Woodlands Bunkhouse is a converte stable set in the 10 acre grounds of Woodlands Centre. It overlooks the Riv Wye and has wonderful views of the Black Mountains. The historic town o Hay on Wye is near by.

The Bunkhouse provides comfortable modern accommodation for families a groups. There's a well equipped kitche and dining room and 22 beds in 9 room The bunkhouse can arrange courses i variety of outdoor activities.

DETAILS

- **Open** - All year. 24 hours.
- **Beds** - 22 in rooms of 1 to 6 plu camping in the grounds.
- **Price/night** - £16 pp + VAT. Reductio for children and large group bookings.

CONTACT: Annie Clipson
Tel: 01497 847272
annie.clipson@oxfordshireoutdoors.co.uk
www.woodlandsoec.org
Glasbury on Wye, Powys, HR3 5LP

RIVER CABIN

251l

ver Cabin, let on a sole use basis for a in of 2 nights, is perfect for 2-4 people. Dog friendly with a secure garden, it erlooks a mill stream which feeds into e River Wye opposite. It has one cosy bunkroom (double bed & 2 bunks), a chen/lounge area, sunny dining porch, atio & private garden with picnic table, pit and BBQ. From Easter-Oct there's lso a small campsite. Located on the ye Valley Walk & NCN 8, it's a fantastic ase for walkers & cyclists. Canoeing, ny trekking, gliding, bike hire, rope and climbing centre all close by.

DETAILS

- **Open** - All year, 24 hour access.
- **Beds** - 4: 1 x 4 (double & bunk beds)
- **Price/night** - From £30 per person per ight, minimum stay 2 nights

CONTACT: Alistair / Nicky Legge
Tel: 07720 717124. 07740 290143
info@rivercabin.co.uk
www.rivercabin.co.uk
rwood, Builth Wells, Powys, LD2 3TQ

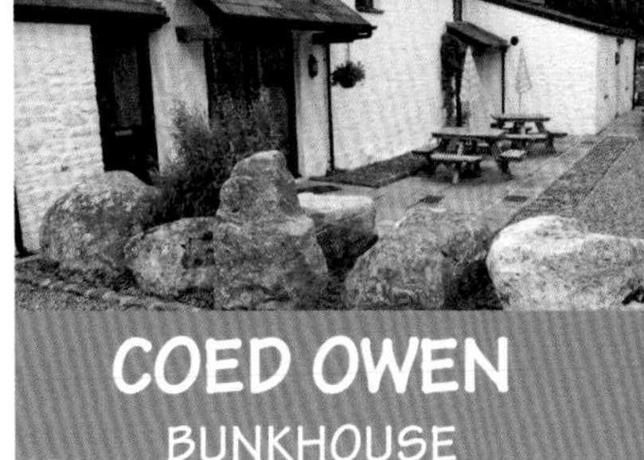

COED OWEN

BUNKHOUSE

251r

Set on a hill farm in the heart of the Brecon Beacons, 2 hours' walk from Pen Y Fan. This Bunkhouse provides well appointed self-catering accommodation; ideal for stag, hen and family parties.

Outdoor activities can be organised or there's direct access onto the mountains and waterfalls close by. Bike Park Wales, Merthyr Tydfil, Penderyn Whiskey and Brecon are all within easy reach. The pub, at the bottom of the drive, serves great food and fine ales.

DETAILS

- **Open** - All year. All day.
- **Beds** - 26: 2x6, 1x10, 1 dbl, 1 twin.
- **Price/night** - From £22pp with bed linen. Min of two nights at weekends.

CONTACT: Molly or Netty Rees
Tel: 07508 544044 (8am-10pm)
info@breconbeaconsbunkhouse.co.uk
www.breconbeaconsbunkhouse.co.uk
Coed Owen Farm, Cwmtaff, Merthyr Tydfil , CF48 2HY

DAN Y GYRN

BUNKHOUSE

Dan y Gyrn Bunkhouse is the perfect base for walkers, cyclists, families or groups. Located in the heart of the Brecon Beacons it provides the ideal base from which to explore this National Park. This comfortable, modern bunkhouse with amazing views is close to Pont ar Daf, the main access route to climb Pen Y Fan, so is great for walking groups. The bunkhouse is also a hit with families with a large garden for children to explore in. Sleeping 15 in 3 rooms this well equipped self-catering bunkhouse is the perfect accommodation for groups.

DETAILS

- **Open** - All year. All day
- **Beds** - 15: 2x6, 1x3 campbeds
- **Price/night** - From £390 for two nights.

CONTACT: National Trust Holidays
Tel: 03443 351296
bunkhouses@nationaltrust.org.uk
www.nationaltrust.org.uk/holidays
Blaenglyn Farm, Libanus, Brecon, Powys, LD3 8NF

CLYNGWYN

BUNKHOUSE

Clyngwyn 4* Bunkhouse sits in the Brecon Beacons, only minutes away from the waterfalls and caves of Ystradfellte and Sgwd Yr Eira. Your deal base for a wide range of outdoor activities. The bunkhouse sleeps up to 19, plus camping, three double B&B ooms and a romantic shepherd's hut in it's own private meadow.

DETAILS

- **Open** - All year. All day.
- **Beds** - Bunkhouse 19. B&B 6. Shepherd's Hut 2.
- **Price/night** - Sun-Thurs: up to 19 people £285, up to 15 £230 or £18pp. Fri/Sat: up to 19 people £325, up to 15 £260. B&B £30pp. Shepherds hut £75 (sleeps 2).

CONTACT: Julie Hurst
Tel: 01639 722930
enquiries@bunkhouse-south-wales.co.uk
www.bunkhouse-south-wales.co.uk
Clyngwyn Farm, Ystradfellte Rd,
Pontneddfechan, Powys, SA11 5US

CRAIG Y NOS

CASTLE

254l

Craig Y Nos Castle sits in the Brecon Beacons. The Nurses Block can be booked on a daily or a room basis. It can also be booked sole use as group accommodation. Offering B&B or self-catering, the choice is yours. The castle provides hearty meals, cosy evenings by the wood burning stoves and a free history tour. Superior B&B rooms are available in the castle.

DETAILS

- **Open** - All year
- **Beds** - Nurses Block: 21: 10x2, 1x1. Castle: 67 rooms: (64 en suite)
- **Price/night** - Nurses Block sole use:- 1 night £350, 2 nights £500, 3 nights £600, 5 nights £700. B&B per twin room: £67.50pn midweek, £87.50pn weekend.

CONTACT: Reception
Tel: 01639 730725
info@craigynoscastle.com
www.craigynoscastle.com
Craig Y Nos Castle, Brecon Road, Penycae, Powys, SA9 1GL

L&A

OUTDOOR CENTRE

254r

L&A is set in a quiet wooded valley an offers accommodation for up to 280 people in self-catering cabins in the Swansea Bay area. There is a bar/caf commercial kitchen, activity hall, meeti rooms and 300 seat dining hall. Set i 80 acres of woodlands and pasture wi open air swimming pool, BBQ and fire pits. L&A are happy to help you organis an event and have extensive links wit activity providers in the area. Close to Afan Aergoed Mountain bike trails.

DETAILS

- **Open** - All day.
- **Beds** - Cabin: 117: 6/8 bed units Bunkhouse: 175:10,16,24,30,40 bed.
- **Price/night** - Bunkhouses: fron £12pp. Cabins: 6 bed £90-£150, 8 be £100-£180. Enquire for group rates.

CONTACT: Nigel or Matthew
Tel: 01639 885509
info@landaoutdoorcentre.co.uk
www.landaoutdoorcentre.co.uk
Goytre, West Glamorgan SA13 2YP

EASTERN SLADE

BARN

255

Eastern Slade Barn is a luxury rmhouse conversion on a working farm the Gower Peninsula. The Gower has glorious beaches, castles & a network of traffic free lanes, ideal for mountain kes. The Coastal Path passes through he farm. Port Eynon seaside village is 30 min walk, while Oxwich Bay with its stle, beach & hotel serving tasty meals is just a 20 min walk. Camping is also vailable and weddings/birthdays can be accommodated.

DETAILS

- **Open** - All year. 24 hours.
- **Beds** - 15: 1x5, 2x2/3 (double with bunk above), 1x2, 2 in lounge
- **Price/night** - £15pp, £180 sole use. High season £20pp, £240 sole use.

CONTACT: Kate
Tel: 07970 969814
tynrheol@hotmail.com
www.easternsladebarngower.co.uk
Eastern Slade Farm, Oxwich, Gower, Swansea, SA3 1NA

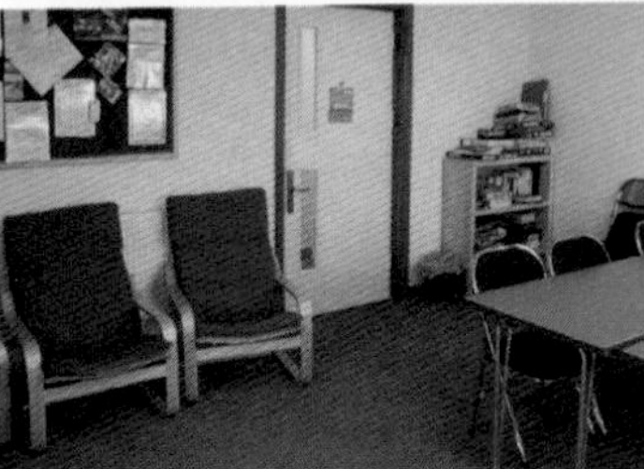

RHOSSILI

BUNKHOUSE

256

Rhossili 4* Bunkhouse is situated at the end of the Gower Peninsula, in an Area of Outstanding Natural Beauty. It is within easy walking distance of three glorious beaches, (including Rhossili Bay voted the best beach in Europe and in the top ten in the World 2017). Ideal for families and groups and perfectly located for a wide range of outdoor activities including walking, surfing, cycling & climbing.

DETAILS

- **Open** - All year except January. Check in 4-9pm; check out by 10:30am.
- **Beds** - 18: 1x4, 2x3, 4x2. 4 sofa-beds in lounge (sole use).
- **Price/night** - Shared (small groups) £16-£20. Full (group of 18) £340. Sole (group of 22) £390.

CONTACT: Josephine Higgins
Tel: 01792 391509
bookings@rhossili.org
www.rhossilibunkhouse.com
Rhossili Bunkhouse, Rhossili, Swansea, SA3 1PL

HARDINGSDOWN

BUNKHOUSE

257l

Hardingsdown Bunkhouse and The Chaffhouse both provide accommodation for families or groups. Comfortable and well appointed they are perfect for exploring Gower and all it has to offer. The properties can be hired individually or together, rates vary with numbers.

DETAILS

- **Open** - All year. 24 hours.
- **Beds** - Bunkhouse 14: 1x5, 1x3, 3x2. Chaffhouse: 12: 1x4 4x2
- **Price/night** - Hardingsdown Bunkhouse: (14 people max) £220 pn. The Chaffhouse: (12 people max) £220 pn. Midweek. £200 pn. Enquire for rates for both units together. Weekly rates available. INDIVIDUALS mid week only, £20 pppn. Prices same for both properties

CONTACT: Allison Tyrrell
Tel: 01792 386222
bunkhousegower@btconnect.com
www.bunkhousegower.co.uk
Lower Hardingsdown Farm, Llangennith, Gower, Swansea, SA3 1HT

PANTYRATHRO

INTERNATIONAL HOSTEL

257r

Llansteffan is a beautiful, quaint village at the tip of the Towi River and Carmarthen Bay. The sandy beaches below the castle offer swimming and relaxation. The virtually traffic free country lanes make the area ideal for cycling.

The Wales Coastal Path is on the doorstep and the city of Carmarthen offers most social and cultural activities. The Pantyrathro International Hostel provides dorm accommodation, private rooms, family rooms and ensuite rooms.

DETAILS

- **Open** - February to January. 24 hours.
- **Beds** - 46: 1x10,1x9,1x6,4x4,1x3,1x2
- **Price/night** - £17pp dorm. Group discounts.

CONTACT: Ken Knuckles
Tel: 01267 241014
kenknuckles@hotmail.com
www.backpackershostelwales.com
Pantyrathro International Hostel, Llansteffan, Carmarthen, SA33 5AJ

LAWRENNY

MILLENNIUM HOSTEL

Once a Victorian village school, the Lawrenny Hostel is superbly placed for exploring South Pembrokeshire. Warm, clean and comfortable, with modern facilities, the accommodation is ideal for individuals or groups, training courses or events. The adjoining village hall is also available to rent and there is a community shop, pub and an award-winning tearoom nearby.

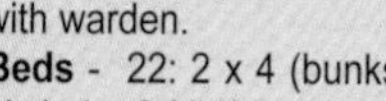

DETAILS

- **Open** - All year. All day. Arrange check in with warden.
- **Beds** - 22: 2 x 4 (bunks), 2 x 4 (dbl + bunks), 1 x 6 (dbl/sgl + bunks)
- **Price/night** - Adults £16, children (4-17) £10. Dbl rooms £37 (couple), £50 (with children). Sole use £250 per night.

CONTACT: Laura Lort-Phillips
Tel: 01646 651270
hostel@lawrennyvillage.co.uk
www.lawrennyhostel.com
Lawrenny Millennium Hostel, Lawrenny,
Pembrokeshire, SA68 0PW

STACKPOLE

OUTDOOR CENTRE

The 147-bed, platinum eco-award-winning. Stackpole Centre is the perfect venue for large families/groups, special interest breaks and outdoor activities. It comprises four large houses, three cottages and a manor house. Close to wild woodlands and stunning beaches.

DETAILS

- **Open** - All year. All day. Reception 9-5.
- **Beds** - Swan House: 13 bedrooms (24 guests). Shearwater House; 7 bedrooms (17 guests). Kestrel House: 12 b/rooms (35 guests). Kingfisher: 10 b/rooms (44 guests). Manor House: 3 b/rooms (9 guests). 3 cottages: 9 b/rooms (18 guests)
- **Price/night** - Whole site £2400, Kingfisher £650, Kestrel £395 Shearwater £295, Swan £550.

CONTACT: Stackpole Reception
Tel: 01646 623 110
stackpole.bookings@nationaltrust.org.uk
www.nationaltrust.org.uk/holidays
The Old Home Farm Yard, Stackpole, nr Pembroke, Pembrokeshire, SA71 5DQ

WARREN FARM

GLAMPING

260

A cosy bunkhouse & beautiful big bell tents, right on the Pembrokeshire Coast Path with fantastic views out to sea. The closest you can stay to excellent climbing at Castlemartin Range, plus brilliant surfing at Freshwater West & Broadhaven South. Within striking distance of many of Pembrokeshire's fabulous tourist attractions. All the accommodation is comfortable and well equipped. Don't delay, come glamping!

DETAILS

- **Open** - All year. Check in 5-6pm, flexible by arrangement.
- **Beds** - Bunkhouse: 12. Bell Tents: 6x8. Camping. Plus an expanding range of pods for couples & individuals.
- **Price/night** - Check website for latest accommodation & prices. From £12pppn

CONTACT: Jane or Hannah, via email
stay@warrenfarm.wales
www.warrenfarm.wales
Warren Farm, Warren, near
Castlemartin, SA71 5HS

UPPER NEESTON

LODGES

261l

Environmentally sensitive barn conversions close to the Milford Haven Waterway in the Pembrokeshire Coast National Park. Ideal for divers, climbers, walkers or family get-togethers. The four independent 5* lodges have fully fitted kitchens and have access to garden/ patio, laundry/drying room, secure storage and ample parking.

DETAILS

- **Open** - All year. Check in from 4pm. Check out before 10.30am.
- **Beds** - 24: Cowshed 10: 1x6,1x4. Barn 8: 1x6,1x2, Granary 1x3. Dairy 1x3
- **Price/night** - From £17.50 (inc linen). Min 2 nights at w/ends (3 nights b/h). Sole use: min 6 Barn, 8 Cowshed. Smaller groups/individuals by agreement.

CONTACT: Sean or Mandy Tilling
Tel: 01646 690750
mail@upperneeston.co.uk
www.upperneeston.co.uk
Upper Neeston Farm, Dale Road, Herbrandston, Milford Haven, SA73 3RY

JAMES JOHN

HAMILTON HOUSE

261r

James John Hamilton House is a new conversion of the first free school in Fishguard, built in 1850 by James John Hamilton. The house provides comfortable, characterful self-catering accommodation for 10 people in four private rooms. Across the garden is Hamilton House Backpackers (pg 262) with an extra 9 beds. It's close to the centre of Fishguard with pubs & cafes. The Pembrokeshire Coastal Path passes through the town and communities of grey seals and dolphins are regularly seen in the local harbours.

DETAILS

- **Open** - All year.
- **Beds** - 10 (+9): 1 x twin, 2 x dbl, 1 x 4 (dbl & bunk) plus 9 beds next door.
- **Price/night** - From £20-£28 pp.

CONTACT: Steve Roberts
Tel: 01348 874288
stephenism@hotmail.com
www.jamesjohnhamilton.co.uk
19a Hamilton St, Fishguard SA65 9HL

HAMILTON

BACKPACKERS

Hamilton Lodge is just one minute's walk from the centre of Fishguard and very close to the Pembrokeshire Coastal Path. Comfortable and friendly, sleeping nine in total with an en suite double and two dorms. Fully equipped kitchen, dining area and lounge. Charming, private garden and covered patio with seating. Free light breakfast included. Groups of up to 18 are welcome in collaboration with James John Hamilton House hostel next door (pg 261r).

DETAILS

- **Open** - All year.
- **Beds** - 9 (+10): 1 x 4, 1 x 3 and 1 x 2. (Plus 10 next door)
- **Price/night** - From £20 to £21 pp in dorms, from £24.50 pp in double en suite.

CONTACT: Quentin Maclaurin
Tel: 01348 874797 or 07505562939
hamiltonbackpackers@hotmail.com
www.hamiltonbackpackers.co.uk
23 Hamilton Street, Fishguard,
Pembrokeshire, SA65 9HL

CAERHAFOD

LODGE

263

Situated between the famous cathedral city of St Davids and the Irish ferry port of Fishguard, the 4* Lodge overlooks the spectacular Pembrokeshire coastline. Within walking distance of the Sloop Inn at Porthgain and the internationally renowned Coastal Path. An ideal stopover for cyclists with The Celtic Trail cycle route passing the bottom of the drive. The lodge sleeps 23 in 5 separate rooms, all en suite with great showers. Dogs welcome by arrangement.

DETAILS

- **Open** - All year. All day. Check in from 4pm, check out 10.30 am.
- **Beds** - 23: 3x4, 1x5, 1x6.
- **Price/night** - Adult £20. U16 £15 when booking 2+ nights. Group rates available

CONTACT: Carolyn Rees
Tel: 01348 837859
Caerhafod@aol.com
www.caerhafod.co.uk
Llanrhian, St Davids, Haverfordwest,
Pembrokeshire, SA62 5BD

CERIDWEN CENTRE

264l

On an organic farm in the Teifi Valley this award winning eco-sensitive location is ideal for holidays, courses, retreats, events and weddings. Accommodation includes; Ceridwen an old smithy sensitively converted into high quality group accommodation for 19, Yurts, Eco Pods, B&B rooms, an up-cycled static caravan, a Romany caravan, a double-decker bus and spaces for tents and caravans.

DETAILS

- **Open** - All year
- **Beds** - 62: Ceridwen 19: 2x4, 5x2, 1x1. Yurts 20: 5x4. Byre 6: 2x3, Bus 6: 3x2. Hopshack 4:2x2. Pod 2:1x2 plus camping.
- **Price/night** - Ceridwen from £861 (2 nights), Glamping from £132 (2 nights)

CONTACT: Simone Broome / Reception
Tel: 01559 370517
info@CeridwenCentre.co.uk
ceridwencentre.co.uk
Drefelin, Drefach-Felindre, Llandysul, Carmarthenshire SA44 5XE

SHAGGY SHEEP

264r

Shaggy Sheep offers budget bunkhouse accommodation in the stunning surroundings of Carmarthenshire, just 25 mins' drive from the Ceredigion coastline and its amazing beaches. Perfect for activity, stag and hen parties. Nestled in the Teifi valley with village pubs and restaurants within walking distance. Bedding is included and facilities include a self-catering kitchen, a lounge, garden and BBQ area. Shaggy Sheep are experts at organising adventure activity holidays.

DETAILS

- **Open** - Jan-Dec. All day.
- **Beds** - 22: 5x4, 1x2
- **Price/night** - Email with numbers and length of stay for a quote

CONTACT: Chris
Tel: 01559 363911
bookings@shaggysheepwales.co.uk
www.shaggysheepwales.com
Old Commerce House, Pontwelly, Llandysul, Carmarthen SA44 4AJ

THE LONG BARN

265

Penrhiw is an organic farm with views over the Teifi Valley. The stunning Ceredigion Coast and the Cambrian Mountains are an easy drive away and the busy small town of Llandysul (1.5 miles) has all essential supplies. The farm's location is ideal for exploring, studying or simply admiring the Welsh countryside. Local activities include fishing, swimming, climbing, abseiling, canoeing, farm walks and cycling.

DETAILS

- **Open** - All year. All day.
- **Beds** - 43: Long Barn 31: 1x15, 1x14, 1x2. Cowshed: 6:1x6. Annex 3: 1x3 (dbl+sgl). Cwtsh 3: 1x3 (dbl+sofa bed)
- **Price/night** - £15pp. Discount for groups and mid week bookings.

CONTACT: Tom or Eva
Tel: 01559 363200 or 07733 026874
cowcher@thelongbarn.co.uk
www.thelongbarn.co.uk
Penrhiw, Capel Dewi, Llandysul, Ceredigion, SA44 4PG

GILFACH WEN

BARN

A homely, high quality, bunkhouse for individuals, extended families or groups on a working farm. The large social area is ideal for reunions or celebrations. The are 7 family bedrooms including one downstairs for disabled. Perfect for exploring Carmarthenshire, Pembrokeshire, Brecon Beacons, Cambrian Mountains and the Gower. Walker, cyclist, dog & equestrian friendly. Village pub close by.

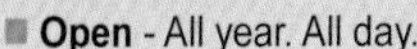

DETAILS

- **Open** - All year. All day.
- **Beds** - 32: 3x6,1x5,1x4,1x3,1x2. 10 double beds & 12 singles in 7 bedrooms.
- **Price/night** - From £17.50pp. Min numbers apply for advance bookings. Last minute individual bookings £20pp.

CONTACT: Jillie
Tel: 07780 476737
info@brechfa-bunkhouse.com
www.brechfa-bunkhouse.com
Gilfach Wen, Brechfa, Carmarthenshire, SA32 7QL

DINEFWR

BUNKHOUSE

On a National Trust estate one mile from Llandeilo, Dinefwr Bunkhouse sits in the heart of an 18th century park enclosing a medieval deer park, next to the historic Newton House. Quite the perfect holiday location for groups or families who enjoy walking or other outdoor activities.

This beautifully presented, characterful bunkhouse sleeps up to 16 in an 8 bed dorm and 2 & 3 bedded rooms and has a well equipped kitchen for self-catering.

GROUPS ONLY

DETAILS

- **Open** - All year. All day
- **Beds** - 16: 1x8, 1x2, 2x3
- **Price/night** - For groups of 8 or less from £160 per night. Extra £20 per person per night for parties with over 8 people.

CONTACT: National Trust Holidays
Tel: 03443 351296
bunkhouses@nationaltrust.org.uk
www.nationaltrust.org.uk/holidays
Dinefwr Park, Llandeilo,
Carmarthenshire, SA19 6RT

TYNCORNEL

HOSTEL

Tyncornel is a former farmhouse set in stunning Cambrian Mountain scenery at the head of the beautiful Doethie Valley. It is one of the most remote hostels in Wales, favoured by walkers, cyclists, and bird watchers. It is on the Cambrian Way long distance footpath. The hostel has 16 places. There is a cosy common room with wood-burning stove, two dormitories with built-in bunk beds and a self-catering kitchen.

DETAILS

- **Open** - All year. Reception 5pm -11pm, 7am -10am.
- **Beds** - 16: 2x8.
- **Price/night** - £14 per adult, £10 (under 18s). Whole hostel bookings £200 and private rooms available. Campers £8.

CONTACT: Janet or Richard
Tel: 01980 629259
Tyncornel.bookings@btinternet.com
www.elenydd-hostels.co.uk
Llanddewi Brefi, Tregaron, Ceredigion, SY25 6PH

DOLGOCH
HOSTEL

Experience the peace of the remote 'ywi valley in an era before electricity at this 17th century farmhouse. Dolgoch is a traditional simple hostel owned by the Elenydd Wilderness Trust. It has hot showers, log burner, self-catering kitchen, dormitories & private rooms. The Lôn Las Cymru and the Cambrian Way pass nearby and there are many ıountain tracks to explore. Ideal for bird-'atchers and lovers of the solitude of the scenic Cambrian Mountains.

DETAILS

- **Open** - All year. 24 hours. Reception 5pm -11pm, 8am -10am.
- **Beds** - 20: 3 rooms inc private rooms.
- **Price/night** - £14 per adult, £10 (under 18). Campers £8

CONTACT: Gillian Keen
Tel: 01440 730226
gill.keen@dolgoch.org
www.elenydd-hostels.co.uk
Dolgoch, Tregaron, Ceredigion, SY25 6NR

STONECROFT
LODGE

270l

Stonecroft Lodge is in Llanwrtyd Wells, the smallest town in Britain. Surrounded by the green fields and mountains of mid Wales, Llanwrtyd is in renowned red kite country and is a great base for mountain biking, walking & pony trekking.

The hostel has private rooms with made-up beds, a fully equipped kitchen, lounge with TV, free laundry and drying, central heating, a large riverside garden and ample parking. The hostel adjoins the Stonecroft Inn for great beer & food.

DETAILS

- **Open** - All year. All day. Call on arrival.
- **Beds** - 27: 1x1, 3x4, 1x6, 4x(dbl+sgl)
- **Price/night** - £16. Discounts for 3+ nights. Phone for sole use rates.

CONTACT: Jane Brown
Tel: 01591 610332
party@stonecroft.co.uk
www.stonecroft.co.uk
Dolecoed Road, Llanwrtyd Wells, Powys, LD5 4RA

PLASNEWYDD
BUNKHOUSE

270r

Set in the beautiful Mid Wales countryside on the Glyndwrs Way, the 4* bunkhouse is an ideal location for exploring or unwinding. Built to the highest standards it provides high quali accommodation for groups or individual It can also be booked for conferences and seminars. Attractions close by include sailing, golf course, outdoor pursuit centre, shooting range, motorbik school and the picturesque market tow of Llanidloes (1/2 mile) with many place to eat and drink.

DETAILS

- **Open** - All year. 24 hours. Arrival and departure times by arrangement.
- **Beds** - 27 in 2 dorms + 1 family room.
- **Price/night** - £20pp + £3 for bedding if required. Sole use £403.

CONTACT: Susan
Tel: 01686 412431 or 07975 913049
susanvaughan67@aol.co.uk
www.plasnewyddbunkhouse.co.uk
Gorn Rd, Llanidloes, Powys, SY18 6LA

BEILI NEUADD

BUNKHOUSE

\ converted 18th century stone barn in stunning countryside just 2 miles from the small market town of Rhayader - the gateway to the Elan Valley and ;ambrian Mountains. On three National Cycle routes and the Trans Cambrian Route, Beili Neuadd offers lovely jardens, ponds and stunning scenery. The centrally heated barn sleeps 16 in 3 en suite rooms and includes a fully quipped kitchen/dining room and drying room. B&B accommodation is also vailable in the main house and there is space to camp in the paddock.

DETAILS

- **Open** - All year. All day.
- **Beds** - 16: 2x6,1x4. B&B: 3 x double.
- **Price/night** - £19 per person, sole occupancy £275. B&B £50pp, £80 for two.

CONTACT: Ruth Ward
Tel: 01597 810211
info@beilineuadd.co.uk
www.beilineuadd.co.uk
Beili Neuadd, Rhayader, LD6 5NS

MID WALES

BUNKHOUSE

Mid Wales Bunkhouse has a superb unspoilt rural location, close to the Elan Valley, for any activity or occasion with a stunning natural garden. Explore or swim in the river. There's walking and biking from the door, even accommodation for your horse. Fully equipped for self catering or meals provided. Authentic tipi and camping. Available for groups of up to 26 or individuals.

DETAILS

- **Open** - All year. 24 hours. Arrive after 3pm (advise if after 7pm), leave by 11am.
- **Beds** - 20
- **Price/night** - £17pp, £90 for private 6-bed room. Sole use of dormitory area (sleeps 14) £195 per night. Sole use of bunkhouse (20 people) £260 per night.

CONTACT: John
Tel: 01597 870081 or 07507 343262
enquiries@bunkhousemidwales.co.uk
www.bunkhousemidwales.co.uk
Woodhouse Farm, St Harmon,
Rhayader, LD6 5LY

HAFREN FOREST

BUNKHOUSE

273l

This former weather station has been converted into a comfortable bunkhouse located on the edge of the Hafren Forest. It is close to Plumlimon, in a quiet rural location between Llanidloes and Machynlleth in the Cambrian Mountains.

A great base for walking, running, cycling (both on and off road), kayaking, wildlife watching, fly fishing, family groups and parties. Fully central heated the bunkhouse has a large dining room, well equipped kitchen and comfortable lounge with TV, DVD and playstation.

  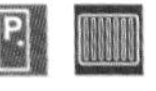     

DETAILS

- **Open** - All year.
- **Beds** - 21: 2x4, 1x5, 1x8
- **Price/night** - £20 per person.

CONTACT: Darren and Sarah
Tel: 07871 740514
mrsh66@btinternet.com
www.hafrenforestbunkhouse.com
Staylittle, nr Llanidloes, Powys, SY19 7DB

BORTH

YOUTH HOSTEL

273r

With 4 miles of stunning beach just 20 metres from the front door, Borth Youth Hostel is perfect for a beach holiday. This Edwardian house has 9 bedrooms with sea views and is a great base for visits to the Centre for Alternative Technology, Aberystwyth or the beautiful Dyfi Biosphere. Snowdonia National Park is just a short drive away making Borth perfect for both mountain biking & surfing. With two classrooms, Borth YHA is idea for school trips too. There's free WiFi, a games & TV room, bike storage & drying room. Breakfast, packed lunch & a licensed bar are available.

DETAILS

- **Open** - All year. Check in 5 - 10.30pm. Check out 8am - 10am
- **Beds** - 60
- **Price/night** - From £18 pp

CONTACT: John Taylor
Tel: 01970 871498
john@borthyouthhostel.co.uk
Borth, Ceredigion, Wales, SY24 5JS

MAES-Y-MOR

Maes-y-Mor offers superior self-catering accommodation at budget prices. With 7 twin & 1 double room plus 1 en suite family room it is ideally situated near the town centre, around the corner from the beach and 5 mins' walk to train/bus stations. Accommodation at the hostel is room-only with self-catering facilities.

All rooms have TVs & tea/coffee making facilities. Car parking and secure bike storage. A 4* double room apartment and a new 4* boutique self-catering house sleeping 7 are also available

DETAILS

- **Open** - All year. 8am to 9.30pm
- **Beds** - 6: Family, double and twin rooms
- **Price/night** - From £38 per person

CONTACT: Mererid or Alaw
Tel: 01970 639270.
maesymor@hotmail.co.uk
www.maesymor.co.uk
25 Bath Street, Aberystwyth, SY23 2NN

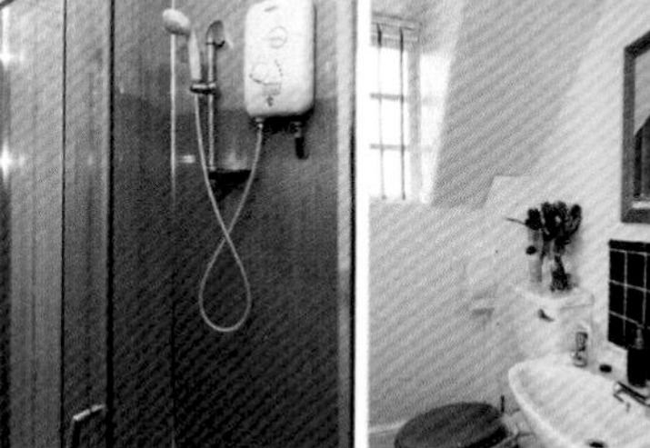

ABERYSTWYTH

UNI BUNKHOUSE

275

Aberystwyth University Bunkhouse is on the Wales Coast Path, close to beaches, dramatic walking and white knuckle mountain biking. Aberystwyth has all the attractions of a Victorian seaside town with the added adventure of an ancient castle and thriving nightlife. Accommodation is in single rooms with shared self-catering kitchens and bathrooms. Meals available. Ideal for education trips, conference, or those looking for a base for a family seaside holiday or outdoor group trip.

DETAILS

- **Open** - All year. Reception 9am-5pm.
- **Beds** - 90 : Individual bedrooms
- **Price/night** - £30 (2+nights) or £36.

Reduced rates for educational groups.

CONTACT: Conference Office
Tel: 01970 621960
constaff@aber.ac.uk
www.aber.ac.uk/en/visitors/bunkhouse/
Penbryn Reception, Aberystwyth University, Penbryn, Penglais, SY23 3BY

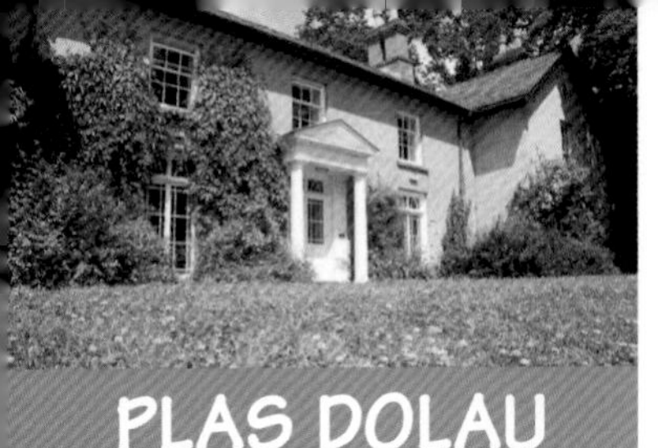

PLAS DOLAU

COUNTRY HOUSE

Plas Dolau is set in 25 acres just 3 miles from Aberystwyth. Ideal for exploring West Wales, walking, cycling, riding, fishing and golf. The warm country mansion has mainly dormitory style accommodation for up to 45 people. An adjoining Swedish style farmhouse can take another 15. There are meeting rooms, dining rooms, games room & outdoor areas. Ideally suited for youth groups, field courses, retreats and house parties. Individuals,couples and families are also welcome.

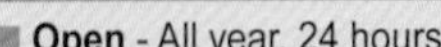

DETAILS

- **Open** - All year. 24 hours.
- **Beds** - 45:+cots. Plus 16 in farmhouse.
- **Price/night** - From £22 (inc breakfast) to £37 (private,en suite,full breakfast). From £650 for the whole mansion.

CONTACT: Pat Twigg
Tel: 01970 617834
pat@plasdolau.co.uk
www.plasdolau.co.uk
Lovesgrove, Aberystwyth, SY23 3HP

CORRIS
HOSTEL

Perfect for group & family celebrations, Corris hostel is a haven from the stresses of the outside world; with its homely & inspiring atmosphere, caring staff & cosy wood fires. Enjoy the gardens with BBQ & campfire areas. In the Dyfi Biosphere & Snowdonia National Park & close to Cadair Idris and Centre for Alternative Technology, it's a walkers & cyclists paradise. On the Mach Loop with a CAMRA pub close by.

DETAILS

- **Open** - Most of year (groups only winter). All day.
- **Beds** - 45: 1x10 1x18 1x4 1x6 1x twin, 1x double+1 1x double+2
- **Price/night** - Adult £20, child £14. Breakfast £4.50. Private rooms extra.

CONTACT: Michael or Debbie or Kevin
Tel: 01654 761686
mail@corrishostel.co.uk
www.corrishostel.co.uk
Old School, Corris, Machynlleth, Powys, SY20 9TQ

HYB BUNKHOUSE

DOLGELLAU

278l

HyB Bunkhouse is in Dolgellau (Lon Las, Sustrans 82), Mid Wales, at the foot of Cader Idris. Centrally located above Medi Gifts, with free parking at rear for up to four cars, there are shops, pubs and restaurants on the doorstep.

HyB backs onto the Mawddach trail near the river Wnion and it is 10 minutes' drive to Coed y Brenin mountain biking centre. This quirky listed building has original features such as oak floors, beams and panelling and offers a good night's sleep.

    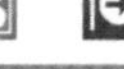 

DETAILS

- **Open** - All year but CLOSED Xmas and New Year.
- **Beds** - 16: 4 x 4 rooms
- **Price/night** - £20 per person. Limited bedding sets available @£5.

CONTACT: Nia
Tel: 01341 421755
post@medi-gifts.com
2-3 Heol y Bont (Bridge St), Dolgellau, Gwynedd, LL40 1AU

PLAS ISA

278r

In the centre of Dolgellau, Plas Isa welcomes independent travellers to this historic Welsh town. Comfortable rooms can be adapted for single, twin, double or group use. The communal lounge and dining room are great for socialising with your group or other guests. It is the perfect base for active holidays in Snowdonia for walkers (Cader Idris, Snowdonia Way), mountain bikers (Coed y Brenin) and cyclists (Mawddach Trail, Lon Las Cymru).

DETAILS

- **Open** - All year. Check in after 3pm, check out before 10am.
- **Beds** - 19: 2x3, 2x4, 1x5
- **Price/night** - From £25pp (family room 3+). Dbl/twin: £30pp. Single: £40pp. U10 £15pp (at least 1 adult in room).

CONTACT: Ian and Hanneke
Tel: 01341 423178 or 07984 737066
info@plasisaguesthouse.co.uk
www.plasisaguesthouse.co.uk
Lion Street, Dolgellau, LL40 1DG

BUNKORAMA

279

Whether you're a lone cyclist or a group of walkers you will love discovering this cosy, clean and comfortable accommodation with breathtaking views of Cader Idris and Cardigan Bay.

Handy for Cycle Route 8, the Cambrian Way & Mawddach Trail and at only £15 per night Bunkorama is an ideal place to make a stopover or spend a few days exploring the mountains, rivers and beaches of the Cambrian Coast.

DETAILS

- **Open** - All year.
- **Beds** - 8: 2x4, plus sofa bed in lounge.
- **Price/night** - £15 pp + £5 per stay if bedding needed and towel available £2 per stay

CONTACT: Graham
Tel: 01341 281134 or 0773 8467196
thebunkorama@gmail.com
www.bunkorama.co.uk
Gwastad Agnes Off Panorama Road,
Barmouth, Gwynedd, LL42 1DX

BUNKHOUSE

AT THE WORKHOUSE

The well equipped, community run bunkhouse at Y Dolydd Llanfyllin Workhouse is handy for Welshpool & Shrewsbury and close to the Berwyn Mountains. With access to a wide range of adventurous activities including Lake Vyrnwy, Pistyll Rhaeadr waterfall (the tallest in the UK) and Revolution bike park. Venue hire for events welcomed, catering/bar available by arrangement. Visit the free History Centre to learn more about the building and the people who lived and worked in it.

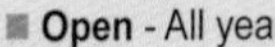

DETAILS

- **Open** - All year.
- **Beds** - 24: 1x4, 1x8, 1x12
- **Price/night** - £15 incl. linen, duvets & pillow. Group discounts may apply.

CONTACT: Tree Marshall
Tel: 07534 354082
bunkhouse@the-workhouse.com
www.the-workhouse.org.uk/
Y Dolydd, Workhouse, Llanfyllin, SY22 5LD

TOAD HALL

281l

oad Hall sits beside the River Dovey, close to Snowdonia National Park nd in the town of Machynlleth. NCN ycle Route 8 and Glyndwrs Way pass near by. The hostel accommodation comprises a four bed-roomed self ntained unit above the family home. A at garden is ideal for camping or bike/ canoe storage.

  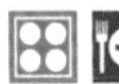  

DETAILS

Open - Not always open, please phone find out and always pre-book. Please acate rooms from 12 -3 pm for cleaning. lo arrivals after 11pm.

Beds - 10: 1x4 (family), 1x2 (twin), 1x2 dbl), 1x2

Price/night - £16 pp + £2 per stay for edding. Reductions for groups.

CONTACT: Will
el: 01654 700597 or 07866 362507 or 07807 849216
willcoyn@hotmail.com
oad Hall, Doll St, Machynlleth, Powys, SY20 8BH

BALA

BACKPACKERS

281r

For outdoor adventures within the Snowdonia National Park, Bala Backpackers offers great value 'hostel-style' accommodation, including; 30+ comfy SINGLE BEDS in bedrooms of 3,4 or 5, 3 private TWIN ROOMS and 3 new EN SUITES. Located in a quiet, sunny, chapel square, in the bustling market town of Bala with its five-mile-long lake and white-water river for raft rides.

DETAILS

- **Open** - All year by arrangement. 8.30-20.30. Front door locked 00.30 - 6.00am.
- **Beds** - Maximum: 45: 2x3, 3x4, 3x5 + 3 twin rooms + 3 en suites.
- **Price/night** - 1 night £21, 2 nights £39, 3 nights £49, weekly £89. Twin room: £49 or en suites from £59. Double holiday-let: £220/4 nights. Sheet-bag hire £3/week.

CONTACT: Stella Shaw
Tel: 01678 521700
info@Bala-Backpackers.co.uk
www.Bala-Backpackers.co.uk
32 Tegid Street, Bala, LL23 7EL

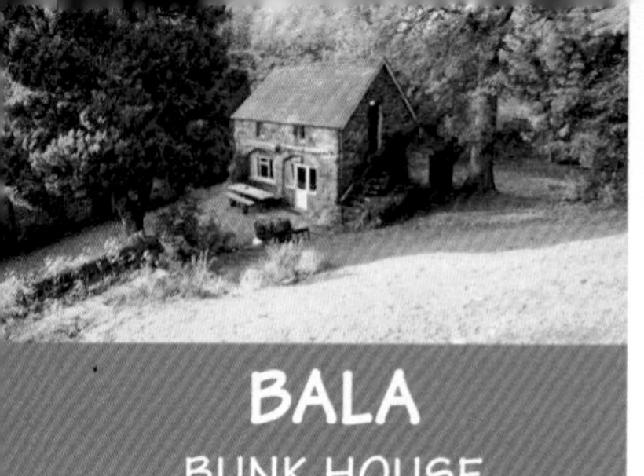

BALA

BUNK HOUSE

282l

A converted 200 year old stone building, Bala Bunk House is full of character. Set back from the road in over an acre of grounds with private parking and views of the Berwyn Hills. Ideal for all types of groups, family parties & individuals. Close to many outdoor activity centres and all amenities. It is the perfect base for walkers & water sport enthusiasts with Bala Lake & the National White Water Centre on the doorstep.

DETAILS

- **Open** - All year. No restrictions. Telephone 9am - 7pm
- **Beds** - 26: 1x2,1x4,1x6,1x8. 1x6 self-contained.
- **Price/night** - Single night from £18 pp, two+ nights from £16.50 pp.

CONTACT: Guy and Jane Williams
Tel: 01678 520738
thehappyunion@btinternet.com
www.balabunkhouse.co.uk
Tomen Y Castell, Llanfor, Bala, Gwynedd, LL23 7HD

TYDDYN BYCHAN

282r

Tyddyn Bychan is an 18th century Welsh farm surrounded by fields. It is an excellent self-catering base for mountain biking, road cycling, canoein walking, climbing, fishing and numero watersports including white water raftir The main bunkhouse sleeps 18 in tw en suite rooms. All bunks are handma to a very high standard. The smaller bunkhouse sleeps 9 in two en suite rooms. All bedding is included. Delicio homemade food is available if booked advance. There is a good parking are well away from the road.

DETAILS

- **Open** - All year. All day.
- **Beds** - 28: 1x10; 1x8; 1x6; 1x3
- **Price/night** - £17 pp including bedding

CONTACT: Lynda
Tel: 01490 420680 or 07523 995741
lynda@tyddynbychan.co.uk
www.tyddynbychan.co.uk
Cefn Brith, Cerrigydrudion, Conwy, LL2 9TS

LLANGOLLEN

HOSTEL

Llangollen Hostel, in the Dee Valley is your perfect location for walking, cycling, canoeing and white water rafting. Families will love visiting the eam railway, horse drawn canal boats and Pontcysyllte Aqueduct - a World leritage Site. The town offers a great ioice of restaurants/pubs and is home o a fringe music and arts festival and e International Eisteddfod. Llandegla, iester, Wrexham and Offa's Dyke Path e all nearby. A warm welcome awaits!

DETAILS

Open - All year. All day.
Beds - 32.
Price/night - From £19pp dorm. £20pp or 3,4,5 or 6 bed room. £45 twin/double r £50 en suite. Family of 4 £60, £10 per xtra child. Book direct for the best prices.

CONTACT: Arlo Dennis
Tel: 01978 861773
info@llangollenhostel.co.uk
www.llangollenhostel.co.uk
Berwyn Street, Llangollen, LL20 8NB

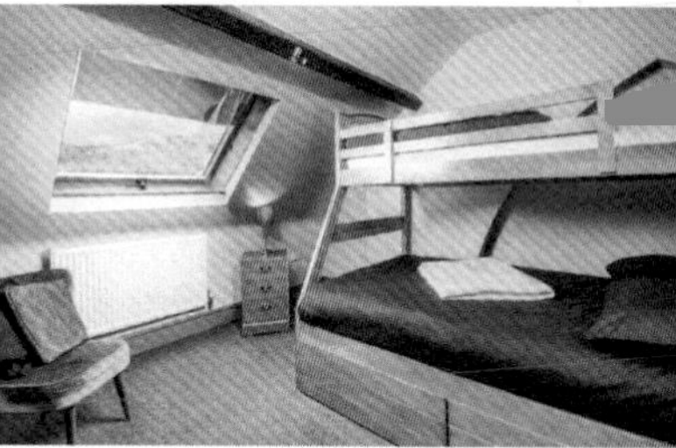

HENDRE ISAF

BASECAMP

2841

This converted Grade 2 stone farm building is the perfect base for enjoying the Snowdonia National Park. Part of the 8,000 hectare Ysbyty Estate, it offers spacious, well appointed group accommodation.

Local attractions include the Tree Top Adventure Course at Betws-y-Coed, Zip World at Penrhyn Quarry, Bethesda, Zip World and Bounce Below at Llechwedd Slate Caverns, Blaenau Ffestiniog and the Plas y Brenin National Mountain Centre.

GROUPS ONLY

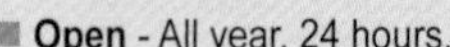

DETAILS

- **Open** - All year. 24 hours.
- **Beds** - 18: 2 x dormitories + 1x1.
- **Price/night** - 2 nights from £380.

CONTACT: National Trust Holidays
Tel: 03443 351296
bunkhouses@nationaltrust.org.uk
www.nationaltrust.org.uk/holidays
National Trust Ysbyty Estate Office,
Dinas, Betws-y-Coed, Conwy, LL24 0HF

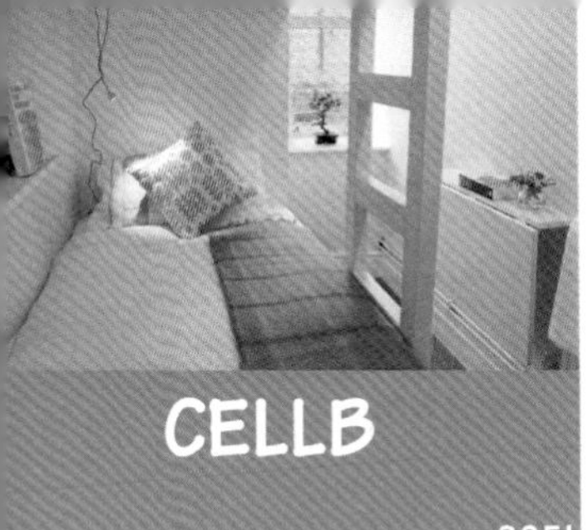

CELLB

285l

fter a long day of adventures, why not
est your weary head in an Edwardian
police house hostel? Conveniently
located in the centre of Blaenau
Ffestiniog. There is a self-catering
tchen, a drying room and secure bike
storage. Need a break from cooking?
There's a restaurant upstairs, or just
njoy a cheeky drink in the bar. What's
nore there's a cinema too! CellB is the
rfect place to recover, recuperate, and
soak up the vibrant landscape.

DETAILS

- **Open** - All year. All day
- **Beds** - 11: 1x6, 1x3, 1x2
- **Price/night** - From £20. Sole use from
:396 for the weekend (Friday-Sunday)
.1,386 for the week.

CONTACT: Reception
Tel: 01766 832001
prisoner@cellb.org
cellb.org
'ark Square, Blaenau Ffestiniog LL41
3AD

TREKS
BUNKHOUSE

285r

Treks 4* Bunkhouse perches in the mountains on the outskirts of the village of Blaenau Ffestiniog. Ideal for those who enjoy the rugged beauty of Snowdonia, it is a former golf club recently converted to provide self-catering accommodation for individuals and groups. There are many attractions nearby including, Llechwedd Slate Caverns, Bounce Below, Zip World Titan, Antur Stiniog, Ffestiniog Railway, Go Below Adventures, Coed y Brenin Mountain Bike Centre, Portmeirion Italian Village, Bala White Water Rafting and Harlech Castle.

DETAILS

- **Open** - All year. Check in 2-8pm.
- **Beds** - 16: 1x6, 1x4, 1x3, 1x2, 1x1
- **Price/night** - £20 per person

CONTACT: Dyfed
Tel: 07796 172318
treksbunkhouse@gmail.com
www.treksbunkhouse.co.uk
Y Cefn, Ffestiniog, Gwynedd, LL41 4PS

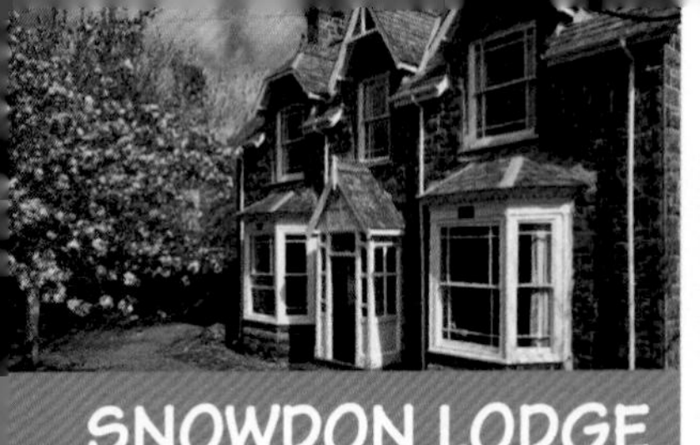

SNOWDON LODGE

GROUP HOSTEL

Stay in the birthplace of Lawrence of Arabia! Snowdon Lodge provides self-catering group accommodation. Located in the village of Tremadog, Snowdon Lodge is perfect for family reunions or groups wanting to explore Snowdonia and the Llyn Peninsula. It has 10 rooms (twins, doubles and small dormitories), an additional lecture room and a large car park leading to woodland walks.

GROUPS ONLY

DETAILS

- **Open** - January - December, All day.
- **Beds** - 35: 2 x 6 (family), 1 x 5, 1 x 6 , 3 x twin, 3 x double
- **Price/night** - Sole use £600 per night. Min of 2 nights, 3 on bank holidays. Discounts for longer stays.

CONTACT: Carl or Anja
Tel: 01766 515354
info@snowdonlodge.co.uk
www.snowdonlodge.co.uk
Lawrence House, Church Street,
Tremadog, Nr Porthmadog, Gwynedd,
Snowdonia, LL49 9PS

MAENTWROG

BUNKHOUSE

287l

Maentwrog bunkhouse is a newly converted cowshed on a working arm. It has a fully equipped kitchen, derfloor heating, TV/DVD, BBQ area, aundry facilities, power washer and ke lockup. Local activities include hill alking (Moelwyn and Cnicht 10 mins ay), white water rafting, Coed y Brenin cling centre, Blaenau Ffestiniog down cycle track, RopeWorks & canyoning. stiniog railway and beautiful beaches e within 15-20 mins' drive. The Welsh stal path passes the end of the lane.

DETAILS

Open - All year.
Beds - 4
Price/night - £18pp bring sleeping ıgs or hire bed linen @£5/person/stay

CONTACT: Mrs Eurliw M Jones
Tel: 01766 590231
emj2@hotmail.co.uk
www.bunkhousesnowdonia.com
len Rhyd Fach, Maentwrog, Blaenau Ffestiniog, Gwynedd, LL41 4HY

VAGABOND

BUNKHOUSE

287r

The Vagabond Bunkhouse/Hostel is in the village of Betws-y-Coed, in the heart of the Snowdonia National Park. This unique bunkhouse has been specifically designed for individuals, families or groups. Very well appointed, it has ready made up beds, free hot drinks, seriously hot showers, a well equipped kitchen and a bar. Catering is available. Outside there's a climbing wall, a power wash and heated dog kennels!

DETAILS

- **Open** - All year. Reception open 7.30-10am and 4.30-7.30pm.
- **Beds** - 36: 2x8, 2x6,2x4
- **Price/night** - £22.00pp. B&B (obligatory at weekends) £27.00. Heated dog kennel £3.00 per night.

CONTACT: Neil Cawthra
Tel: 01690 710850 or 07816 076546
neilcawthra@mail.com
www.thevagabond.co.uk
Craiglan, Betws-y-Coed, Conway, LL24 0AW

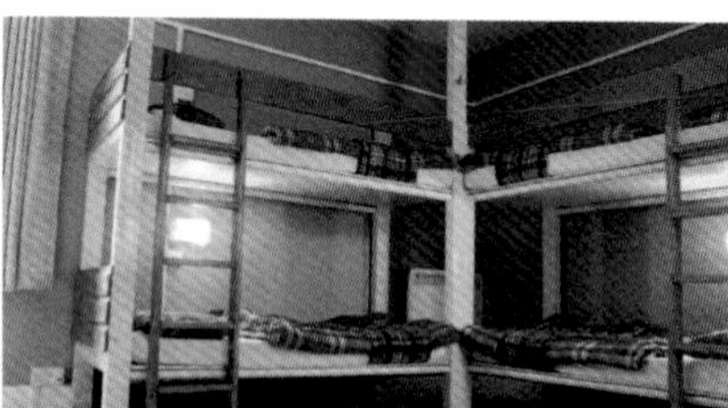

WOODLANDS

CENTRE

288l

This large Victorian property has been specially adapted to provide self-catering accommodation for groups of up to 33. The eight dormitories vary in size from one to ten beds, complete with duvets and linen. The Centre is centrally heated and has a common room, games room, large kitchen, drying room and hot showers. Located in Betws-y-Coed, Woodlands Centre is an ideal base for outdoor activities in Snowdonia.

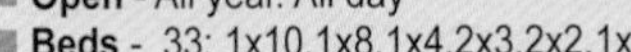

DETAILS

- **Open** - All year. All day
- **Beds** - 33: 1x10,1x8,1x4,2x3,2x2,1x1
- **Price/night** - £18.15 pp. Sole Use: youth groups £216.44. Adult only groups £471.90. Further reductions for members and uniformed organisations-see website.

CONTACT: Lisa Pratt
Tel: 01690 710863
BookingOffice@WoodlandsCentre.com
www.woodlandscentre.com
Vicarage Road, Betws-y-Coed, Conwy, LL24 0AD

SNOWDONIA

MOUNTAIN HOSTEL

288r

In the heart of the Ogwen Valley with stunning views over Snowdonia, this hostel is the perfect base for walkers climbers and cyclists with the best routes straight from the door. For adventure seekers Zip World is within walking distance and the Anglesey Beaches are a short drive. Recently refurbished, Snowdonia Mountain hostel is comfortable and well equipped.

Sorry No stag or hen parties.

DETAILS

- **Open** - All Year (sole use Nov- Mar)
- **Beds** - 26: 2x6, 2x4, 1x4 (self contained flat),1x2
- **Price/night** - From £20

CONTACT: Neil Martinson
Tel: 01248 600416
info@snowdoniamountainhostel.com
www.snowdoniamountainhostel.com
Snowdonia Mountain Hostel, Tai Newyddion, Nant Ffrancon, Bangor LL57 3DQ

LLEDR HOUSE

Lledr House nestles in Snowdonia ational Park. Once YHA and now newly efurbished, guests delight in the luxury mattresses, modern bathrooms, well uipped kitchen and extended car park. ndividuals, groups and families enjoy ne clean, comfortable accommodation. Betws-y-Coed, Llyn Elsi and Zip World high rope course close by.

DETAILS

- **Open** - Open March to November incl. Check in from 5pm till 10.30pm.
- **Beds** - 37: House 32: 1x9, 2x4,1x6, 2x2, 2x2(dbl), 2x1. Cabin 5: 1x5
- **Price/night** - From £19pp. Single rooms £22.50. Sole Use: £550 (min 3 nights on BH). Cabin £120 (min 2 nights).

CONTACT: Brian or Melanie Quilter
Tel: 01690 750202 or 07915 397705 or 07915 397660
Lledrhouse@aol.com
lledrhouse.co.uk
ont-y-Pant, Dolwyddelan, North Wales, LL25 0DQ

CONWY VALLEY

BACKPACKERS BARN

Conwy Valley Backpackers is situated on a peaceful organic farm in the heart of the beautiful Conwy Valley, with excellent access to Snowdonia. Centrally heated with a fully equipped self-catering kitchen, log fires and hot showers. Secure bike/canoe storage. Grazing for horses and tourist information are available. Local activities range from fishing and hiking to white water rafting and mountain biking. Surf Snowdonia is within walking distance and Zip World is a short drive away.

DETAILS

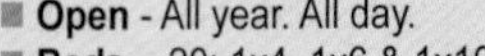

- **Open** - All year. All day.
- **Beds** - 20: 1x4, 1x6 & 1x10
- **Price/night** - From £20pp. Sole use from £275. £3pp bed linen hire.

CONTACT: Claudia
Tel: 01492 660504 or 07956 851425
info@conwyvalleybarn.com
www.conwyvalleybarn.com
Pyllau Gloewon Farm, Tal-y-Bont,
Conwy, Gwynedd, LL32 8YX

LLANDUDNO

HOSTEL

Llandudno Hostel is a Victorian 4* boutique, award-winning hostel where individuals, families & groups (including schools) are welcome all year. Set in the heart of the Victorian seaside town of Llandudno, it's your perfect base for shopping & exploring many local attractions, including blue flag beaches, dry slope skiing, Zip World, Surf Snowdonia, bronze age copper mine, traditional pier, museums & fishing trips.

DETAILS

- **Open** - All year (telephone in winter prior to arrival). All day.
- **Beds** - 46: 2x8,2x6,4x2,1x4,1xfamily(6)
- **Price/night** - From £23 per person, £53 per private twin room, £60 per private twin en suite. Group and family rates on request. Special offers autumn/winter

CONTACT: James or Melissa
Tel: 01492 877430
info@llandudnohostel.co.uk
www.llandudnohostel.co.uk
4 Charlton Street, Llandudno, LL30 2AA

PLATTS FARM

BUNKHOUSE

Platt's Farm Campsite and 3* Bunkhouse is situated in a range of Victorian farm buildings, in the charming village of Llanfairfechan. Close to the A55, the Bunkhouse lies at the start/end of the 14 Welsh 3000 Peaks walks in the Snowdonia National Park, within a 10 min walk of the Wales Coastal Path and on the NCN 5 Cycle Route. Shops, pubs and cafés are within 5 mins' walk. Just 15 mins from Zipworld, Bethesda & 20 mins from Surf Snowdonia.

DETAILS

- **Open** - All year. Check out before 11am, check in after 2pm.
- **Beds** - 10
- **Price/night** - £15.50 pp. Sole use £155 per night.

CONTACT: Sam Davies
Tel: 01248 680105
sam@plattsfarm.com
www.plattsfarm.com
Platts Farm Bunkhouse, Aber Road, Llanfairfechan, Conwy, LL33 0HL

CABAN CYSGU

BUNKHOUSE

Caban Cysgu, run by the community of Gerlan, offers purpose-built accommodation at the foot of the Carneddau. Perfect for walking in Snowdonia, it's a great base for the 'Fourteen 3000ft Peaks' long-distance hallenge & The Slate Trail. Just 5 mins rom Zip World; the longest and fastest ip line in Europe. There are also plenty of mountain bike trails on the doorstep while road cyclists have the Sustrans oute 'Lôn Las Ogwen' just a mile away. For climbers, Idwal is close by, while Afon Ogwen is popular with canoeists.

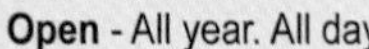

DETAILS

- **Open** - All year. All day.
- **Beds** - 16 : 1x5, 1x2, 1x1, 1x8
- **Price/night** - From £14 - £16

CONTACT: Dewi Emyln, Manager
Tel: 01248 605573 or 07464676753
dewi@cabancysgu-gerlan.co.uk
www.cabancysgu-gerlan.co.uk
Ffordd Gerlan, Gerlan, Bethesda, Bangor, LL57 3ST

LODGE DINORWIG

294

On the edge of Snowdonia National Park, Lodge Dinorwig, a former school, has a 14 bed bunkroom. Breakfast is included and evening meals can be booked but there is no self-catering. Perfectly located for all the high adrenaline activities Snowdonia has to offer and with easy access to attractions such as Bounce Below as well as Snowdon and Llanberis. The on-site café will provide tea and cake after a day in the mountains.

DETAILS

- **Open** - All year. Check in from 3pm, check out by 11am.
- **Beds** - 14: 1x14
- **Price/night** - From £25-£29. Sole use from £300-£350 including breakfast

CONTACT: Simon and Sonni
Tel: 01286 871632
info@lodge-dinorwig.co.uk
www.lodge-dinorwig.co.uk/
Dinorwig, Caernarfon, Gwynedd, LL55 3EY

OLD SCHOOL

LODGE

295

In the small mountain village of Deiniolen, in the heart of Snowdonia, not far from Llanberis, The Old School Lodge is the perfect base for groups of all kinds wishing to explore the rugged splendour of North Wales. Perfect for groups of walkers or climbers, the Lodge provides high quality accommodation for those looking for a warm comfortable base to return to after a day on the Welsh Mountains. Facilities include a well equipped self-catering kitchen, lounge, games room & resources room.

  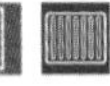      

DETAILS

- **Open** - All year. All day.
- **Beds** - 38: 1x6,7x4,2x2
- **Price/night** - £19.00pp, Scouts and Guides: £14.25. Minimum stay 2 nights, minimum charge based on 12 people.

CONTACT: Booking Secretary
Tel: 01516 324943
activities@oldschoollodge.org.uk
www.oldschoollodge.org.uk
Deiniolen, Caernarfon LL55 3HH

ARETE

OUTDOOR CENTRE

The Arete Outdoor Centre, in Snowdonia National Park, offers excellent access to the stunning coastline, mountains & lakes of North Wales and Anglesey. With comfortable, affordable, bunkhouse accommodation and large kitchens this is a great base for groups of friends or family. The team can advise on how best to spend your stay and a range of exciting outdoor activities are available through the centre's well qualified staff.

       GROUPS ONLY

DETAILS

- **Open** - All year. All day.
- **Beds** - 100+ in 22 rooms split into three blocks of 20, 58 and 30+
- **Price/night** - Catered from £30pp, self-catering from £15 pp. Sole use deals.

CONTACT: Gareth Davies
Tel: 01286 672136
info@aretecentre.co.uk
www.aretecentre.co.uk
Arete Outdoor Education Centre,
Llanrug, Caernarfon, Gwynedd, LL55 4AP

PENTRE BACH

BUNKHOUSE

Situated between Waunfawr and Betws Garmon, Pentre Bach Bunkhouse provides dog friendly accommodation, outdoor activities and a campsite. The ground floor of the bunkhouse has a dining/cooking area while upstairs there are alpine sleeping platforms with mattresses for 16. Showers, toilets and washing/drying facilities, shared with the campsite, are just across the yard.

DETAILS

- **Open** - All year. All day. Enquires 9am - 10pm. Arrive from 4pm, leave by 11am.
- **Beds** - 16: 1x16.
- **Price/night** - £13 per person (inc gas, electric & showers). Sole use bookings negotiable according to group size.

CONTACT: Karen Neil
Tel: 01286 650643 (5-10pm) or 07798 733939 (9-5pm)
info@bachventures.co.uk
www.pentrebachbunkhouse.co.uk
Pentre Bach, Waunfawr, Caernarfon, Gwynedd, LL54 7AJ

RHYD DDU

OUTDOOR CENTRE

The Rhyd Ddu Bunkhouse provides group accommodation at the foot of Snowdon and the Nantlle Ridge. Sleeping 31 in 6 bedrooms, it has a fully equipped kitchen and a large communal dining room with a big screen - great for movie nights! Glorious views, central heating, fast WiFi, parking, secure bike storage, drying room and a large garden. Bring your own sleeping bag, pillow case and towel. A pub, café, and steam train station are all within 2 minutes' walk.

GROUPS ONLY

DETAILS

- **Open** - All year. All day. Check in from 4pm, check out by 11am.
- **Beds** - 31: 1x12, 1x5, 3x4, 1x2
- **Price/night** - Sole use from £250 per night. Minimum stay of 2 nights.

CONTACT: Robat
Tel: 01286 882688
stay@canolfan-rhyd-ddu.cymru
www.snowdonia-bunkhouse.wales
Rhyd Ddu Outdoor Centre, Rhyd Ddu, Snowdonia, Wales LL54 6TL

CWM PENNANT

TRAINING CENTRE & HOSTEL

Cwm Pennant Hostel is a welcoming 56 bed hostel offering relaxed accommodation for individuals, families and groups. Breakfast, dinner & packed lunches available if required. Set within stunning grounds in the Snowdonia National Park, it has fantastic views of the Cwm Pennant valley & Moel Hebog.

DETAILS

- **Open** - All year (Nov-Feb advance booking of large groups only). Reception 9am-12noon, 3.30-8pm.
- **Beds** - 56: 4x4, 1x6, 1x8, 1x10, 1x16.
- **Price/night** - £20 (adult), £17 (under 12's), under 2's free. From £1,500 for two nights sole use. Breakfast from £4.50. Packed lunches £6.50 and evening meals £7.50 are available on request.

CONTACT:
Tel: 01766 530888
bookings@cwmpennanthostel.com
www.cwmpennanthostel.com
Golan, Garndolbenmaen, Gwynedd,
LL51 9AQ

TOTTERS

300l

Totters sits in the heart of the historic castle town of Caernarfon just 30m from the Menai Straits. Close to many pubs and restaurants but with good public transport to the Snowdonia National Park. The hostel is a 200 year old, five floored town house with five bedrooms sleeping either 4 or 6 and a huge double/ family en suite. Opposite there is a self-catering town house sleeping 6.

DETAILS

- **Open** - All year. All day. Check in by 10 pm.
- **Beds** - 28: 3x6, 2x4, 1x2 (en suite), 1x2 (twin)
- **Price/night** - £19.50pp in a dorm. £55 for a double/twin en suite. £47.50 for a twin. Discounts for groups.

CONTACT: Bob/Henryette
Tel: 01286 672963 Mob: 07979 830470
totters.hostel@googlemail.com
www.totters.co.uk
Plas Porth Yr Aur, 2 High Street,
Caernarfon, Gwynedd, LL55 1RN

PARC ELERNION

CAMPING BARN

300r

Set within SSSI woodland, close to Trefor with its lovely sandy beach & harbour and with easy access to the Wales Coast Path, this little camping barn sleeps 2 on Westlake camp beds. BYO sleeping bags & towels. There is a well equipped kitchenette. The washing & toilet facilites are shared with the caravan site. A holiday cottage & tent pitches are also available. Perfect for the Welsh coast, castles & Snowdonia.

DETAILS

- **Open** - Arrive after 3pm, depart before 11am
- **Beds** - Camping barn: 2. Cottage: 4. + Camping
- **Price/night** - From £15, minimum booking 2 nights Friday/Saturday.

CONTACT: Jeff Webster
Tel: 01286 660857 or 07811 300630
jeff@parc-elernion.co.uk
www.parc-elernion.co.uk
Clynnog Rd, Trefor, Caernarfon,
Gwynedd, LL54 5AA

ABERSOCH

SGUBOR UNNOS

Bunkhouse accommodation on a family farm in the village of Llangian. Just one mile from Abersoch which is famed for watersports, the bunkhouse is an ideal base for walking the Llyn Coast Path, surfing, cycling, golf, fishing and sailing. Spinning and knitting courses using the farm's own wool are available. The three modern bunkrooms are ideal for individuals or groups with a fully equipped kitchen/lounge, disabled facilities, secure storage and parking.

DETAILS

- **Open** - All year. All day.
- **Beds** - 14: 2x4, 1x6
- **Price/night** - £20 (adult), £10 (under 10 years), including a light breakfast and bed linen. Discount for 3+ nights.

CONTACT: Phil or Meinir
Tel: 01758 713527
enquiries@tanrallt.com
www.tanrallt.com
Fferm Tanrallt Farm, Llangian, Abersoch, Gwynedd, LL53 7LN

ABERDARON

FARM BUNKHOUSE 302l

Aberdaron Farm Bunkhouse is two miles from Aberdaron village, it has underfloor heating and a large comfortable social room. Bring sleeping bags or hire duvet sets for £3. Whistling Sands is close by and Bardsey Island lies across The Sound off the tip of the Llyn Peninsula. Pets allowed (with notice). Holiday cottages/camping also available.

DETAILS

- **Open** - All year. All day (arrive after 4pm and leave by 11am).
- **Beds** - 15: 1x8, 1x4 (en suite), 1x3 (en suite)
- **Price/night** - £16pp, £18 pp (en suite) inc breakfast. Enquire for sole use of room/bunkhouse/family room prices. Minimum of 3 days on bank holidays.

CONTACT: Gillian Jones
Tel: 01758 760345 or 07794 147195
enquiries@aberdaronfarmholidays.co.uk
www.aberdaronfarmholidays.co.uk
Y Gweithdy, Anelog, Aberdaron, Pwllheli, LL53 8BT

ANGLESEY

302r OUTDOOR CENTRE

Anglesey Outdoors is an ideal base for groups, individuals or families. It is just a mile from Porthdafarch Beach & the coastal path and only 2km from Sustrans Cycle Route 8. It has four self contained areas each with their own self-catering & bathroom facilities. These can be hired individually or together. Full catering an option and there's an on-site bar/bistro. Yurts and cabans also available.

  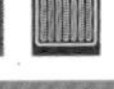    

DETAILS

- **Open** - All year. 24 hour access.
- **Beds** - 68: Main Centre 33: 1x7,4x5,1x4,1x2. Maris Annexe 10: 5x2. Ty Pen Annexe 8: 1x4,2x2. Gogarth Dorms 16: 1x7,1x7,1x2.
- **Price/night** - £12pp (Gogarth Dorms) to £24pp ensuite twin. Ask about sole use.

CONTACT: Penny Hurndall
Tel: 01407 769351
penny@angleseyoutdoors.com
www.angleseyoutdoors.com
Porthdafarch Road, Holyhead, Anglesey LL65 2LP

OUTDOOR
ALTERNATIVE

This purpose built 4* centre is quietly tucked away in Rhoscolyn, an Area of Outstanding Natural Beauty on the Anglesey Coast. Just 5 mins' walk to the sandy beach at Borthwen and a stone's throw from the Anglesey Coastal Path. Perfect for friends & families, outdoor groups, schools and universities. Your Ideal base for kayaking, climbing, sailing, walking, bird watching or beach holidays. Careful energy use is encouraged, with composting and recycling. Nearby Holyhead has ferry links to Ireland.

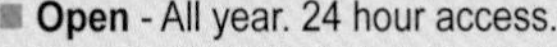

DETAILS

- **Open** - All year. 24 hour access.
- **Beds** - 20: 2x2, 1x4, 2x6. 20: 1x3, 3x4, 1x5.
- **Price/night** - £22pp. £385 for sole use.

CONTACT: Jacqui Short
Tel: 01407 860469
enquiries@outdooralternative.co.uk
www.outdooralternative.co.uk
Cerrig-yr-Adar, Rhoscolyn, Holyhead, Anglesey, LL65 2NQ

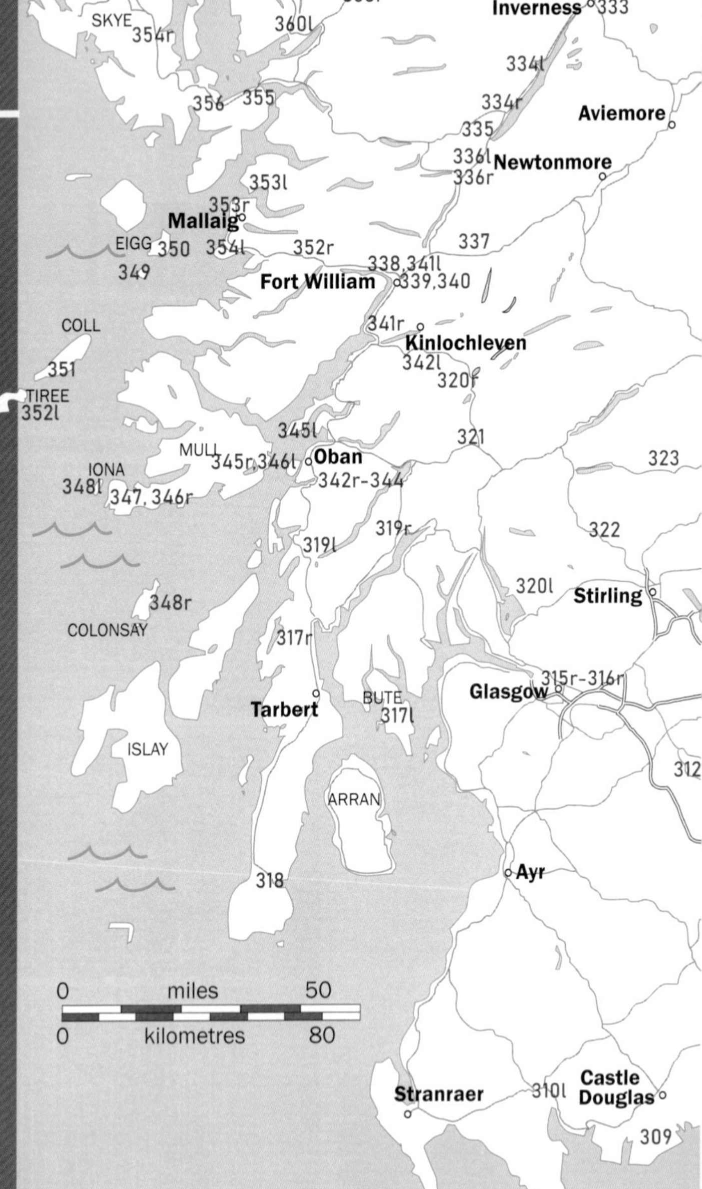
360r
Inverness
333
SKYE
354r
360l
334l
356
355
334r
Aviemore
335
336l
Newtonmore
336r
353l
353r
Mallaig
EIGG
350
354l
352r
337
349
338,341l
Fort William
339,340
COLL
341r
Kinlochleven
351
342l
320f
TIREE
352l
345l
321
MULL
345r,346l
Oban
323
IONA
348l
342r-344
347, 346r
319r
322
319l
320l
Stirling
348r
COLONSAY
317r
315r-316r
Glasgow
Tarbert
BUTE
317l
ISLAY
312
ARRAN
Ayr
318
0
miles
50
0
kilometres
80
Castle
Douglas
Stranraer
310l
309

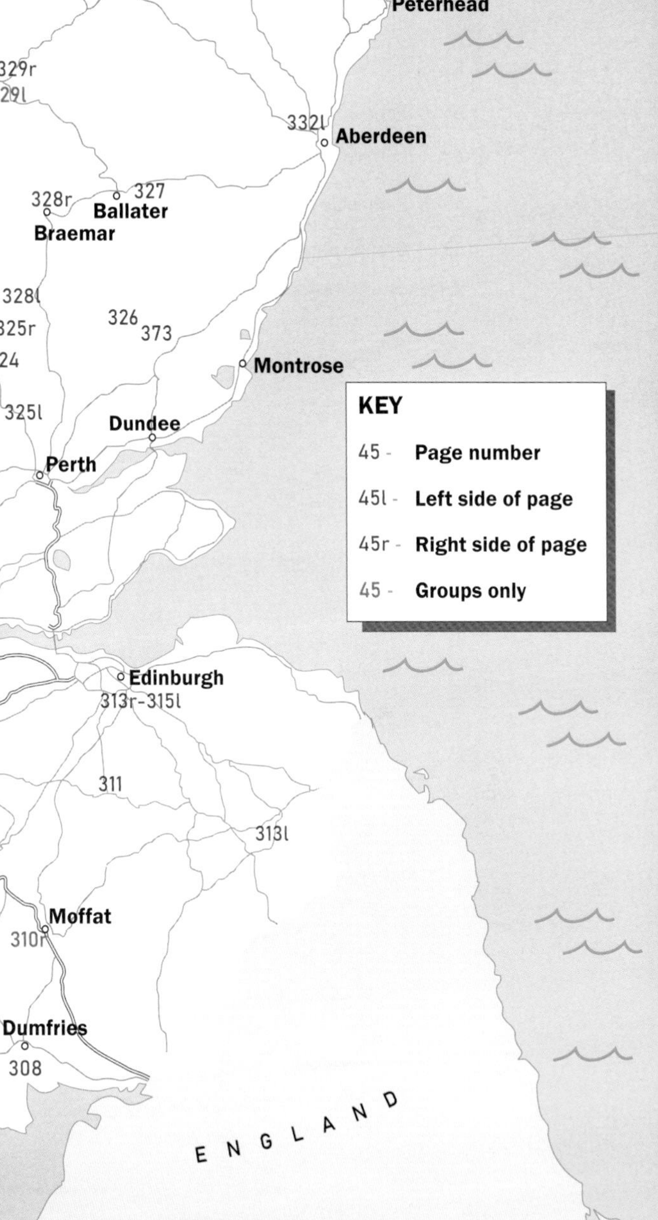

KEY

45 - Page number

45l - Left side of page

45r - Right side of page

45 - Groups only

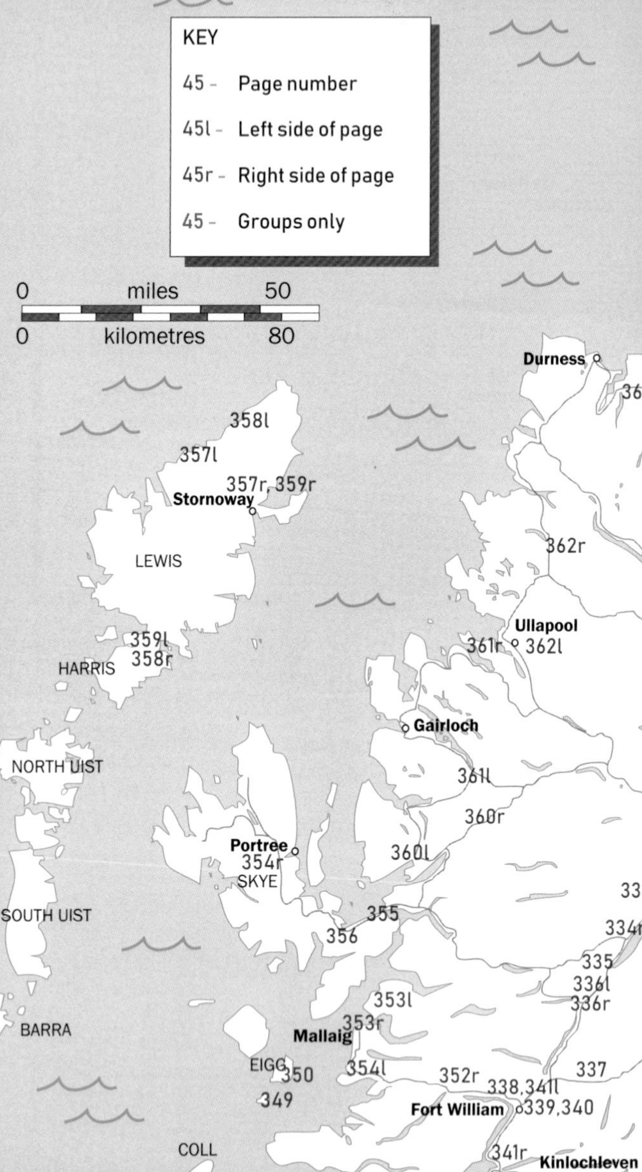
KEY
45 – Page number
45l – Left side of page
45r – Right side of page
45 – Groups only
0 miles 50
0 kilometres 80
Durness
366
358l
357l
357r, 359r
Stornoway
LEWIS
362r
Ullapool
361r
362l
359l
358r
HARRIS
Gairloch
NORTH UIST
361l
360r
Portree
354r
SKYE
360l
SOUTH UIST
355
356
334r
335
336l
336r
353l
353r
BARRA
Mallaig
EIGG
350
354l
352r
337
338,341l
349
Fort William
339,340
COLL
341r
Kinlochleven
351
342l
320r

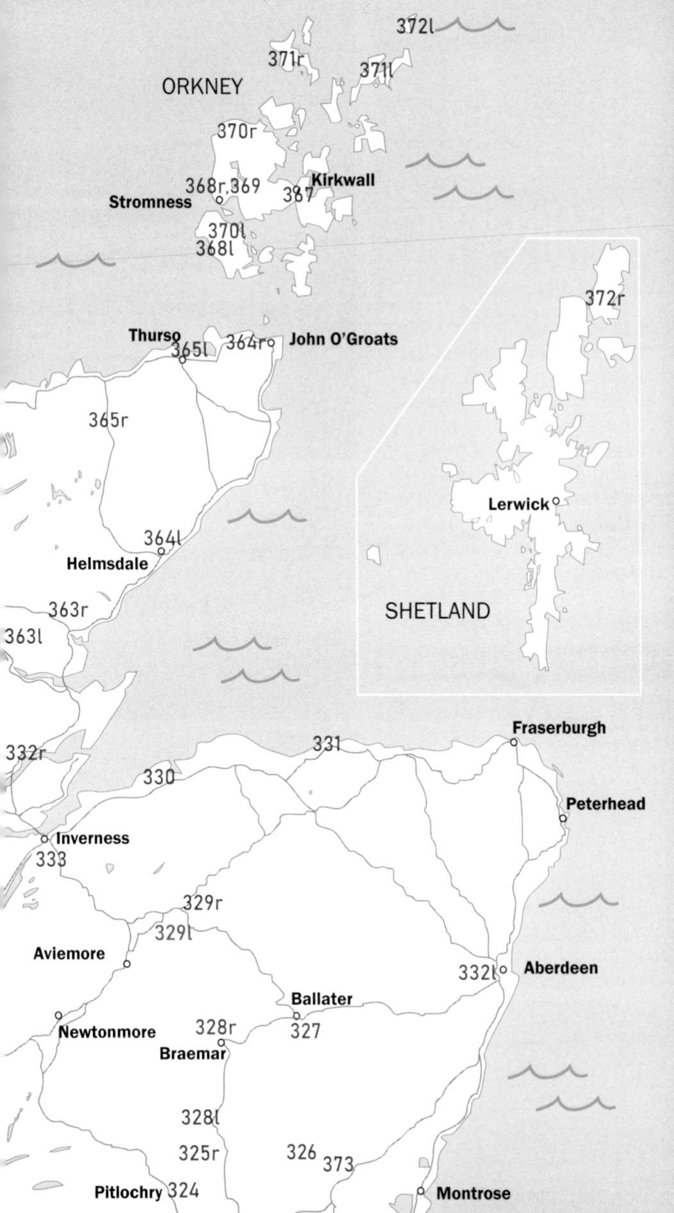

372l
371r
371l
ORKNEY
370r
Kirkwall
368r,369
367
Stromness
370l
368l
372r
Thurso
365l
364r
John O'Groats
365r
Lerwick
364l
Helmsdale
SHETLAND
363r
363l
Fraserburgh
332r
331
330
Peterhead
Inverness
333
329r
329l
Aviemore
332l
Aberdeen
Ballater
Newtonmore
328r
327
Braemar
328l
325r
326
373
Pitlochry
324
Montrose

MARTHROWN

OF MABIE

Marthrown is set in the heart of Mabie Forest, 6 miles south of Dumfries. It has a sauna, a wood burning spring water hot tub, a large BBQ, garden areas, a challenge course and plenty of room for groups. There are a variety of mountain bike routes and the 7Stanes mountain bike trails are nearby. Catered meals available for groups. As well as the bunkhouse, there are also Mongolian yurts, an American style tipi and the jewel in the crown is the Iron Age Roundhouse for parties or weddings.

DETAILS

- **Open** - All year. 24 hours - late arrival by arrangement.
- **Beds** - 26: 1x8,1x7,1x6,1x5 + Roundhouse, 2 Yurts, Tipi and camping.
- **Price/night** - £16 to £19.50.

CONTACT: Mike or Pam Hazlehurst
Tel: 01387 247900
pamhazlehurst@hotmail.com
www.marthrownofmabie.co.uk
Mabie Forest, Dumfries, DG2 8HB

CASTLE CREAVIE

HAY BARN HOSTEL

This comfortable family friendly hostel sleeps 6. It is set on a working farm and is surrounded by spectacular Galloway countryside. The hugely spacious open plan design has oak floors, comfy beds, dining area, wood burning stove, separate kitchen with basic cooking facilities, washroom & W.C. There are also: hot showers, washing/drying facilities, bike wash and store. Breakfast and farm produce available. The ideal base for walkers and cyclists with 7Stanes and NCN Route 7 close by.

DETAILS

- **Open** - All year. All day.
- **Beds** - 6: 1x4, 1x2
- **Price/night** - £20pp bed linen provided & beds made up. £80 for sole use. Electricity included.

CONTACT: Charlie and Elaine Wannop
Tel: 01557 500238
elaine@castlecreavie.co.uk
www.castlecreavie.co.uk
Castle Creavie, Kirkcudbright, DG6 4QE

BARHOLM ACCOMMODATION

310l

Barholm Enterprise Centre houses a variety of businesses including an Arts and Crafts Co-operative and Barholm Accommodation which has en suite shared and private rooms.

Perfect for cyclists, walkers, fishermen or those who generally enjoy the outdoors. Facilities include a communal kitchenette (fridge/freezer, kettle, toaster and microwave), sitting room with TV, on-site cycle hire and bike repair facilities & electric car charging.

DETAILS

- **Open** - All year. All day
- **Beds** - 25: 1x6, 1x5, 1x4, 1x1, 2x1+ camp bed, 1x2+ camp bed
- **Price/night** - From £16.50

CONTACT: Jenny Adams
Tel: 01671 820810
jenny.barholm@gmail.com
barholm-centre.co.uk
St Johns Street, Creetown, Dumfries and Galloway, DG8 7JE

WELL ROAD CENTRE

310r

The Well Road Centre sits in its own grounds in the charming town of Moffat. It is ideal for all types of groups conferences, residential workshops, sports, social events and outdoor activity clubs. The Centre has two spacious meeting rooms, a large brigh self-catering kitchen, dining room fully equipped for 65, games hall for indoo activities and table tennis room. Bring your own sleeping bags or linens for single duvets. Ample parking & storage

DETAILS

- **Open** - All year. All day.
- **Beds** - 70: in 13 rooms (2 en suite).
- **Price/night** - From £830 for two nights mid week for up to 30 people. £25 pp for 31+ . From £955 for two nights weekend for up to 35 people. £25pp for 31+.

CONTACT: Ben Larmour
Tel: 01683 221040
Ben8363@aol.com
www.wellroadcentre.com
Well Road Centre, Moffat, DG10 9BT

CLEIKUM MILL

LODGE

Cleikum Mill Lodge is a modernised character building in the heart of the Tweed Valley. The Mill sleeps 12, 8 in the Lower Mill and 4 in the Upper Mill. Book individual rooms, a floor or the whole Mill. Innerleithen, a 7Stanes trail centre, is on the NCR1 and Southern Upland Way. It has a shop, pubs and cafés.

DETAILS

- **Open** - All year. All day. Check in after 4pm, check out before 10am.
- **Beds** - 12: Lower Mill: 1x2, 2x3. Upper Mill: 2x2
- **Price/night** - £35 single, £56 twin, £71 triple room. Apartment for four £112. Discounts for sole use bookings for 3 nights or more. The longer you stay the higher the discount.

CONTACT: Graham
Tel: 07790 592747
hello@cleikum-mill-lodge.co.uk
www.cleikum-mill-lodge.co.uk
7 Cleikum Mill, High St, Innerleithen, Scottish Borders EH44 6QT

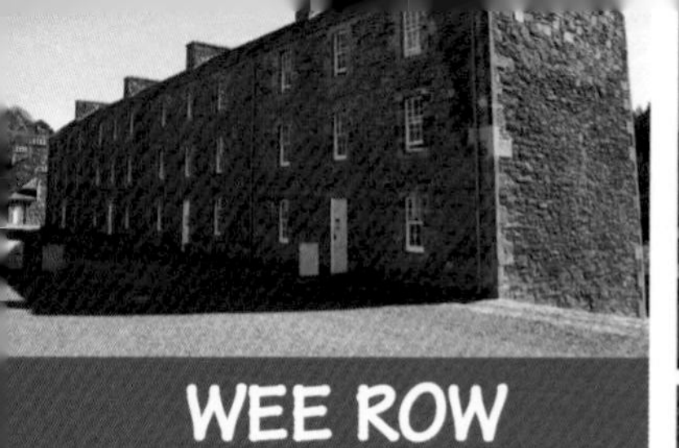

WEE ROW

HOSTEL

Located in the heart of New Lanark World Heritage Site and just one hour's drive from either Glasgow or Edinburgh, Wee Row is the perfect base for your holiday. The award winning New Lanark Visitor Centre is on the doorstep; step back in time and rediscover life in this working mill village. The hostel sleeps 62 in 18 private rooms (all en suite) and has terrific views over the River Clyde and surrounding countryside. Facilities include bike storage, laundry and drying room. Breakfasts and evening meals are available at the New Lanark Mill Hotel.

DETAILS

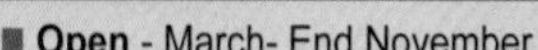

- **Open** - March- End November
- **Beds** - 62: 6x2, 1x3, 3x3, 8x4 +Studio
- **Price/night** - From £19.50 per person

CONTACT: Reception
Tel: 01555 666710
weerowhostel@newlanark.org
www.newlanarkhostel.co.uk
Wee Row Hostel, Wee Row, New Lanark, Lanark, Lanarkshire, ML11 9DJ

KIRK YETHOLM

FRIENDS OF NATURE

313l

Kirk Yetholm Friends of Nature House is perfectly located at the start/end of the Pennine Way. It is also close to St. Cuthbert's Way, the Borderloop Cycle Route and Sustrans Route 84. It's a great base too for local day hikes, ideal for individuals, families and small groups. Recently upgraded, the house offers a comfortable, friendly and peaceful retreat. Evening meals and breakfast are available in the adjacent hotel.

DETAILS

- **Open** - All year (Nov-Feb groups only). Reception 5pm-11pm & 8am-10am.
- **Beds** - 22: 1x7, 1x5, 1x4, 2x2 (twin), 1x2 (bunk).
- **Price/night** - From £18, under 18's from £15. Discounts for IFN / SYHA / HI.

CONTACT: The Manager
Tel: 01573 420639
kirkyetholm@thefriendsofnature.org.uk
www.thefriendsofnature.org.uk
Friends of Nature House,Waukford,Kirk Yetholm,Kelso,Roxburghshire,TD5 8PG

EURO HOSTEL

EDINBURGH HALLS

313r

Euro Hostel Edinburgh Halls is the perfect place to base your summer visit to Edinburgh. Available from 4th June to 31st August you can have an apartment to yourself or share with others for a great budget stay. Located in the heart of the Old Town close to the Royal Mile, it's perfect for backpackers, shoppers, groups or those visiting the famous Edinburgh Festival. Single or twin private bedrooms are available or you can rent a whole apartment for up to 12.

DETAILS

- **Open** - 4th June - 31st August. Check-in from 3pm and check out by 11am
- **Beds** - 338
- **Price/night** - From £20

CONTACT: Rosanna Burns or Debbie-Jo McIntyre
Tel: 08454 900461
edinburgh@eurohostels.co.uk
www.eurohostels.co.uk/edinburgh/
Kincaids Court, Guthrie Street, Edinburgh, EH1 1JT

ROYAL MILE
BACKPACKERS

314l

Royal Mile Backpackers is a small and lively hostel with its own special character! Perfectly located on the Royal Mile, the most famous street in Edinburgh, Royal Mile Backpackers is the ideal place to stay for the independent traveller.

The comfortable beds and cosy common areas will make you feel at home and the friendly staff are always on hand to help you make the most of your time in Edinburgh.

DETAILS

- **Open** - All year. All day. Reception 6.30 am - 3 am (24 hrs during August).
- **Beds** - 46
- **Price/night** - From £11 per person. ID required for check in.

CONTACT: Receptionist
Tel: 0131 557 6120
royalmile@scotlandstophostels.com
www.royalmilebackpackers.com
105 High Street, Edinburgh, EH1 1SG

CASTLE ROCK
HOSTEL

314r

In a wonderful location, facing south wi a sunny aspect and panoramic views over the city, Castle Rock Hostel is jus steps away from the city centre with th historic Royal Mile, the busy pubs anc late-late nightlife of the Grassmarket ar Cowgate. Then, of course, there is the famous Edinburgh Castle. Most of the rooms have no traffic noise and there a loads of great facilities, 24-hour receptic and no curfew. With its beautiful and dramatic skyline, Edinburgh is truly on of the world's great cities.

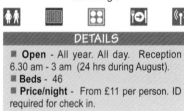

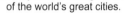

DETAILS

- **Open** - All year. Reception 24 hours.
- **Beds** - 302
- **Price/night** - From £14 per person. ID required for check in.

CONTACT: Receptionist
Tel: 0131 225 9666
castlerock@scotlandstophostels.com
www.castlerockedinburgh.com
15 Johnston Terrace, Edinburgh, EH1 2PW

HIGH STREET

HOSTEL

315l

The High Street Hostel has become a hugely popular destination for world travellers since opening in 1985 and is one of Europe's best regarded and nost atmospheric hostels. Located just ff the historic Royal Mile in a 470 year old building, it is your perfect base for exploring all the city's many attractions and of course its wonderful nightlife.

Providing excellence in location, ambience and facilities, the hostel is ghly recommended by more than ten of e world's top backpacker travel guides. Come along and see for yourself!

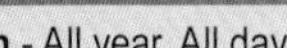

DETAILS

- **Open** - All year. All day.
- **Beds** - 156.
- **Price/night** - From £14 per person. ID required for check in.

CONTACT: Reception
Tel: 0131 557 3984
highstreet@scotlandstophostels.com
www.highstreethostel.com
8 Blackfriars St., Edinburgh, EH1 1NE

EURO HOSTEL

GLASGOW

315r

Your smarter alternative to a hotel in the city, just five mins' walk from Central Station, with friendly staff, a lively bar and clean comfortable private & shared en suite rooms. Perfect for clubbing, shopping and discovering the city's cultural heritage and live music scene. Or for visiting family, coast to coast cycle rides/city cultural walks, sporting events, or shopping & good nights out. The VIP suites are ideal for all types of groups.

DETAILS

- **Open** - All year. Late and early check outs available.
- **Beds** - 444 rooms: single, doubles, 2, 4, 8 and 14 person all en suite
- **Price/night** - Beds from £10. Rooms from £20. VIP suites from £14pp. Ask about group discounts and special offers.

CONTACT: Reception
Tel: 0141 222 2828
glasgow@eurohostels.co.uk
www.eurohostels.co.uk/glasgow
318 Clyde Street, Glasgow, G1 4NR

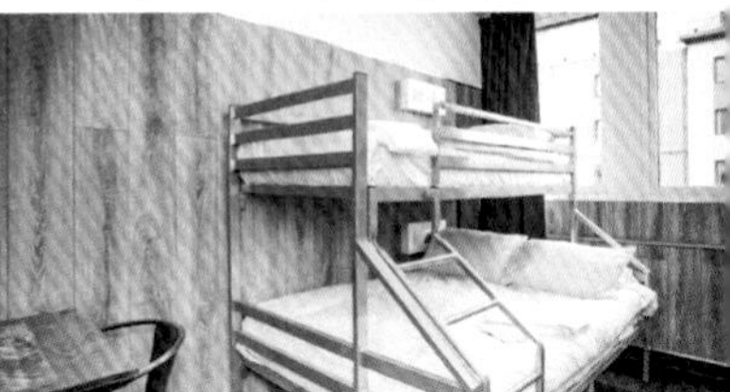

BLYTHSWOOD
HOUSE

316l

In the heart of Glasgow city centre. Blythswood House is the perfect base from which to explore everything the city has to offer. The single rooms are grouped in flats of 2,6,7 or 8 so perfect for individuals or groups wanting to visit Glasgow in the summer. All rooms are en suite and each flat has self-catering facilities. Easily accessible from the city's train and bus stations Blythswood House welcomes walkers and cyclists.

DETAILS

- **Open** - June - Early September
- **Beds** - 170 single rooms within flats 2, 6, 7, or 8 some doubles available.
- **Price/night** - Individual £38, £230pp per week, Student discounts available. 15% reduction for 6+ people

CONTACT: Rebecca Forsyth
Tel: 0141 566 1121
accommodation@gsa.ac.uk
www.gsa.ac.uk/visit-gsa
200 West Regent Street, Glasgow, G2 4DQ

TARTAN
LODGE

316r

On Alexandra Parade, near Denistoun and 20 minutes' walk from Glasgow city centre, Tartan Lodge, is set within a former 19th century church and Masonic Lodge. You will find affordable accommodation for budget and business travellers with a selection of double and twin en suite bedrooms and shared dormitories with family facilities. Towels can be hired.

DETAILS

- **Open** - All year. Check in from 2pm. Check out by 11am
- **Beds** - 93: 5 x double, 2 x twin, 1 x triple. Dorms: 2x3, 8x4, 1x4 female, 2x6, 1x6 female, 2x8
- **Price/night** - Dorms from £10pp. Private rooms from £50 per room

CONTACT: Reception
Tel: 0141 554 5970
info@tartanlodge.co.uk
www.tartanlodge.co.uk
235 Alexandra Parade, Glasgow, G31 3AW

BUTE

BACKPACKERS

317l

3ute Backpackers is a well established 4* hostel, located on the seafront of ·othesay, Isle of Bute. It accommodates ıp to 45 people in 14 bedrooms (single/ ·win/double/family, some en suite). The nain house has a sea front sun lounge with TV, free WiFi, a fully equipped self-catering kitchen & a laundry room. ˈhere are regular live music sessions & ·pen mic nights. Plenty of free on street parking and a secure bike shed.

DETAILS

- **Open** - All year. 24hr access, no curfew. Reception 9am - 10pm
- **Beds** - 45 beds: 14 bedrooms; 4 family rooms, 4 twin rooms, 6 bunk rooms.
- **Price/night** - £20pp dorm, £22.50pp twin, £25pp single.

CONTACT: Reception
Tel: 01700 501876
butebackpackers@hotmail.com
www.butebackpackers.co.uk
The Pier View, 36 Argyle Street,
Rothesay, Isle of Bute, PA20 0AX

ARGYLL

BACKPACKERS

317r

If you enjoy spectacular views and watching wildlife in modern comfortable self-catering accommodation then you'll love Argyll Backbackers! Located on the banks of Loch Fyne, just minutes from Cycle Route 78 in the hamlet of Inverneil and perfect for island hopping to/from Arran and Islay. You'll be able to stock up on supplies from Tarbert or Ardrishaig / Lochgilphead, depending on your route.

DETAILS

- **Open** - 1st April until 31 October. 1st November - 31 March sole use only.
- **Beds** - 22: 2x2(dbl), 2x2(bunks), 2x4(bunks) en suite, 1x6(bunks) en suite.
- **Price/night** - £23pp (£21pp if 3 nights or more). Sole use: 1 Nov-31 Mar, £450pn; 20th Dec-6 Jan, £490pn.

CONTACT: Pam Richmond
Tel: 01546 603366 Mobile:07786 157727
argyllbackpackers@sky.com
www.argyllbackpackers.com/
Loch Fyne Lodge, Inverneil, Ardrishaig,
Argyll, PA30 8ES

CAMPBELTOWN
BACKPACKERS

318

The Campbeltown Backpackers is housed in the Old Schoolhouse, a Grade B listed building. The hostel offers easy access to the facilities of Campbeltown including swimming pool, gym, cinema and distillery tours.

It is a good stop along the Kintyre Way which gives walkers spectacular views of the surrounding islands. The area also enjoys very good windsurfing, surfing, mountain bike routes and other major cycle trails.

DETAILS

- **Open** - All year. Leave by 10.30am on day of departure.
- **Beds** - 16: 1x6, 1x10
- **Price/night** - £22 per person

CONTACT: Alan
Tel: 01586 551188
info@campbeltownbackpackers.co.uk
www.campbeltownbackpackers.co.uk
Kintyre Amenity Trust, Big Kiln,
Campbeltown, Argyll, PA28 6JF

TORRAN BAY
HOSTEL

319l

With 16 en suite rooms, Torran Bay Hostel lies at the southern end of Loch Awe and offers the perfect base for your Highland holiday. Enjoy excellent free fishing or launch your boat from Torran Farm land and spend the day on the 25 mile long loch. Other activities include hiking, cycling, bird watching or golf. Prices includes continental breakfast and all rooms have TV, DVD and WiFi.

DETAILS

- **Open** - All year. All day.
- **Beds** - 34: 10 x 2 or double, 2 x double and single, 1 x 4 , 2 x 3
- **Price/night** - From £50 to £72 per room including continental breakfast and parking. Group bookings welcome. Note prices are per room, not per person.

CONTACT: Sheila Brolly
Tel: 01546 810133
sheilabro1@hotmail.co.uk
www.torranbayhostel.co.uk
Torran Farm, Ford, Lochgilphead. PA31 8RH

INVERARAY
HOSTEL

319r

The historic town of Inveraray, on the western shore of Loch Fyne, is a superb location for exploring Scotland's Southern Highlands and Islands. Inverarary Hostel is perfect for independent holidaymakers who enjoy socialising with other guests from many different backgrounds. The hostel offers simple, comfortable accommodation in private rooms & shared dorms, an excellent self-catering kitchen, communal dining area and a cosy wee lounge.

DETAILS

- **Open** - April-Sept.Reception 8-10am/3.30-9.30pm. No daytime access.
- **Beds** - 21 in 10 rooms
- **Price/night** - From £20pp. Breakfast £3.90.

CONTACT: Dawn or Ruben
Tel: 01499 302454
info@inverarayhostel.co.uk
www.inverarayhostel.co.uk
Dalmally Road, Inveraray, Argyll, PA32 8XD

BALMAHA

BUNKHOUSE

320l

On the banks of Loch Lomond on the West Highland Way, Balmaha Bunkhouse offers quality accommodation. Continental breakfast, bedding, WiFi, tea & coffee are included. Ideal for hen, stag and family get-togethers. Plus a private self-catering chalet (The Roost) sleeps 4 and B&B (en suite) in the main house. Kayaks and Canadian canoes can be hired on site.

DETAILS

- **Open** - Arrive 2pm-7pm, leave by 10am
- **Beds** - Bunkhouse 14: 1x6,1x4 (family),1x2 (double/twin),1x2 (twin); The Roost 4: 1x4; B&B: 1xdbl, 1xtwin, 1x single
- **Price/night** - £25pp incl. cont. b/fast. Sole use: B/H £350. The Roost £90. Dog £5pn. B&B (hot breakfast): Dbl £80, twin £80, single £35/40. No cards.

CONTACT:
balmahahouse.co.uk
www.balmahahouse.co.uk
Balmaha, Loch Lomond, G63 0JQ

KINGSHOUSE

BUNKHOUSE

320r

Within the grounds of the famous Kingshouse Hotel, this brand new, purpose built bunkhouse is right on the West Highland Way amid spectacular Scottish mountain scenery. With 32 beds across 10 rooms there is ample storage for your bags and each bunk has a locker, reading light, power socket, linen and towels. Ideal for travellers needing a stopping point or as a base to explore all that Glencoe has to offer and beyond. You'll find skiing, walking and mountain biking on the doorstep. The Way Inn cafe also offers all day dining and packed lunches. Open from 7am to 11pm daily.

DETAILS

- **Open** - All year.
- **Beds** - 32: 1x6, 4x4, 5x2
- **Price/night** - From £35 per person.

CONTACT:
Tel: 01855 851259
contact@kingshousehotel.co.uk
www.kingshousehotel.co.uk/bunkhouse
Glencoe, Argyll, PH49 4HY

BY THE WAY

HOSTEL & CAMPSITE

By The Way Hostel & Campsite lies in the Loch Lomond National Park, between Arrochar's peaks & Glencoe. There's excellent walking, climbing and white water rafting. The accommodation includes camping, various huts: hobbit houses, posh pods, glamping & trekker huts, camping cabins & a purpose built 4* hostel with twin, double & dormitory rooms, with great self-catering facilities. For more comfort still there are 2 chalets; one with three bedrooms, one with two.

DETAILS

- **Open** - Hostel/huts closed from end Oct to end March. Camping from April to end Sept. 8am - 10am & 2pm - 8pm.
- **Beds** - 26 hostel; 36 huts; 50 camping.
- **Price/night** - Hostel dorms from £20.00pp. Huts vary. Camping £8pp.

CONTACT: Kirsty Burnett
Tel: 01838 400333
info@TyndrumByTheWay.com
www.TyndrumByTheWay.com
Lower Station Rd, Tyndrum, FK20 8RY

CALLANDER
HOSTEL

Situated in the town of Callander at the start of the Loch Lomond and Trossachs National Park, Callander Hostel is a great location for tourists and outdoor enthusiasts alike. With outstanding views over Ben Ledi this Visit Scotland 5* Hostel has comfortable beds, en suite rooms and a fully equipped self-catering kitchen. Everything you need for the perfect retreat. The gardens have a children's play area, gas BBQ and seating.

DETAILS

- **Open** - All year. All day. Open 24 hours.
- **Beds** - 28: 2 x 8 bed dorms, 1 x 6, 1 x twin/double, 1 x family room (4)
- **Price/night** - From £18.50 per person in dorm, from £60 per twin/double en suite room.

CONTACT: Patricia
Tel: 01877 331465
bookings@callanderhostel.co.uk
www.callanderhostel.co.uk
6 Bridgend, Callander, FK17 8AH

COMRIE

CROFT

323

Comrie Croft is a perfect rural retreat r mountain bikers, hikers, families and backpackers, just over an hour from Edinburgh & Glasgow. The 4* hostel ffers cosy, home style rooms which are also available for sole group use and eddings. On-site facilities include The Tea Garden café, bike shop and lots of grin enducing mountain bike trails, amily-friendly valley routes and a well tocked farm shop. A footpath takes you the vibrant village of Comrie and gives ccess to stunning glens and mountains.

DETAILS

- **Open** - All year. All day.
- **Beds** - 56 + 46 + 14 (3 units)
- **Price/night** - From £18, U18 free in arent's room. Enquire for sole use.

CONTACT:
Tel: 01764 670140
info@comriecroft.com
www.comriecroft.com
Comrie Croft, By Crieff/Comrie,
Perthshire, PH7 4JZ

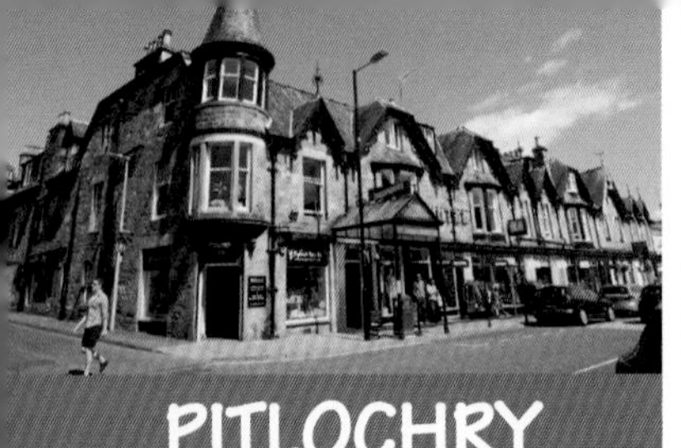

PITLOCHRY

BACKPACKERS HOTEL

Located in the centre of beautiful Pitlochry, this friendly, cosy hostel is an old Victorian hotel literally bursting with character and provides dormitory and en suite private rooms. Comfy beds come with fitted sheets, duvets and 2 fluffy pillows and private rooms have fresh towels. The bright spacious lounge has comfy sofas and as many free hot drinks as you can drink. There's free WiFi, games, musical instruments and a free pool table. A great place to meet like minded people. You won't want to leave!

DETAILS

- **Open** - March to Nov. 7.30am-1pm and 5pm-10pm (times may vary).
- **Beds** - 79.
- **Price/night** - From £18pp for dorms. Private rooms from £25pp

CONTACT: Receptionist
Tel: 01796 470044
info@pitlochrybackpackershotel.com
www.pitlochrybackpackershotel.com
134 Atholl Road, Pitlochry, PH16 5AB

JESSIE MACS

325l

the centre of Birnam just 10 mins' walk rom Dunkeld, this refurbished Victorian anse offers a mix of self-catering hostel and B&B accommodation. Your perfect ase to discover the mountains, waters, rich culture and heritage of Big Tree ountry. Jessie Mac's has doubles, bunk rooms and family rooms, all en suite. One double has wheelchair access.

 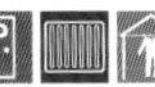    

DETAILS

- **Open** - Check in: 4pm - 6.30 pm. Check out: by 10.30am.
- **Beds** - 21: 4x2, 2x4, 1x5
- **Price/night** - Dorm £22pp +continental breakfast £27, +cooked breakfast £30. Double £29.50pp (based on 2 sharing) or £35 single occ. Child £11 in shared room. Infants free. Group rates available.

CONTACT: Dot Mechan
Tel: 01350 727324
info@jessiemacs.co.uk
www.jessiemacs.co.uk
Murthly Terrace, Birnam, Dunkeld PH8 0BG

KINDROGAN

FIELD STUDIES CENTRE

325r

Set in wooded grounds on the banks of the river Ardle in the picturesque Scottish Highlands. Rooms range from en suite dorms to singles with shared facilties in a mixture of bunks and single beds. Bedding (make your own bed) & towels, full breakfast, WiFi, tea & coffee all included. A home-made supper and well stocked bar are also available upon request. Classrooms & conference capability available.

DETAILS

- **Open** - All year. Reception 8.30am-5pm
- **Beds** - 116
- **Price/night** - B&B: shared facilities £30, en suite £40, single occupancy £50. Packed lunch £5 (make your own). Supper £10 (6-7pm) all prices include VAT

CONTACT: Jason Lock
Tel: 01250 870150
enquiries.kd@field-studies-council.org
www.field-studies-council.org/kindrogan
Enocdhu, Blairgowrie, Perth and Kinross, PH10 7PG

PROSEN

HOSTEL

Glenprosen is the most intimate of the Angus Glens on the southernmost edge of the Cairngorms National Park. Two Munros; the Mayar and Driesh link Glenprosen to the Cairngorms plateau. Prosen Hostel is also close to the upgraded East Cairngorms footpath network. Converted to the latest and greenest specification, the 4* hostel offers cosy, quality accommodation for 18. With 4 rooms, sleeping 4, 4 and 6 in bunks and a family room sleeping 4. You can also hire the nearby village hall.

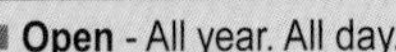

DETAILS

- **Open** - All year. All day.
- **Beds** - 18:1x6, 3x4
- **Price/night** - £18 - £22 pp. Min periods & prices apply for Xmas and New Year.

CONTACT: Hector or Robert
Tel: 01575 540302
hectormaclean@compuserve.com
www.prosenhostel.co.uk
Prosen Hostel, Balnaboth, Kirriemuir, Angus, DD8 4SA

BALLATER
HOSTEL

Ballater Hostel lies in the centre of Ballater, near Balmoral, on the east side of the Cairngorms National Park. raditional dorms & private rooms, along with a large open plan kitchen/dining/ ommunal area make a great space to relax . Drying room and cycle storage available. Either book whole hostel, a om or just a bed with no minimum stay. xcellent facilities, comfortable beds and warm and friendly welcome awaits you - the kettle is always on!

DETAILS

- **Open** - All year. Reception open 8-10am & 5-10pm. No access 10am-5pm.
- **Beds** - 29: 1x8, 1x6, 1x4, 1x2, 3x3 (family)
- **Price/night** - Dorm beds from £18.70. Private rooms from £29.33

CONTACT: Dominique & Daniel
Tel: 01339 753752
info@ballater-hostel.com
www.ballater-hostel.com
Bridge Square, Ballater, AB35 5QJ

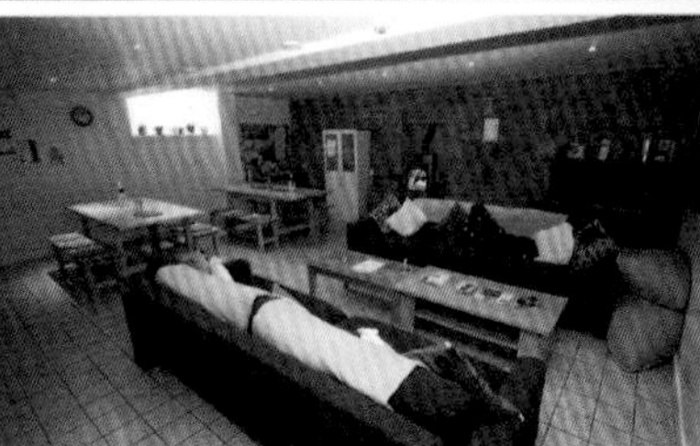

GULABIN
LODGE

328l

Gulabin Lodge nestles in Glenshee at the foot of Beinn Gulabin and is the nearest accommodation to the Glenshee ski slopes. The 4* lodge offers excellent accommodation for individuals, families, stag and hen groups & school residentials. On-site there are many outdoor activities including mountain bike hire. During the winter there's a ski school with equipment hire. Meals & transport to and from airports /stations available for groups. A 12/14 bed house is also available.

DETAILS

- **Open** - All year. 24 hours.
- **Beds** - 37: 9 rooms available.
- **Price/night** - From £20pp. Contact for fully catered stays and private rooms.

CONTACT: Darren and Tereza
Tel: 01250 885255/ 07799 847014
info@gulabinlodge.co.uk
www.gulabinoutdoors.co.uk
Spittal of Glenshee, By Blairgowrie, PH10 7QE

BRAEMAR LODGE
BUNKHOUSE

328r

Surrounded by the beauty and tranquillity of Deeside, Braemar Lodge Hotel and Bunkhouse are just a two minute walk from the village. Braemar Lodge Hotel a former Victorian shooting lodge, is set in extensive grounds. The great value bunkhouse provides comfortable accommodation for up to 12 people within the hotel grounds. The bunkhouse is equipped with two shower rooms, one of which is suitable for wheelchairs. There's a generous, fully equipped, self catering kitchen, but you are welcome to sample the excellent hotel meals. All bed linen and towels are supplied.

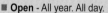

DETAILS

- **Open** - All year. All day.
- **Beds** - 12: 3x4
- **Price/night** - From £17 per person

CONTACT: Reception
Tel: 01339 741627
mail@braemarlodge.co.uk
www.braemarlodge.co.uk
6 Glenshee Rd, Braemar, AB35 5YQ

ABERNETHY

BUNKHOUSE

329l

Sharing a car park with the Speyside Way, the converted Nethy Station offers all that a group of 12-26 could expect from a bunkhouse. It is well equipped and fully central heated. Most rooms have triple bunks and there is a 2 bunk room with unusual access, known as Narnia, as you get there through a wardrobe! Self-catering or catered options. Close to winter sports areas. The bunkhouse is only 200 yards from the local shop, butcher and pub.

DETAILS

- **Open** - All year. Anytime.
- **Beds** - 26: 2x9, 4x2
- **Price/night** - £16.90 per person. After the minimum of 12 you just pay for those who stay. 10% discount midweek and 20% discount for stays of over 4 nights.

CONTACT: Patricia or Richard
Tel: 01479 821370
info@nethy.org
www.nethy.org
Station Road, Nethy Bridge, PH25 3DN

ARDENBEG

BUNKHOUSE

329r

Part of the award-winning Craggan Outdoors activity centre, Ardenbeg offers good value, well appointed bunkhouse accommodation with the extra benefit of a large private garden with BBQ, picnic tables & a children's play area. The property is situated on a quiet residential street in Grantown-on-Spey, the historic capital of Strathspey, just a 15 mins' drive from Aviemore and all its amenities. For adventures even closer at hand you can organise a whole host of activities through Craggan Outdoors.

DETAILS

- **Open** - All year. 24 hours access.
- **Beds** - 23: 1x4, 1x5, 1x6, 1x8.
- **Price/night** - £19.20 - £26pp, subject to number of people & duration of stay.

CONTACT: Keith & Jill Ballam
Tel: 01479 873283 / 01479 872824
info@cragganoutdoors.co.uk
www.cragganoutdoors.co.uk
Grant Road, Grantown-on-Spey, Moray
PH26 3LD

FINDHORN

VILLAGE HOSTEL

Findhorn Village Hostel is just a stone's throw from the beautiful Moray Coast. Great wildlife sites and the Speyside distilleries are within reach. The hostel provides newly renovated self-catering accommodation for groups or individuals. There are shared bunkrooms, a two person room and an en suite family room. A new annex (6 beds) has a small kitchenette and en suite shower rooms.

DETAILS

- **Open** - All year. Office hours 10am-3pm Mon to Fri.
- **Beds** - 34: 28 in hostel & 6 in annex; 2x8; 1x2; 1x4/5
- **Price/night** - Individual bunks £17. Groups of 10 or more people £15/bed. Bed linen is priced separately at £3.50.

CONTACT: Richard
Tel: 01309 692339 or 07496 230266
findhornvillagecentre@gmail.com
www.findhornvillagehostel.com
Church Place, Findhorn, Forres, Moray, IV36 3YR

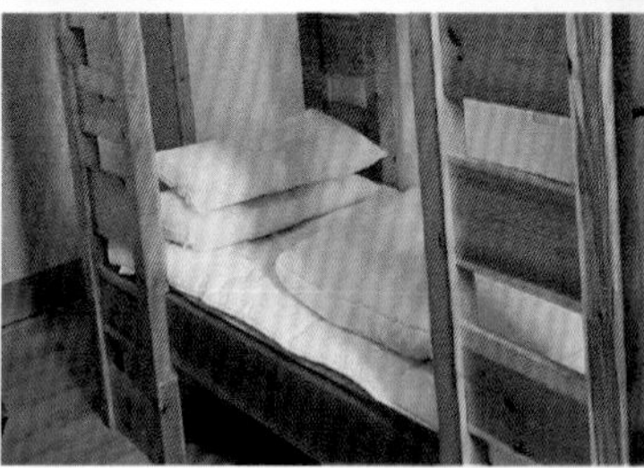

THE SAIL LOFT

BUNKHOUSE

331

Situated on the shore of the Moray Firth coast in Portsoy, The Sail Loft has a stunning location. Converted from a former sail making loft, The Sail Loft is modern and well equipped. It provides self-catering accommodation for 25 in a mixture of single accessible, twin, triple and bunk rooms, with secure cycle storage, cycle wash-down facilities and an outdoor wood fired hot tub. The Sail Loft is a short easy walk from Portsoy town centre and its charming 17th century historic harbour. You can take part in traditional skills too, including wooden boat building. Groups welcome.

DETAILS

- **Open** - All year.
- **Beds** - 25
- **Price/night** - From £23 per person.

CONTACT: Ian Tillett
Tel: 01261 842695 or 01261 842222
contact@portsoysailloft.org
www.portsoysailloft.org/
Back Green, Portsoy, AB45 2AF

CRAIBSTONE

ESTATE

332l

Hostel accommodation - 5 minutes from Aberdeen Airport and 5 miles north from Aberdeen city centre. The accommodation is well placed for touring much of the North East of Scotland.

Easy access to the 'Granite City' with its striking granite architecture and rich and inspiring history. Families enjoy Codonas Amusement Park located at Aberdeen beach. Visit the dolphins that skirt the fringes of the busy harbour.

DETAILS

- **Open** - 24/06/19 to 16/08/19
- **Beds** - 103 beds in 95 rooms.
- **Price/night** - Standard room £15, en-suite room £20, twin en-suite £35.

CONTACT: Gwen Bruce
Tel: 01224 711012
accommodation@sruc.ac.uk
www.sruc.ac.uk
Accommodation Office, Scotland's Rural College, Ferguson Building, Craibstone Estate, Bucksburn, Aberdeen, AB21 9YA

BLACK ROCK

BUNKHOUSE

332r

Situated in beautiful Glenglass and sheltered by Ben Wyvis, this comfortable bunkhouse is an ideal base for touring the Highlands. The bunkhouse is at the eastern end of a hikers' route across Scotland and on the Land's End to John O'Groats route. The village has a general shop, Post Office, bus service and an inn (serving good bar meals and breakfasts) 250m away. There is also a camping ground. All areas of the bunkhouse are easily accessible by wheelchair and suitable for the disabled.

DETAILS

- **Open** - April 1st to October 31st. 24hr access. New arrivals 12noon -7pm.
- **Beds** - 16 : 4 x 4.
- **Price/night** - £17 per person. 10% off for groups of 8

CONTACT: Lillian
Tel: 01349 830917
blackrockholidays@gmail.com
www.blackrockscotland.com
Evanton, Dingwall, Ross-shire, IV16 9UN

INVERNESS

STUDENT HOTEL

The cosy and friendly Student Hotel enjoys panoramic views of the town and the mountains beyond. Your perfect place to unwind, just yards from the city's varied night-life and a few mins' walk from bus and train stations. Relax in the fabulous lounge with real log fire and drink as much free tea, coffee & hot chocolate as you like. Visit the beautiful ancient pine forest of Glen Affric or the Culloden Battlefield. Famous Loch Ness lies just a few miles upstream and of course has its own special wild animal.

DETAILS

- **Open** - All year. All day. Reception 7am - 10.30pm.
- **Beds** - 57
- **Price/night** - From £18 per night. ID required for check in.

CONTACT: Receptionist
Tel: 01463 236556
info@invernessstudenthotel.com
www.invernessstudenthotel.com
8 Culduthel Road, Inverness, IV2 4AB

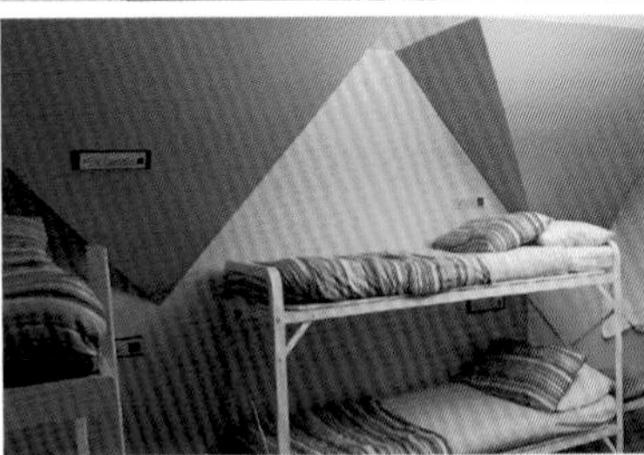

LOCH NESS

BACKPACKERS LODGE

334l

This 18th century Highland farmhouse provides warm & friendly hostel accommodation. Ideally situated within walking distance of Loch Ness, Urquhart Castle, on the Great Glen Way and with pubs, restaurants and supermarket close by. Residents only bar offers over 70 Scottish beers and 25 Scotch whiskies. Horse riding, fishing, watersports and mountain biking can all be arranged locally. Free parking and free WiFi. Bike storage available except in Jul/Aug.

DETAILS

- **Open** - All year. All day.
- **Beds** - Dorm beds: 32. Family rooms: 2. Private doubles/twins: 3
- **Price/night** - From £17pp. Discounts apply to groups or long term stays

CONTACT: Patrick & Nikki Kipfmiller
Tel: 01456 450807
info@lochness-backpackers.com
www.lochness-backpackers.com
Coiltie Farmhouse, East Lewiston,
Drumnadrochit, Inverness, IV63 6UJ

THE LOCHSIDE

HOSTEL

334r

Perched right on the banks of Loch Ness, the Lochside Hostel has amazing views up and down the loch and can give you direct access to the water's edge. Why not go for a dip in Scotland's largest water body? Take a walk to watch for wildlife? Or even hunt the elusive Nessie!? The Great Glen walking route passes the front door and the End to End cycle route is nearby. Drumnadrochit is just 12 miles away by boat. Recently opened by MacBackpackers, an award-winning tour company who also own 3 hostels in Edinburgh, a great stay awaits

DETAILS

- **Open** - Check in 2pm, check out 10am
- **Beds** - 47: 3x2 (twin), 2x4 (female), 5x4, 1x5, 1x8 all mixed dorms.
- **Price/night** - From £15

CONTACT: Reception
Tel: 01320 351274
lochness@macbackpackers.com
lochsidehostel.com
Altsigh, Inverness. IV63 7YD

MORAGS LODGE

LOCH NESS

A multi-award winning 4* hostel with a range of rooms to meet all needs and budgets in the bustling village of Fort Augustus on the banks of Loch Ness. Your perfect base to explore the Loch Ness area and an ideal stop off on the Great Glen Way. Surrounded by stunning mountain scenery and set in wooded grounds the hostel boasts 24 hour self-catering facilities, excellent home-made cheap meal options, a rustic bar, free WiFi, bike hire and ample car parking.

DETAILS

- **Open** - All year. Check in from 4pm (earlier by arrangement).
- **Beds** - 75: 1x7, 6x6, 6x4, 4x2/3
- **Price/night** - From £24pp in dorm beds. Doubles/twins from £30pp. Family rooms from £80.

CONTACT: Claire
Tel: 01320 366289
info@moragslodge.com
www.moragslodge.com
Bunoich Brae, Fort Augustus, PH32 4DG

SADDLE MOUNTAIN

HOSTEL

336l

Saddle Mountain Hostel is a small and friendly 4* hostel in Invergarry, between Loch Ness and Fort William and at the junction with the road to Skye. The comfortable hostel sleeps 24 people in 5 rooms. It has a large kitchen, dining room and lounge, free WiFi, a purpose-built drying room and bike storage. A great location for Munro bagging, walking, cycling, scenic tours, water sports, fishing and wildlife watching.

 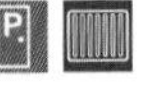      

DETAILS

- **Open** - All year except Nov. Closed Tues & Wed Dec-Easter. Check in 4.30-10pm.
- **Beds** - 24: 2x6, 1x5 (1 dbl, 3 singles), 1x4, 1x3 (1 dbl, 1 single).
- **Price/night** - From £18pp Whole hostel prices available on request.

CONTACT: Helen or Gregor
Tel: 01809 501412
info@saddlemountainhostel.co.uk
www.saddlemountainhostel.co.uk
Mandally Road, Invergarry, PH35 4HP

GREAT GLEN

HOSTEL

336r

Located between mountains and lochs 20 miles north of Fort William and 10 miles south of Loch Ness, the Great Glen Hostel is your ideal base. Perfect for touring the Highlands, bagging Munros or paddling rivers and lochs. It's only a short walk to the Great Glen Way The hostel provides comfortable, well appointed accommodation in twin, family and dormitory rooms and has a shop where you can buy your essentials.

DETAILS

- **Open** - All year. All day. Please call first Nov-March.
- **Beds** - 49: 3x2, 1x3, 4x5, 2x6, 1x8
- **Price/night** - Dorm beds from £22. Twin rooms from £25 pp. Whole hostel for sole use from £500 per night.

CONTACT: The Manager
Tel: 01809 501430
bookings@greatglenhostel.com
www.greatglenhostel.com
South Laggan, Spean Bridge, Invernesshire, PH34 4EA

ÀITE

CRUINNICHIDH

ite Cruinnichidh, 15 miles northeast of ort William, occupies a unique sheltered spot adjacent to the Monessie Gorge where you can explore remote glens, nountain passes and lochs. The hostel as a fully equipped kitchen/dining room, sitting room, excellent showers, sauna, seminar room and garden. All bedding s provided. There is a good selection of naps, board games and books. Guests are encouraged to socialise and enjoy the natural environment that the hostel has to offer.

DETAILS

- **Open** - All year. All day.
- **Beds** - 28: 1x6, 4x4, 1x twin, 1x double, 1x family/double en suite.
- **Price/night** - From £18 per person.

CONTACT: Gavin or Nicola
Tel: 01397 712315
gavin@highland-hostel.co.uk
www.highland-hostel.co.uk
1 Achluachrach, By Roy Bridge, Near Fort William, PH31 4AW

SMIDDY

BUNKHOUSE

Find a friendly welcome at this warm & comfortable hostel for your group or family. Enjoy the loch-side location overlooking the Caledonian Canal, 4 miles from Fort William & Ben Nevis, with the meeting of the West Highland Way and Great Glen Way on your doorstep. Perfect for the outdoor enthusiast with advice/instruction/guiding from resident instructors for walking/climbing, river, loch and sea kayaking & dinghy sailing. Equipment hire available. AALS licensed & DofE approved for activity expeditions.

DETAILS

- **Open** - All year. All day (with key).
- **Beds** - 24: 3x4, 2x6.
- **Price/night** - From £16-£22.50 (incl bedding).

CONTACT: John or Tina
Tel: 01397 772467
enquiry@highland-mountain-guides.co.uk
www.accommodation-fortwilliam.co.uk
Snowgoose Mountain Centre, Station Road, Corpach, Fort William, PH33 7JH

BANK STREET LODGE

Bank Street Lodge is 100 metres from Fort William High Street with its shops, pubs & restaurants. There is a fully equipped kitchen with cooker, fridge, microwave, cutlery and crockery. The common room lounge has a TV, it also provides tables and chairs for meals and a snack vending machine. All bedding is provided. Some rooms are en-suite (twins, doubles and family). Some of the en-suite rooms have recently been refurbished. WiFi is also available in the lounge/TV room. 3 Star STB rating.

DETAILS

- **Open** - All year except Xmas. All day access. Entry from 1pm, depart by 10am.
- **Beds** - 43: 6x4, 4x3, 1x7
- **Price/night** - From £18 to £25 per person. Group rates available.

CONTACT: Reception
Tel: 01397 700070
bankstreetlodge@btconnect.com
www.bankstreetlodge.co.uk
Bank Street, Fort William, PH33 6AY

FORT WILLIAM
BACKPACKERS

340

Surrounded by spectacular mountain scenery, Fort William is a mecca for those with a spirit of adventure. You can start (or end) the West Highland Way in Fort William, hike or bike along mountain trails, go for a boat trip on the sea loch or just take it easy amidst the wonderful scenery. Even in winter Fort William stays busy with skiing, snow-boarding, mountaineering and ice-climbing. Set on a hillside above the town, with wonderful views, this cosy hostel provides all you'll need after a day in the hills.

DETAILS

- **Open** - All year. All day. Reception 7am-noon & 5pm-10.30pm
- **Beds** - 38
- **Price/night** - From £18 per person. ID required for check-in.

CONTACT: Receptionist
Tel: 01397 700711
info@fortwilliambackpackers.com
www.fortwilliambackpackers.com
Alma Road, Fort William, PH33 6HB

COORIE DOON

CABIN

341l

deally situated next to the road to the es, the Caledonian Canal (route of the reat Glen Way) and close to the West Highland Way, Nevis Range and the Glencoe Mountain Resort, this stylish abin offers easy access to world-class king, climbing, skiing, mountain biking, simply enjoying the amazing view. Es, e owner and a mountaineer, is happy offer advice. After a day of adventures return to the luxury of a drying room, underfloor heating and hot showers!

   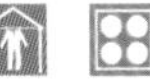   

DETAILS

- **Open** - All year. Check in 4pm-10pm, heck out 10am.
- **Beds** - 6: 2x3 (each room has one ouble and a single bed)
- **Price/night** - From £100 ask for details

CONTACT: Es Tresidder
Tel: 07503 775874
e.tresidder@gmail.com
www.fb.com/CoorieDoon
Coorie Doon, Old Banavie Road,
Banavie, Fort William, PH33 7PZ

CORRAN

BUNKHOUSE

341r

Corran Bunkhouse lies on the shore of Loch Linnhe, 8 miles south of Fort William and 7 miles north of Glencoe. With two fully equipped, 5* self-catering bunkhouses; one sleeping 12 (plus 9 in an annexe) and the other 20, it is an ideal base for small and large groups. All bedrooms are en suite. There are fully equipped kitchen/dining areas, drying room, central heating, laundry facilities, private parking and a steam room situated in the smaller bunkhouse. Children are welcome.

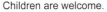

DETAILS

- **Open** - All year. Check in 4 - 9.30pm.
- **Beds** - 41: 11x2, 2x3, 2x4, 1x5
- **Price/night** - £27.50pp. £25pp groups. £40 single occupancy (Nov.- March)

CONTACT: Alan & Halina
Tel: 01855 821000
corranbunkhouse@btconnect.com
www.corranbunkhouse.co.uk
Corran Ferry Approach Road, Onich,
Fort William, PH33 6SE

GLENCOE

INDEPENDENT HOSTEL

342l

Glencoe Independent Hostel lies in secluded woodland midway between Glencoe village and Clachaig Inn with access to world class cycling, walking, climbing and kayaking. The Glencoe Ski Centre and The West Highland Way are just 20 mins away. The hostel has 4 rooms with comfortable communal spaces. Also available are an alpine bunkhouse sleeping 16, 4 luxury caravans and 3 luxury log cabins.

DETAILS

- **Open** - All year (phone in Nov and Dec). 9am - 9 pm.
- **Beds** - 65: hostel:26, bunkhouse:16, caravans: 4x2-4, cabins: 2x2, 1x3
- **Price/night** - From £12.50 to £50 per person.

CONTACT: Keith or Davina
Tel: 01855 811906
info@glencoehostel.co.uk
www.glencoehostel.co.uk
Glencoe Independent Hostel, Glencoe, Argyll, PH49 4HX

BACKPACKERS

PLUS OBAN

342r

Many people's favourite hostel thank to its friendly atmosphere, the beautif seaside town setting and its excellen facilities. Enjoy free WiFi, free breakfa free all-day hot drinks, clean spaciou rooms, secure bike storage, laundry service, communal areas, strong hot showers, comfortable beds and a wel equipped self-catering kitchen. The live town of Oban has direct ferry access the many beautiful Scottish Isles.

DETAILS

- **Open** - All year. Reception 8am t 10:30am and 4pm to 10pm.
- **Beds** - 50-60 dorm beds, family double, twin rooms, some en suite.
- **Price/night** - Dorms FROM £17pp Private rooms FROM £22pp.

CONTACT: Receptionist
Tel: 01631 567189
info@backpackersplus.com
www.backpackersplus.com
The Old Church, Breadalbane St, Oban, Argyll, PA34 5PH

OBAN
BACKPACKERS

Perfectly situated in the heart of Oban, the gateway to the Isles, just 10 mins' walk from the bus, train & ferry terminals. This friendly hostel is a great place to stay and unwind. The fabulous sociable lounge has a real fire, pool table, free WiFi, comfy sofas and unlimited free hot drinks. The kitchen is fully equipped, perfect for cooking your favourite meals. Large dorm beds come complete with bedding including 2 comfy pillows. The hot powerful showers are legendary! Knowledgeable and friendly staff will help you make the most of your time in Oban.

DETAILS

- **Open** - March - Nov. 7am - 10pm.
- **Beds** - 54: 1x12, 1x10, 1x8, 4x6
- **Price/night** - From £18. Whole hostel bookings please email for quote.

CONTACT: Reception
Tel: 01631 562107
info@obanbackpackers.com
www.obanbackpackers.com
Breadalbane Street, Oban, PA34 5NZ

CORRAN
HOUSE

344

Experience a warm welcome & value accommodation in Oban for singles, couples, families and groups. Enjoy a large self-catering kitchen, spacious TV lounge, comfortable rooms & big beds. Corran House is perfect for exploring Argyll and the inner Hebrides & is close to the bus, train and ferry. Downstairs try Markie Dans bar for tasty meals, live music and great Highland hospitality.

DETAILS

- **Open** - All year. Reception 3-10pm. Check in only after 3pm.
- **Beds** - 52: 26 bunks, 5x4 1x6. Plus guest rooms: 26
- **Price/night** - Bunks £18/£20 en suite. Guest rooms £27.50-£40pp (2 sharing). Singles from £45. Winter discounts.

CONTACT:
Tel: 01631 566040
enquiries@corranhouseoban.co.uk
www.corranhouseoban.co.uk
1 Victoria Crescent, Corran Esplanade,
Oban, Argyll, PA34 5PN

LISMORE
BUNKHOUSE

345l

This super warm and comfy eco bunkhouse on a traditional croft is the perfect base from which to explore the magical Isle of Lismore. The bunkhouse sleeps 12 in a mix of en suite dorms and private rooms and for larger groups the campsite has 5 pitches and hook ups for 2 camper vans. The Isle of Lismore is just 7 miles by car ferry from Oban and is a tranquil, unspoilt island surrounded by stunning mountain scenery. Perfect for wildlife and history lovers as well as walkers, cyclists and those wanting to get away from it all. Bike hire available.

DETAILS

- **Open** - All year.
- **Beds** - 12
- **Price/night** - From £18pp. Exclusive hire available.

CONTACT: Clare
Tel: 07720 975433
lismorebunkhouse@gmail.com
www.fb.com/thelismorebunkhouse/
Isle of Lismore, PA34 5UG

CRAIGNURE
BUNKHOUSE

345r

Craignure, a superior eco-sensitive bunkhouse, purpose built in 2014, is the perfect base for your Mull adventure. Set on the water's edge close to the ferry port, there's the Craignure Inn next door for traditional island hospitality. The 4 well appointed bunkrooms have en suite showers and there's a spacious well appointed communal area with kitchen, ample dining and relaxing space.

DETAILS

- **Open** - All year. Closed 11am-4pm for cleaning.
- **Beds** - 20: 2x4, 2x6
- **Price/night** - £24 per person. 4 berth rooms £90, 6 berth rooms £135. Whole hostel £420 by prior arrangement. Discounted rates for multiple nights.

CONTACT: Chris, Claire or Ivan
Tel: 01680 812043 or 07900 692973
info@craignure-bunkhouse.co.uk
www.craignure-bunkhouse.co.uk/
Craignure Bunkhouse, Craignure, Isle Of Mull, Argyll And Bute, PA65 6AY

SHIELING HOLIDAYS

HOSTEL TENTS

346l

Stay in a Shieling Tent on the Isle of Mull. Choose from private en suite or standard Sheilings, budget-bed tents for small groups or book a bed in the Shared Shieling Hostel Tent. Clean, bright & spacious, there's also a tented common room with basic kitchen facilities, multi-fuel stove, free WiFi and TV. Views across Craignure Bay and towards Ben Nevis. Otters live on the site, wildlife abounds & eagles soar above.

DETAILS

- **Open** - Easter-Oct.Reception 8am-8pm
- **Beds** - 106: Ensuite 8×6. Standard 3×6. Budget-bed 6×4. Shared Shieling Hostel Tents 2×8 (single sex). Plus Cottages (2×4).
- **Price/night** - From £20pp. See accommodation's website for more details

CONTACT: Carol Perry
Tel: 01680 812496
info@isleofmullcampsite.co.uk
www.shielingholidays.co.uk
Craignure, Isle of Mull, Argyll, PA65 6AY

ROSS OF MULL

BUNKROOMS

346r

Ross of Mull Bunkrooms are located le: than a mile from the ferry link to Iona a Fionnphort. Ideal for exploring the supe wildlife, rich history, shell-sand beache and unspoilt environment of the Ross of Mull, loved by outdoor enthusiasts. The perfect base for day trips to Staffa the Treshnish Isles and Iona. There is well-equipped kitchen, woodburner an stunning views. Larger groups could consider Achaban House (see page 34 next door which sleeps 14.

DETAILS

- **Open** - March - October. November - February whole bunkhouse only
- **Beds** - 8: 2x4
- **Price/night** - 4 bunk room:£96 (4 people), £83 (3 people), £70 (2 people). Sole use £170. Towel hire £2.

CONTACT: Rachel Ball
Tel: 07759 615200
info@rossofmullbunkrooms.co.uk
www.rossofmullbunkrooms.co.uk
Fionnphort, Isle of Mull PA66 6BL

ACHABAN

HOUSE

)n the beautiful Ross of Mull, Achaban House is perfect for those wanting ıxurious B&B on the Ross of Mull with the option to self-cater. Close to the Fionnphort ferry to Iona & day trips to affa, Lunga & the Treshnish Isles. Ideal for walkers, cyclists or wildlife lovers. Rooms are en suite or with private athrooms, breakfast is included. Larger groups welcome at the Ross Of Mull 3unkrooms next door (see page 346r).

DETAILS

- **Open** - All year. All day.
- **Beds** - 14: 1x5, 2x2 (twin), 2x2 (double), 1x1
- **Price/night** - Single room £47. Double/ twin rooms £77. Family 5 bed room £104-139. Sole use of whole house £400.

CONTACT: Matt Oliver
Tel: 01681 700205
info@achabanhouse.co.uk
www.achabanhouse.co.uk
chaban House, Fionnphort, Isle of Mull, PA66 6BL

IONA HOSTEL

348l

Tucked into the rocky outcrops on a working croft, Iona Eco Hostel has spectacular views of the isles and mountains beyond. The land has been worked for generations, creating the familiar Hebridean patchwork of wildflower meadow, crops and grazing land. It offers quiet sanctuary for those that seek it, within easy reach of island activities. Whether travelling on your own, with friends, or as a group, Iona Hostel promises a warm welcome. Tourist board 4 star. Green Tourism Gold.

DETAILS

- **Open** - All year. Closed 11am-1pm for cleaning - no curfew.
- **Beds** - 21: 1x2, 2x4, 1x5, 1x6.
- **Price/night** - £23.00 adult / £19.00 under 10's (bedding included).

CONTACT: John MacLean
Tel: 01681 700781
info@ionahostel.co.uk
www.ionahostel.co.uk
Iona Hostel, Iona, Argyll, PA76 6SW

COLONSAY

BACKPACKERS LODGE

348r

Come to Colonsay Backpackers Lodge and savour the idyll of this Inner Hebridean island. Explore the magnificent sandy beaches, ancient forests and beautiful lochs. Wildlife abounds; spot dolphins, seals, otters and many rare birds. The pub, café & shop are 3 miles away. Or buy fresh lobster, crab and oysters from the fishir boats. The lodge is a refurbished forme gamekeeper's house with bothies. Centrally heated, it has 2 twin, 3 twin bunk and 2 three-bedded rooms. Free Wifi.

DETAILS

- **Open** - March to October. 24 hours
- **Beds** - 16: 5x2, 2x3
- **Price/night** - £28pp twin, £22pp bothy

CONTACT: The Manager
Tel: 01951 200312
cottages@colonsayholidays.co.uk
www.colonsayholidays.co.uk
Colonsay Estate Cottages, Isle of Colonsay, Argyll, PA61 7YP

ISLE OF MUCK

BUNKHOUSE

349

This self-catering hostel can also be hired as a holiday cottage. The bunkhouse overlooks the ferry port of Port Mor, it is near to The Craft Shop & Tearoom and to the island's Community Hall. The Isle of Muck is just 2 miles long by 1 mile wide and has a population of 46 people. With a rich cultural heritage and amazing wildlife, Muck is the perfect place to unwind. BYO towel, sleeping bag and supplies (no shops on Muck).

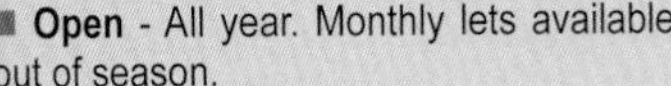

DETAILS

- **Open** - All year. Monthly lets available out of season.
- **Beds** - 8: 3x2(bunks) 1x2 (double)
- **Price/night** - £20pp (plus £5 per stay if bed linen is required). £80 sole use. £490 for a weeks sole use.

CONTACT: Georgia Gillies
Tel: 07833 195654
bunkhouse@isleofmuck.com
www.isleofmuck.com
Isle of Muck, Port Mor, Isle of Muck,
PH41 2RP

GLEBE BARN

Glebe Barn offers 4* homely accommodation on the extraordinary Isle of Eigg within 1 mile of the island shop & café/restaurant. Outstanding sea views and sleeping up to 22 in twin, triple, family & dorm rooms. Perfect for individuals, families or groups. Also two person mezzanine apartment.

DETAILS

- **Open** - Groups all year; individuals from April to October. Open 24 hours.
- **Beds** - 22: 1x2, 2x3, 1x6, 1x8.
- **Price/night** - Dormitory bed: £21 (1-2 nights), £19 (3+ nights), £17 (6+ nights). Twin room £47 (1-2 nights), £43 (3+ nights), £39 (6+nights). Triple room £63 (1-2 nights), £57 (3+ nights), £51 (6+ nights). Contact for quote for groups.

CONTACT: Tamsin or Stuart
Tel: 01687 315099
mccarthy@glebebarn.co.uk
www.glebebarn.co.uk
Glebe Barn, Isle of Eigg, Inner Hebrides, PH42 4RL

COLL

BUNKHOUSE

351

;oll Bunkhouse 5* self-catering hostel ccommodation is a mile from the ferry :rminal & close to local amenities. Ideal ır groups or individuals, short or longer stays. A half hour from the mainland ɔy plane, under 3 hours by ferry. This beautiful Hebridean island is ideal for walking, stargazing, wildlife, cycling, /ater sports or chilling amidst stunning ;enery. Visit quiet and beautiful spaces and beaches and enjoy fine island ɔspitality. A warm welcome awaits you.

DETAILS

- **Open** - All year. 24 hours.
- **Beds** - 16: 2x6, 1x4
- **Price/night** - £22pp (dorm). Private 'ooms from £110 (quin), £80 (quad), £65 triple), £50 (twin). Discount of 10% to 55% for sole use for 2 nights or more.

CONTACT: Jane
Tel: 01879 230217
jane@developmentcoll.org.uk
www.collbunkhouse.com
ırinagour, Isle of Coll, Argyll, PA78 6SY

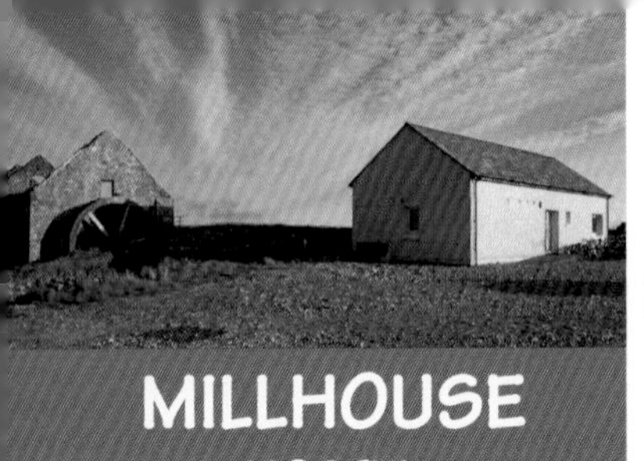

MILLHOUSE

HOSTEL

352l

Tiree is an idyllic Hebridean island surrounded by white beaches and crystal clear seas. Perfect for outdoor pursuits & wildlife enthusiasts, Millhouse offers you 4* facilities and free WiFi. You can hire bikes, visit the lighthouse museum, watch the seals or enjoy watersports at Loch Bhasapol (200m away). For walkers Tiree Pilgrimage route passes close by. Tiree has a resident RSPB warden and there are handy bird and otter hides for you to use.

DETAILS

- **Open** - Mar-Oct. (Winter by arrangement). Open all day. Check in 4pm. Check out 10am.
- **Beds** - Hostel 16 : 2 x 2/3, 2 x 5.
- **Price/night** - Dorm from £24pp. Private room from £42pp.

CONTACT: Kris Milne
Tel: 01879 220802 Mob: 07786 708154
mail@tireemillhouse.co.uk
www.tireemillhouse.co.uk
Cornaigmore, Isle of Tiree, PA77 6XA

GLENFINNAN

SLEEPING CAR

352r

Glenfinnan Sleeping Car provides uniq accommodation in an historic railway carriage next to Glenfinnan Station & close to Glenfinnan Viaduct (featured i Harry Potter films). An ideal location fo the mountains, a good starting point fo bothy expeditions & a useful stop-ove en route to Skye. Fully equipped kitche shower & drying room. The dining coac provides excellent meals in the daytim & evening meals are available close b

DETAILS

- **Open** - All year (call for winter openin details). 24 hours.
- **Beds** - 10
- **Price/night** - £35 per twin bun compartment per night (£25 single occ. £5 bedding/towel hire. £150 sole use.

CONTACT: Amy or Paul
Tel: 01397 722295
glenfinnanstationmuseum@gmail.co
www.glenfinnanstationmuseum.co.u
Glenfinnan Station, Glenfinnan, nr For William, PH37 4LT

KNOYDART

BUNKHOUSE

353l

‹noydart is a remote peninsula on the vest coast of Scotland reachable only oy boat or long hike. Community run, the Bunkhouse uses hydro electricity & promotes responsible tourism. Set amid wild, remote terrain overlooking a mesmerising beach. Ten mins' walk to pub, PO, shop & ferry at Inverie. 3 edrooms and comfy communal areas. anger service & deer stalking available. Stunning dark skies, so bring a torch!

DETAILS

- **Open** - All year (no staff at Christmas & imited service New Year's Day).
- **Beds** - 26: 1x7, 1x8, 1x11
- **Price/night** - £18 per adult, £10 for ınder 16's. Block bookings £395. Special ates for schools, youth groups & DofE..

CONTACT: Fiona
Tel: 01687 462163
bunkhouse@knoydart.org
www.knoydart-foundation.com
verie, Knoydart, By Mallaig, Inverness-shire PH41 4PL

SHEENAS

BACKPACKERS

353r

The Backpackers Lodge, the oldest croft house in Mallaig, offers a homely base from which to explore the Inner Hebrides, the famous white sands of Morar and the remote peninsula of Knoydart. Mallaig is a working fishing village with all the excitement of the boats landing. You can see the seals playing in the harbour and take whale and dolphin watching trips. The hostel provides excellent budget accommodation with central heating, a well equipped kitchen/common room and free WiFi. Hot water and heating provided by renewable energy.

DETAILS

- **Open** - All year. 9am-8pm
- **Beds** - 12: 2 x 6
- **Price/night** - £22 per person.

CONTACT: Norman or Sheena
Tel: 01687 462764
backpackers@btinternet.com
www.mallaigbackpackers.co.uk
Harbour View, Mallaig, Inverness-shire, PH41 4PU

ARISAIG

BUNKHOUSE

354l

This recently renovated bunkhouse provides good value accommodation for individuals and small groups right next door to the Arisaig Hotel and the Crofter's Rest pub. A perfect stop-off en route to the Scottish islands or as a base to explore this beautiful part of the north west coast.Sea kayaking and archery available from the hotel. Trips to the small islands start from Arisaig Marine over the road. Cycle hire is available. Or take part in an evening of tradional music making in the pub.

DETAILS

- **Open** - All year. All day
- **Beds** - 14: 2x2, 2x3, 1x4
- **Price/night** - Bed in dorm: £25. Twin £50. Triple £75

CONTACT: The Arisaig Hotel
Tel: 01687 450210
bookings@arisaigbunkhouse.co.uk
www.arisaigbunkhouse.co.uk
Main Street, Arisaig, Inverness-shire
PH39 4NH

PORTREE

INDEPENDENT HOSTEL

354r

Originally the post office, Portree Host on the Isle of Skye sleeps 60 in small family rooms and dorms. All bedding is provided, there is a fully equipped kitchen/dining area (continental breakfa is available on request) & a well equipped launderette. Close to the bus terminus, it is an ideal base for touring the island & is walking distance to a wid variety of shops. From the hostel there are pleasant coastal & woodland walks Bike and car hire are available locally. Portree has an annual Folk Festival in July & Highland Games in August.

DETAILS

- **Open** - All year. No curfew
- **Beds** - 60
- **Price/night** - Prices start at £21pp

CONTACT: Patt
Tel: 01478 613737
skyehostel@yahoo.co.uk
www.hostelskye.co.uk
The Old Post Office, The Green, Portree
Isle of Skye, IV51 9BT

SKYE
BACKPACKERS

355

Whether your visit to Skye is to tackle the mighty mountains, meet the legendary faeries or simply to chill out, Skye Backpackers is the place for you. Located in the fishing village of Kyleakin surrounded by mountains and sea, the hostel has dorm, double and twin rooms. All beds come with sheets, duvets and pillows. There is a fully equipped self-catering kitchen, a sunny dining area, as much free tea, coffee & hot chocolate as you can drink, free WiFi, a cosy lounge with a real fire and spectacular views.

DETAILS

- **Open** - All year. All day. Reception 7am-12am & 5pm-10pm (times may vary).
- **Beds** - 39
- **Price/night** - From £15pp. ID required for check in.

CONTACT: Receptionist
Tel: 01599 534510
info@skyebackpackers.com
www.skyebackpackers.com
Benmhor, Kyleakin, Skye, IV41 8PH

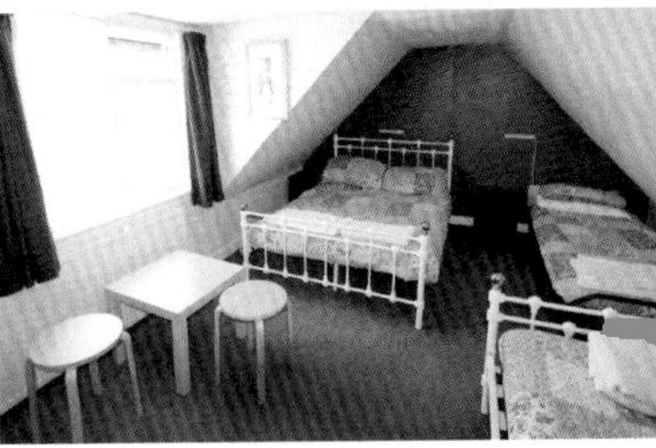

SKYE BASECAMP

Skye Basecamp is a fabulous centrally located hostel with individual beds in small dormitories & private en suite rooms. Perfect for lovers of the great outdoors, with hot showers, comfy beds and a great drying room. Shops & bars all within walking distance. Knowledgeable staff and enthusiastic guests create a fantastic atmosphere. Join us for sunset panoramas across the shores of Broadford Bay or take a stroll to the beach with its resident otters.

DETAILS

- **Open** - All year. All day. Check in 4-10pm.
- **Beds** - 37
- **Price/night** - Seasonal from £20pp. Discounts for groups/sole use.

CONTACT: Catriona & Mike Lates
Tel: 01471 820044
bookings@skyebasecamp.co.uk
www.skyebasecamp.co.uk/
Lime Park, Broadford, Isle of Skye IV49 9AE

GEARRANNAN

HOSTEL & BUNKHOUSE

357l

Part of the Gearrannan Blackhouse Village on the Isle of Lewis, the earrannan Hostel has been refurbished to sleep 13 including a 3 bed family room. Warm and cosy it has a well quipped kitchen & two modern shower rooms. The bunkhouse (groups only) leeps 14 in bunks. The perfect base for many local attractions from surfing to country walks, archaeology to cycling. There are also 3 holiday cottages.

DETAILS

- **Open** - All year.
- **Beds** - Hostel: 13: 1x10 1x3. Bunkhouse: 14: 2x6 1x2. Black houses: 1x2, 2x3-5
- **Price/night** - From £20 per person. Family room £65.

CONTACT: Mairi
Tel: 01851 643416
info@gearrannan.com
www.gearrannan.com
5a Gearrannan Carloway Isle of Lewis
HS2 9AL

HEB

HOSTEL

357r

The Heb Hostel is a family-run backpackers hostel in the heart of Stornoway on the enchanting Isle of Lewis. It is an ideal stop/stay for travellers visiting the Hebrides. Cyclists, walkers, surfers, families and groups are all welcome. Clean, comfortable, friendly and relaxed, Heb Hostel aims to provide you with a quality stay at budget prices. There are many facilities, including a common room with peat fire, free WiFi, local guides and information.

 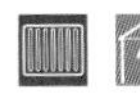    

DETAILS

- **Open** - All year. All day. Please phone for access code if warden not around.
- **Beds** - 26: 1x8, 2x7,1x4 (family dorm).
- **Price/night** - £19 pp. Family dorm: £75 for family, £84 for adults only.

CONTACT: Christine Macintosh
Tel: 01851 709889
christine@hebhostel.com
www.hebhostel.com
25 Kenneth St, Stornoway, Isle of Lewis,
HS1 2DR

GALSON FARM

HOSTEL

358l

This fully equipped hostel on the Isle of Lewis enjoys stunning views of the Atlantic coast towards the Butt of Lewis Lighthouse. It provides the perfect haven from which to explore the west side of Lewis, with sandy beaches, wildlife and historic sites on the doorstep. A short walk through the croft takes you to the shore and river, where there is an abundance of birds & otters are regular visitors. The hostel has one dormitory with 6 beds, two shower/toilet rooms and a kitchen/dining room. Towels, bedding, bike shed & drying facilities are included.

DETAILS

- **Open** - All year. All day.
- **Beds** - 6: 1x6
- **Price/night** - £20pp. Sole use £110 .

CONTACT: Elaine & Richard
Tel: 01851 850492 or 07970 219682
GalsonFarm@yahoo.com
www.galsonfarm.co.uk
Galson Farm House, South Galson, Isle of Lewis, HS2 0SH

N°5

DRINISHADER

358r

N°5 Drinishader is on the Isle of Harris, miles from Tarbert and 8 miles from the famous white sandy beaches. Situated above Drinishader harbour, overlooking the beautiful East Loch Tarbert, the hostel and self-catering units provide a variety of accommodation for individuals families and groups. Pick-up services from Tarbert can be arranged for a smal cost. Your perfect base for coastal/hill walking, cycling, kayaking, boat trips, sightseeing and bird/wildlife watching. Breakfast and packed lunches can be provided.

DETAILS

- **Open** - All year. Reception 7am-10pm
- **Beds** - 20
- **Price/night** - From £21pp. Reductions for families, groups and longer stays.

CONTACT: Alyson
Tel: 01859 511255 or 07833 474743
info@number5.biz
www.number5.biz
5 Drinishader, Isle of Harris, HS3 3DX

BACKPACKERS
STOP

359l

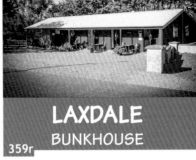

Situated in the village of Tarbert on the sle of Harris, the Backpackers Stop is a comfortable hostel for travellers. Close o the ferry, bus, shops, cafés, bars and estaurants. The Backpackers Stop is a handy base for exploring Harris, as well as whilst walking or cycling the islands. deal when arriving by ferry. Self-catering kitchen, lounge and shared dorms. .inen, duvets and towels provided. USB ockets, free WiFi.Tea & coffee available all day. Basic self service breakfast provided. Keycode entry.

DETAILS

- **Open** - 1st March - 10th November. All year round for large groups/private use.
- **Beds** - 22: 4 rooms
- **Price/night** - £22 per person.

CONTACT: Lee
Tel: 01859 502742 or 07708 746745
bpackers_stop@hotmail.com
www.backpackers-stop.co.uk
Main Street, Tarbert, Isle of Harris, HS3 3DJ

LAXDALE
BUNKHOUSE

359r

Laxdale Bunkhouse, on the Isle of Lewis, lies within Laxdale Holiday Park, a small family-run park set in peaceful leafy surroundings. Just 1.5 miles away from the town of Stornoway, it's an ideal base for exploring the island. Built in 1998, the bunkhouse has four rooms of four bunks. There is a drying room, a spacious fully equipped dining kitchen, a comfortable TV lounge and BBQ area. Toilets/ showers are located in the building & are suitable for the disabled. Wigwams are also available.

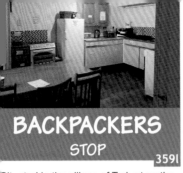

DETAILS

- **Open** - March to Nov. 9am - 10pm.
- **Beds** - 16: 4x4.
- **Price/night** - £18 adult, £16 child, £65 room (3 or less people) £250 sole use.

CONTACT: Gordon Macleod
Tel: 01851 706966 / 01851 703234
info@laxdaleholidaypark.com
www.laxdaleholidaypark.com
Laxdale Holiday Park, 6 Laxdale Lane, Stornoway, Isle of Lewis, HS2 0DR

SANACHAN

BUNKHOUSE

360l

Sanachan Bunkhouse, in Kishorn, is the perfect base for walking, climbing, kayaking, cycling & sailing in Wester Ross. After a fun filled day, your group can return to a warm fire, comfy bunks, hot showers and simple living.

There is parking for six cars and beds for fifteen, split between two rooms (bring a sleeping bag).The bunkhouse is well equipped for self-catering, with enough tables & chairs for everyone. Laundry/ drying, outside recreation and BBQ.

GROUPS ONLY

DETAILS

- **Open** - All year.
- **Beds** - 15: 1x7, 1x8
- **Price/night** - £17 pp. Discounted student rate of £15 pp.

CONTACT: Sean and Sophie
Tel: 01520 733484
bookings@ourscottishadventure.com
www.ourscottishadventure.com/
Sanachan Bunkhouse, Kishorn,
Strathcarron, Ross-shire, IV54 8XA

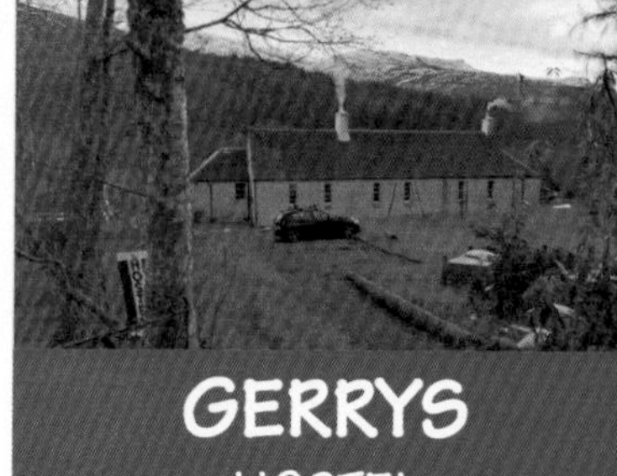

GERRYS

HOSTEL

360r

Gerry's Hostel is situated in an excellen mountaineering and wilderness area on the most scenic railway in Britain. It is on the Cape Wrath Trails, The T.G.O Challenge Route and is 0.5 miles from the Coulin Pass at Craig. It sleeps 20; 10 in a large dormitory with comfy beds the rest in 5/6 bed family rooms. Meals and draught ale are a 15 min drive away Your perfect base for many activities including walking, climbing, fishing, cycling, golfing and wildlife watching.

DETAILS

- **Open** - All year. Check in after 4pm
- **Beds** - 20: 1x10, 2x5 or 6
- **Price/night** - From £19pp main dorm. Family room from £19pp (min 3 guests). Twins and doubles £25pp.

CONTACT: Simon Howkins
Tel: 07894 984294, 01520 766232
s.howkins@gmail.com
www.gerryshostel.com/
Craig Achnashellach, Strathcarron,
Wester Ross, IV54 8YU

KINLOCHEWE

BUNKHOUSE

361l

Walkers, climbers and mountain ikers enjoying the Torridon Mountains and wilderness areas will be warmly velcomed at the Kinlochewe Hotel and unkhouse. Situated on the North Coast 500 road route, within 20 miles of over 20 Munros, the bunkhouse boasts a vell equipped, self-catering kitchen, an fficient drying room, hot showers and a 2 bunk dormitory. The hotel bar serves xcellent home-made food and is in the 2018 Good Beer Guide.

DETAILS

- **Open** - All year. 8am - 10pm.
- **Beds** - 12.
- **Price/night** - £17.50pp. Discount for group bookings with sole occupancy for 2 nights or more.

CONTACT: Dave and Karen Twist
Tel: 01445 760253
info@kinlochewehotel.co.uk
www.kinlochewehotel.co.uk
Kinlochewe by Achnasheen, Wester Ross, IV22 2PA

BADRALLACH

BOTHY & CAMPSITE

361r

On the tranquil shores of Little Loch Broom overlooking one of Scotland's finest mountain ranges, Badrallach Bothy and Campsite offer a fine base for walking and climbing. Fish in the rivers, hill lochs and sea or simply enjoy the flora and fauna. Hot showers, spotless accommodation, an unbelievable price and total peace make the Bothy and Campsite a firm favourite. There is also a holiday cottage for hire.

DETAILS

- **Open** - All year. All day.
- **Beds** - 12+ (alpine style platforms) 20 at a squeeze. Mats required.
- **Price/night** - £8pp, £2 per vehicle. £100 sole use. See @badrallachcampsite facebook page for camping/cottage fees.

CONTACT: Chris Davidson
Tel: 07435 123 190
mail@badrallach.com
www.badrallach.com
Croft No 9, Badrallach, Dundonnell, Ross-shire, IV23 2QP

THE CEILIDH PLACE

BUNKHOUSE

362l

The Ceilidh Place, in the centre of Ullapool, is a unique small complex, consisting of a music venue/performance space, restaurant, hotel, bar, bookshop, coffee shop, gallery and bunkhouse. There are regular ceilidhs, concerts & plays. The bunkhouse (group only) does not have self-catering facilities but the coffee shop is open from 8.30am to late evening all week including weekends. Rooms are also available in the hotel. The village of Ullapool is a small exciting port and fishing town, with ferries from the Outer Hebrides. Hill walkers and families especially love staying here.

DETAILS

- **Open** - All year.
- **Beds** - Bunkhouse: 32,
- **Price/night** - Get in touch for prices.

CONTACT: Effie
Tel: 01854 612103
stay@theceilidhplace.com
www.theceilidhplace.com
14 West Argyle St. Ullapool, IV26 2TY

INCHNADAMPH

LODGE

362r

Inchnadamph Lodge has been tastefully converted to provide luxury hostel accommodation at a budget price. There's a large self-catering kitchen, a games room, a lounge and a dining room. Food is usually available at the Inchnadamph Hotel just across the river. Based at the foot of Ben More Assynt and overlooking Loch Assynt, explore one of the wildest areas in the Highlands from the door.

DETAILS

- **Open** - Mid March to Mid Oct. All day
- **Beds** - 30: 2x8, 2x6 (dormitory). 14 (twin/double/family).
- **Price/night** - £20-24pp (dormitory), £30-£34(twin)pp including continental breakfast and linen. Group discounts.

CONTACT: Chris
Tel: 01571 822218
info@inch-lodge.co.uk
www.inch-lodge.co.uk
Inchnadamph, Assynt, Nr Lochinver,
Sutherland, IV27 4HL

BUNKHOUSE
@ INVERSHIN HOTEL

363l

Situated within a small hotel in the north Highlands, the bunkhouse consists of 4 rooms with a shared shower room & toilet. Guests can enjoy the hotel facilities; comfortable reception area, cosy bar with real fire, real ale and regular music sessions. Cyclists, walkers, bikers, fishermen, Munro baggers, families and individuals are all welcome. The bunkhouse is just off the North Coast 500 road route. No self-catering facilities but breakfast & evening meals are available.

DETAILS

- **Open** - April-end Sept. Check in 4pm.
- **Beds** - 10: 2x twin, 2x triple (bunkbeds)
- **Price/night** - £20pp. Breakfast: £5 or £10. Discount for groups of 6 or more.

CONTACT: Angus or Cheryl
Tel: 01549 421202
enquiries@invershin.com
www.invershin.com
Invershin Hotel, Lairg, Sutherland, IV27 4ET

SLEEPERZZZ.COM

363r

Stay on a first class train in Rogart in the heart of the Highlands, halfway between Inverness and John O'Groats! Two railway carriages have been tastefully converted. One sleeps 9, and one is subdivided to sleep 4 and 2. There are two beds per room, a kitchen, dining room, sitting room, showers & toilets. All bedding is included. Close by you will find a shop, post office and pub with restaurant.

DETAILS

- **Open** - April to Sept inclusive. 24 hours.
- **Beds** - 15: 1x9, 1x4+1x2
- **Price/night** - From £20pp, under 12yrs £14pp. Stay 2 nights & save £1pp per night. Alternatively £1 discount from the first night if you arrive by cycle or rail.

CONTACT: Kate
Tel: 01408 641343
kate@sleeperzzz.com
www.sleeperzzz.com
Rogart Station, Pittentrail, Sutherland, Highlands, IV28 3XA

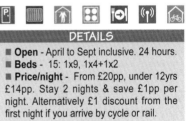

HELMSDALE HOSTEL

364l

Set in the scenic coastal village of Helmsdale, the hostel (which was completely refurbished last year) offers spacious en suite accommodation including a fully equipped kitchen and comfortable lounge area with log burning stove. On the NC500 and Lands End John O'Groats route, the hostel is popular with 'end to enders' and walkers exploring the Far North Marilyn Hills. It is also a perfect stop on the way to Orkney. Dogs on request. Groups welcome.

DETAILS

- **Open** - All Year (Nov-Mar advanced booking essential).
- **Beds** - 24: 6x4 (en-suite)
- **Price/night** - Adults from £25. Children from £15. Discount for sole use..

CONTACT: Irene
Tel: 07971 516287 or 07971 922356
irene.drummond@btinternet.com
stay@helmsdalehostel.co.uk
Stafford Street, Helmsdale, Sutherland, KW8 6JR

HIGHLAND HAVEN

364r

The Highland Haven is new and offers unique group accommodation in the fa north of Scotland. Its stunning location on the NC500 enjoys magnificent views over to Orkney and Dunnet Head.

A perfect base for cyclists, walkers. families and friends. The Highland Have provides everything you need to relax & recharge and perfect dark skies for sta gazing. Experience the ultimate group getaway - affordable & luxurious.

DETAILS

- **Open** - All year. All day.
- **Beds** - 10: 1x6, 1x4 plus 2 sofa beds
- **Price/night** - Burrow (sleeps 4) £140. Barn (sleeps 6) £200. Sole use (10 + sofa bed) £300.

CONTACT: Bronagh Braidwood (BB)
Tel: 01955 611499
thehighlandhaven@gmail.com
thehighlandhaven.co.uk
St Johns, East Mey, Thurso, Caithness KW14 8XL

SANDRAS
HOSTEL

3651

Thurso is the northern-most town on the UK mainland. The cliffs are alive with guillemots, kittiwakes, fulmars & puffins, while the sea is home to seals & porpoises. The 4* hostel has en suites in all rooms, (some have TVs). Using their own backpacking experience, the owners ensure you will enjoy a level of comfort and service second to none. Surfing, pony trekking, fishing, quad biking, coastal walks and boat trips are all available nearby. On the NC500 route.

DETAILS

- **Open** - All year
- **Beds** - 26: 2x4 1x6 1x3 4x2
- **Price/night** - Dorm £20pp. Double/twin £46. Family room £75 (4 people), £90 (5 people). Breakfast is included in the price.

CONTACT: George or James
Tel: 01847 894575
info@sandras-backpackers.co.uk
www.sandras-backpackers.co.uk
24-26 Princes Street, Thurso, Caithness, KW14 7BQ

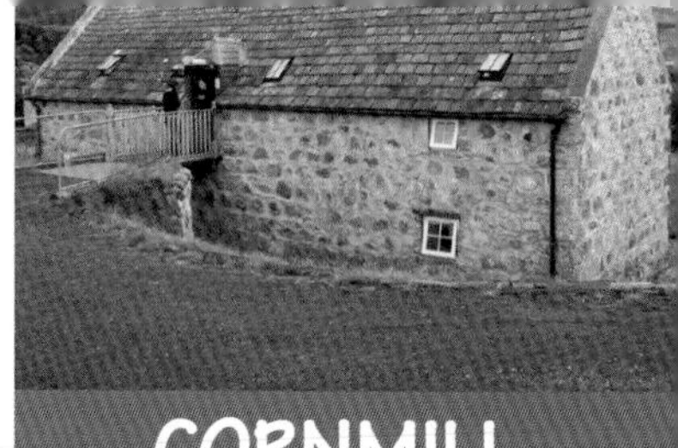

CORNMILL
BUNKHOUSE

365r

Cornmill Bunkhouse is situated on a traditional croft. The mill was built in the early 1800s and was active until 1920s. It is now 4* accommodation for individuals or groups. Guests are reminded of their historic setting; the smaller bunkroom has a patio door looking onto the workings of the old mill with its large wooden cog driving wheels. Activities can be organised for groups including laser tagging & shooting. Hen and stag parties welcome.

DETAILS

- **Open** - All year, advanced notice required 1st Oct - 1st April. All day.
- **Beds** - 14: 1x8,1x6
- **Price/night** - £18 per person. Discounts available for group bookings.

CONTACT: Sandy Murray
Tel: 01641 571219 Mob: 07808 197350
sandy.murray2@btinternet.com
www.achumore.co.uk
Cornmill Bunkhouse, Achumore, Strathhalladale, Sutherland, KW13 6YT

KYLE OF TONGUE

HOSTEL

Kyle of Tongue Hostel is a stone lodge, magnificently situated on the romantic shores of the Kyle of Tongue on the north coast of Scotland. It has supreme panoramic views of Castle Varich, Ben Hope and the queen of Scottish mountains - Ben Loyal. Beautifully furnished, like a boutique hotel, but with all the friendliness of a hostel. There are comfortable private bedrooms, roomy shared dormitories and relaxing communal areas. Full camping services are also available

DETAILS

- **Open** - All year. Check in from 4pm.
- **Beds** - 36
- **Price/night** - Dormitory beds from £21, Private rooms from £50

CONTACT: Richard Mackay
Tel: 01847 611789
kothostelandhp@btinternet.com
www.tonguehostelandholidaypark.co.uk
Kyle of Tongue Hostel & Holiday Park,
Tongue, By Lairg, Sutherland, IV27 4XH

ORCADES HOSTEL

Orcades Hostel in Kirkwall, the capital of Orkney, is an excellent base for exploring the Isles. Accommodation is in doubles, twins, 4 & 6 bedded rooms. Each bedroom has en suite toilet/shower rooms. TVs and all bedding is provided. There is a stylish kitchen, a lounge with DVD & games and WiFi throughout the building. A warm and friendly welcome awaits you at this comfortable 4 star hostel.

DETAILS

- **Open** - All year. Check in after 2pm. Check out by 10am on day of departure.
- **Beds** - 34: doubles, twin, 4 and 6 bed
- **Price/night** - £20 pp in a shared room, £26 pp in a double or twin room (£52 for the room), £42 for single occupancy of a double/twin room. Winter rates available.

CONTACT: Erik or Sandra
Tel: 01856 873745
orcadeshostel@hotmail.co.uk
www.orcadeshostel.com
Muddisdale Road, Kirkwall, KW15 1RS

HOY
CENTRE

368l

Surrounded by magnificent scenery, the Hoy Centre is ideally situated for a peaceful and relaxing holiday. It's also an ideal venue for outdoor education, weddings, workshops, clubs or family gatherings. Offering high quality, 4* accommodation, the centre has a well equipped kitchen, comfortable lounge & a large dining hall. All rooms are en suite with twin beds and one set of bunks. Hoy is an RSPB reserve comprising 3,500ha of upland heath and cliffs with a large variety of wildlife including arctic hares.

DETAILS

- **Open** - All year.
- **Beds** - 32
- **Price/night** - Please phone for prices for singles, families or groups. Either on a daily or residential basis.

CONTACT: Customer Services
Tel: 018566 873535 ext 2901
stromnesscs@orkney.gov.uk
www.orkney.gov.uk
Hoy Centre, Hoy, Orkney, KW16 3NJ

HAMNAVOE
HOSTEL

368r

Accommodation on the waterfront at Stromness, Orkney, close to the ferry. Single, family and twin rooms with glorious views. Light, airy kitchen and a large dining table with views of the harbour. Lounge with comfortable seating, TV, DVDs and books. Laundry room, WiFi, free long stay car park. Visit the nearby islands of Graemsay and Hoy, check out the World Heritage sites. Relax in the tranquility of island life.

DETAILS

- **Open** - All year. All day. No curfew. Check in after 2pm (reconfirm if not arriving before 7pm), check out by 10am.
- **Beds** - 13: 1x4, 1x1, 4x2.
- **Price/night** - From £21pp. Private rooms £23pp

CONTACT: Mr George Argo
Tel: 01856 851202
info@hamnavoehostel.co.uk
www.hamnavoehostel.co.uk
10a North End Road, Stromness, Orkney, KW16 3AG

BROWNS

HOSTEL & HOUSES

roviding nightly or weekly self-catering ccommodation in the captivating small town of Stromness, Orkney. Within walking/cycling distance of the ancient Maeshowe, Ring of Brodgar and Skara Brae. Stromness has a museum, art entre, festival, scuba diving, free fishing and ferries from mainland Scotland. acilities include well equipped kitchens, comfy sitting rooms and beds in single, double, twin, triple and family rooms, all with towels and bedding provided. Computers with internet and WiFi. Cycle storage & free car park up the lane.

  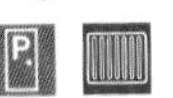      

DETAILS

- **Open** - All year. All day. No curfew.
- **Beds** - 28: 3x1,4x2,3x3,2x4
- **Price/night** - From £20.

CONTACT: Sylvia Brown
Tel: 01856 850661
info@brownsorkney.co.uk
www.brownsorkney.co.uk
45/47 Victoria Street, Stromness,
Orkney, KW16 3BS

RACKWICK

HOSTEL

Three Star Rackwick Hostel in Hoy has 2 bedrooms containing 4 beds each (2 bunk beds per room). In the scenic Rackwick Valley in the north of Hoy, the hostel overlooks Rackwick Bay considered one of the most beautiful places in Orkney. There's a small kitchen with a good range of utensils, and a separate dining area. Singles, families and groups are welcome for private room or whole hostel bookings. Car parking and bike storage behind hostel. Walkers and Cyclist Welcome

DETAILS

- **Open** - April - September
- **Beds** - 8: 2x4
- **Price/night** - For prices please check accommodation's website or phone.

CONTACT: Customer Services
Tel: 01856 850907 or 01856 873535 ext 2901
stromnesscs@orkney.gov.uk
www.orkney.gov.uk
Rackwick Hostel, Rackwick, Hoy,
Orkney, KW16 3NJ

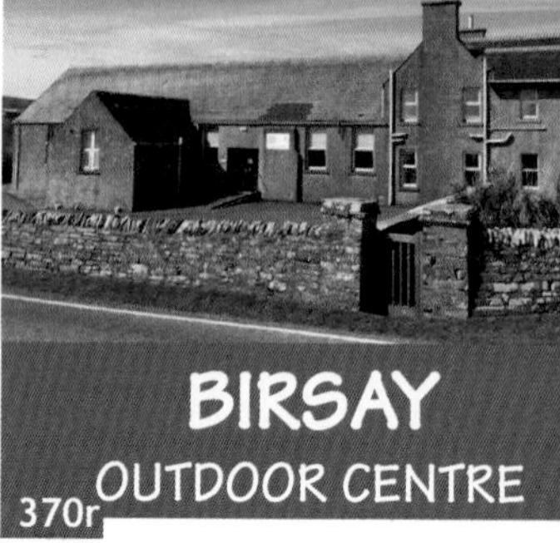

BIRSAY

OUTDOOR CENTRE

Birsay Hostel in the northwest corner c the Orkney mainland offers comfortabl accommodation for up to 26 in 5 bedrooms. An ideal venue for outdoor education trips, weddings, clubs or family gatherings. It has a well equippe kitchen, dining area, drying room, disabled access and all bed linen is provided. There is a campsite in the extensive grounds. Close to spectacul coast, RSPB reserves and the remains of early Christian, Neolithic and Norse settlements. UNESCO heritage sites.

DETAILS

- **Open** - April - Sept. Open all year for group bookings.
- **Beds** - 26: 2x4,1x2,1x6,1x10
- **Price/night** - Prices on enquiry. Private rooms or whole hostel bookings.

CONTACT: Customer Services
Tel: 01856 850907 or 01856 873535 ext 290
stromnesscs@orkney.gov.uk
www.orkney.gov.uk
Birsay, Orkney, KW17 2LY

AYRES ROCK

HOSTEL

371l

Sanday is the perfect place to take time out, with long stretches of unspoilt sandy beaches, an abundance of birds, seals and other wildlife, glittering seas, clear air and spectacular skies. Those lucky enough to live here enjoy a rare quality of life in a small, friendly and safe community. Enjoy the views over the Holms of Ire from the conservatory in this 4* hostel.

DETAILS

- **Open** - All year. 8am to 10pm.
- **Beds** - 8 : 2x2 (twin), 1x4 (en suite).
- **Price/night** - From £19.50pp. Twin room single occupant £23.50. Groups from £60. Camping pods from £18.50pp Twin pod £35. Cooked breakfast £7.50 Evening meals from £12.50

CONTACT: Julie or Paul
Tel: 01857 600410
sandayhostel@gmail.com
www.ayres-rock-hostel-orkney.com
Ayre, Coo Road, Sanday, Orkney KW17 2AY

CHALMERSQUOY

ACCOMMODATION

371r

Chalmersquoy offers four-star quality hostel accommodation and camping in Westray on Orkney, the Queen of the Isles. The barn hostel has an excellent kitchen and lounge. There is a double room, a family room and three twin bunk rooms, all with sea views. Explore the cliffs, beaches and seabirds on the island or visit the Heritage Centre, shops and local crafts. Bar and food available at Pierowall Hotel, 5 mins' walk away. The famous fish and chip shop is open Wednesday and Saturday evenings.

DETAILS

- **Open** - All year. If we're in, we're open.
- **Beds** - 12: 3x2 (bunk), 1x2 (dbl), 1x4
- **Price/night** - £24pp or £210 per night for exclusive use.

CONTACT: Michael & Teenie Harcus
Tel: 01857 677214

enquiries@chalmersquoywestray.co.uk
www.chalmersquoywestray.co.uk
Chalmersquoy, Westray, Orkney, KW17 2BZ

OBSERVATORY
HOSTEL

372l

On a 34 acre croft managed by the North Ronaldsay Bird Observatory on the most northern isle of Orkney. Adjacent to a shell sand beach visited by seals and unique seaweed-eating sheep. Spectacular bird migrations and outstanding views. Ideal accommodation for those interested in wildlife but welcomes all. The hostel sleeps 10 in three dormitories with a self-catering kitchen. Lounge bar and meals available in the Observatory Guest House.

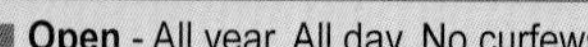

DETAILS

- **Open** - All year. All day. No curfews.
- **Beds** - 10: 2x4,1x2 + Guesthouse.
- **Price/night** - Hostel £18-£19, half board from £39.50. Guest house private rooms £56 - £73.50 half board.

CONTACT: Duty Warden
Tel: 01857 633200
nrbo@nrbo.prestel.co.uk
www.nrbo.co.uk
NRBO, North Ronaldsay, Orkney Islands, KW17 2BE

GARDIESFAULD
HOSTEL

372r

Gardiesfauld Hostel is on Unst, the most northerly of the Shetland Isles wit spectacular cliffs sculpted by the Atlant Ocean on the west and secluded, sand beaches on the east with rocky outcrop where seals and otters appear. On the picturesque shore at Uyeasound, this refurbished hostel has good facilities and a relaxed atmosphere. There is a kitchen, dining room, lounge, conservatory and rooms with en suite facilities as well as a garden when you can pitch a tent or park your caravan.

DETAILS

- **Open** - April to October. Open in winter for pre-bookings. Open all day.
- **Beds** - 35: 1x11, 2x6, 2x5, 1x2
- **Price/night** - Adults £16, U16's £9. Camping £8, U16s £4. Hook ups £18

CONTACT: Warden
Tel: 01957 755279
enquiries@gardiesfauld.shetland.co.uk
www.gardiesfauld.shetland.co.uk
Uyeasound, Unst, Shetland, ZE2 9DW

AUCHLISHIE

BUNKHOUSE

A brand new family owned bunkhouse situated in Kirriemuir, at the gateway to the Glens of Isla, Prosen and Clova.

he bunkhouse offers excellent facilities to the outdoor enthusiast wanting to xperience and enjoy the proximity to the Cairngorms National Park.

An architect designed, purpose built bunkhouse with full kitchen, shower and drying room facilities. Cosy duvets, pillows and bed linen provided, towels available to hire.

   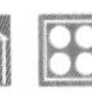   

DETAILS

- **Open** - All year
- **Beds** - 24
- **Price/night** - From £25 per person

CONTACT: James or Nicky
Tel: 07867 476300
yard@auchlishie.co.uk
www.auchlishie-bunkhouse.co.uk
Auchlishie Farm, Kirriemuir, Angus DD8 4LS

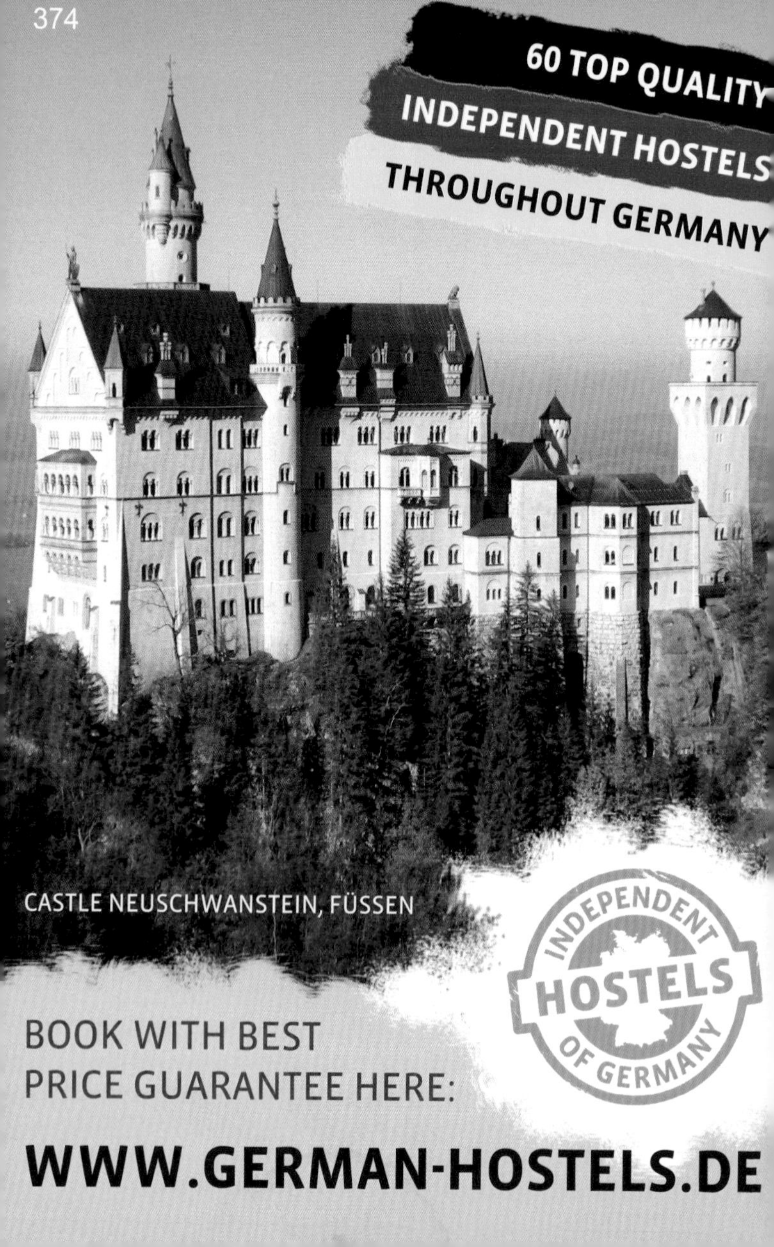
60 TOP QUALITY
INDEPENDENT HOSTELS
THROUGHOUT GERMANY
CASTLE NEUSCHWANSTEIN, FÜSSEN
INDEPENDENT HOSTELS OF GERMANY
BOOK WITH BEST
PRICE GUARANTEE HERE:
WWW.GERMAN-HOSTELS.DE

swiss
hostels
Photo: maennlichen.ch

BOOK DIRECT ON OUR WEBSITE

Every booking placed through the Independent Hostels' website is a direct booking, with 100% of your payment and all your communications going direct to the accommodation.

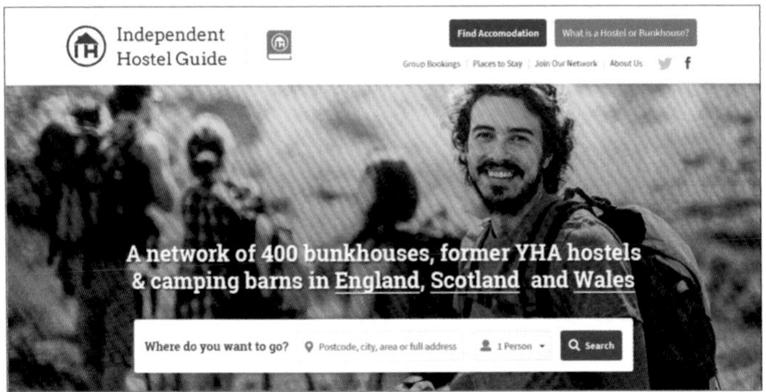

When you book with other websites they withhold up to 20% of your money as commission and often don't provide contact with your hosts.

BOOK DIRECT BECAUSE

- **Everything you pay goes to your hosts**
- **You can chat with the staff and discuss your needs**
- **You may get preferential treatment**

Everything you pay and everything you say goes to your hosts.

Be good to your hosts

AND BOOK DIRECT

BENEFITS FOR ACCOMMODATION OWNERS

We support your own marketing and provide direct bookings from the right kind of people.

We actively promote your accommodation on Twitter, Facebook, Instagram & Pinterest.

We promote your accommodation on our website, in our guidebook, in leaflets supplied to Tourist Information Centres and on the Long Distance Walkers' website.

Our group booking service provides you with enquiries from all types of group leaders.

We promote your accommodation at festivals and shows in the UK. We provide you with IHUK branded signs, mugs, leaflets and books.

Our message boards host conversations between accommodation owners. We keep you in touch with industry news and we provide exclusive deals.

With a friendly efficient service.

Official IH Member
Independent Hostels UK
The largest network of hostels, bunkhouses & group accommodation in England, Scotland and Wales

WHAT IS INDEPENDENT HOSTELS UK ?

IHUK IS THE LARGEST NETWORK OF HOSTELS & BUNKHOUSES IN THE UK.
The network's website is viewed millions of times each year and we distribute thousands of guidebooks and tens of thousands of leaflets via bookshops, hostels, information centres and events.
To join IHUK visit Independenthostels.co.uk/join or phone 01629 580427
B48

INDEX

INDEX

INDEX

INDEX

INDEX